Scientists and
National Policy-Making

Scientists and
National Policy-Making

EDITED BY

ROBERT GILPIN AND

CHRISTOPHER WRIGHT

Columbia University Press

NEW YORK AND LONDON

Preface

In the increasing number and variety of interactions between social affairs and science and technology, two constant factors stand out: the clear need to establish policies for many of these interactions on a national basis and the involvement of men of science in this process. To understand the activities of natural scientists in the development of national policies is both an intellectual challenge and a practical necessity. This study of the policy process must complement studies of particular problem areas affected by scientific discoveries and technological developments. It is apparent that without improved understanding of the parts played by scientists in national policy-making, we are unlikely to anticipate the full range of social effects of particular scientific developments or to recognize related fundamental changes in our political processes.

The correctness and adequacy of the numerous opinions and alarms that are being expressed on this subject can only be judged with the help of comparative studies and empirical data that are only now beginning to be collected. It is a matter for concern that empirical knowledge may not catch up with the flow of impressionistic writing about a subject that is so much in the public eye and so demanding of political decisions as is science in its relation to national security, public welfare, and the resources for science itself. Development of this knowledge is likely to require close collaboration, if not a synthesis, of various academic disciplines and, ideally, should be basic enough to have predictive value rather than be a mere summary of the past. Nothing approximating a comprehensive social science of science or, more exactly, science affairs now exists. Even the limits of the subject are not yet apparent, but at least they are beginning to be described and defined by inquiries such as the one of which this volume forms a part.

In seeking to foster the social science of science, the Columbia University Council for Atomic Age Studies has been acutely aware of the special difficulties imposed upon scholarly study by the need for contemporary and future orientations and for integration of the results of practical experience with theoretical inquiries. The composite nature of this symposium volume is thus due partly to the need to collect and disseminate ideas and information that will accelerate the production of works reflecting an individual scholar's full mastery of the subject and partly to the need to stimulate a continuing dialogue between men of affairs and scholars in the social sciences. The dialogue is sustained here by essays which reflect the particular preoccupations, knowledge, and analyses of such persons as well as their individual, and occasionally inimitable, literary styles. The ten authors of these essays have, however, all had opportunities for exchanging views with each other and with other participants in seminars and conferences held by the Council for Atomic Age Studies. In this way a measure of agreement was achieved on the issues and general focus of attention.

The first of the Council's study conferences designed to encourage research on problems of governmental use and support of science and scientists was convened by Philip C. Jessup, then Co-chairman of the Council and now a judge on the International Court of Justice, in June of 1959 at the home of the American Academy of Arts and Sciences in Brookline, Massachusetts. The three authors whose essays were first published elsewhere were among the participants at this conference, and two of them, Wallace Sayre and Warner Schilling, received some further assistance from the Council in connection with their studies. In the winter of 1962 the Council conducted a series of four interinstitutional seminar meetings at Columbia University under the chairmanship of William T. R. Fox, Professor of International Relations and Director of the Institute of War and Peace Studies and now also Co-chairman of the Council. A number of Council Monographs were prepared in connection with the seminar and a larger conference on civil-science relations was subsequently held at Gould House, Dobbs Ferry, New York, in October of 1962. All ten authors were present at this conference, which was chaired by Mr. Fox and was jointly sponsored and supported by the Council and the Committee on National Security Policy Research of the Social Science Research Council. The monographs and reprints which served as drafts for most of the essays in this volume provided a basis for discussion on this occasion.

Although the authors alone remain responsible for their statements and the editors for matters involving editorial discretion, the Council wishes to acknowledge with thanks the invaluable comments and encouragement of all the natural and social scientists and men of affairs who participated with the authors and chairmen in one or more of these private discussions. These include the following persons who participated as private individuals although they were associated with the federal government: Richard H. Bolt, Richard G. Hewlett, Thomas L. Hughes, Robert Jastrow, Arthur Levine, Col. George A. Lincoln, J. Kenneth Mansfield, James T. Ramey, Carroll L. Shartle, Elmer B. Staats, and Alan T. Waterman.

Participants from private institutions other than Columbia University, who in many cases have also had considerable governmental experience, included James P. Baxter, III, Lincoln P. Bloomfield, A. Hunter Dupree, John P. Fox, Morton Grodzins, W. Eric Gustafson, Morton H. Halperin, Pendleton Herring, John C. Honey, Norman Kaplan, William W. Kaufmann, James E. King, Jr., Sanford Lakoff, Avery Leiserson, Gene M. Lyons, Thomas F. Malone, James McCormack, Jr., Norman Milleron, Max Millikan, Richard H. Nolte, Robert E. Osgood, James A. Perkins, E. Raymond Platig, Edward M. Purcell, Robert B. Sheeks, Hans Speier, Norman W. Storer, M. H. Trytten, Alvin M. Weinberg, Anthony J. Wiener, Carroll L. Wilson, and Bryce Wood.

Participants from Columbia University included Bernard Barber, Andre Cournand, W. Maurice Ewing, Ralph S. Halford, Menelaos D. Hassialis, Samuel P. Huntington, Robert K. Merton, Claire M. Nader, Richard E. Neustadt, and David B. Truman.

The various phases of the Council's inquiries into government and science would not have been possible without either the able staff assistance of Nancy S. Kaufman, Jeri H. Thomas, and Julie Yastishak or the financial support of the Carnegie Corporation of New York through its grant to Columbia University for support of various Council activities.

The editors wish also to acknowledge with gratitude the expert and courteous service rendered by the staff of the Columbia University Press despite the difficulty of expediting the publication of a volume having so many authors.

Christopher Wright,
EXECUTIVE DIRECTOR
COUNCIL FOR ATOMIC AGE STUDIES

New York City
September, 1963

Contents

Introduction: Natural Scientists in Policy-Making

ROBERT GILPIN

Assistant Professor of Politics and Public Affairs and Faculty Associate of the Center of International Studies at Princeton University

Delivering the annual Godkin Lectures in late 1960, Sir Charles Snow, scientist, novelist, and civil servant, told a Harvard University audience a fascinating tale about the "culpable" behavior of Winston Churchill's wartime scientific adviser F. A. Lindemann (Lord Cherwell). While hoping to intrigue and entertain his listeners, Sir Charles meant his tale to be a moral one, and in his last lecture to a highly responsive audience he warned his American friends that the moral of his cautionary tale applied to them. They must be on guard, he warned, against the machinations of scientific advisers in high places; in this lecture he provided the United States with a few simple rules for protection against the type of evil he believed had been visited upon England by Lord Cherwell.[1]

The paradox of Sir Charles's tale is that though it was directed against a scientist it ended with an impassioned plea for increased numbers of scientists to participate in political life. Only they, Snow tells us, have a sense of the future and the knowledge to guide mankind out of the perilous present. Snow concluded that the age of rapid change produced by science requires that there be "scientists active in all levels of government."

Sir Charles's desire for increased participation of scientists in government has been more than fulfilled in the United States. American scientists have become very much a part of America's governing elite and are today found active in all levels of government.[2]

---

[1] Sir Charles's Godkin Lectures were published under the title *Science and Government* (Cambridge, Mass., Harvard University Press, 1961).

[2] In general, the contributors to this volume use "scientist" to refer to natural

Throughout the executive branch of the national government, natural scientists now contribute significantly to broad policy decisions. As has happened so frequently in the past, the pluralism of American society has again accommodated a rising social group whose contributions to national life necessitate that its leadership gain power within the political system.

Unfortunately, the study of the political participation of natural scientists has lagged far behind the activities of scientists.[3] Science and government in the United States have been intimately related since the beginning of the Republic, and scientists had gained an unprecedented place in American government before the end of World War II, yet the first and foremost book on scientists and policy-making, *Government and Science* by Don K. Price, was not written until 1954. While other studies have followed Price's book, the literature which seeks to comprehend and evaluate scientists as participants in government still leaves the field of inquiry largely unexploited.[4]

---

scientists and, to a lesser extent, engineers. In addition, however, several authors are interested in the role of social scientists such as the "scientific strategists" in the making of public policy. For this latter subject see especially the essays by Bernard Brodie and Albert Wohlstetter in this volume.

[3] Harold D. Lasswell proposed such studies in his Presidential Address at the American Political Science Association annual meeting on September 6, 1956. See "The Political Science of Science," *The American Political Science Review*, L, No. 4 (December, 1956), 961–79. In 1945 Robert K. Merton made a similar appeal to all social scientists. See "Role of the Intellectual in Public Bureaucracy," chap. VII of his *Social Theory and Social Structure* (Glencoe, Ill., Free Press, 1959).

[4] Contemporary relations between government and science are discussed by J. Stefan Dupré and Sanford A. Lakoff, *Science and the Nation: Policy and Politics* (Englewood Cliffs, N.J., Prentice-Hall, 1962) and James L. McCamy, *Science and Public Administration* (University, Ala., University of Alabama Press, 1960). For a case study of scientists in politics, see this writer's *American Scientists and Nuclear Weapons Policy* (Princeton, N.J., Princeton University Press, 1962). Writings on the sociology of science which touch on the subject of scientists and policy-making include: Bernard Barber, *Science and the Social Order* (Glencoe, Ill., Free Press, 1952) and Bernard Barber and Walter Hirsch, eds., *The Sociology of Science: A Reader* (New York, Free Press of Glencoe, 1962). See also Bernard Barber, "Sociology of Science: A Trend Report and Bibliography," *Current Sociology*, V, No. 2 (Paris, 1957).

Science and government at the local and state level in the United States is also an important area in political science. The principal work is by Frederic N. Cleaveland, *Science and State Government* (Chapel Hill, N.C., University of North Carolina Press, 1959).

In the present study of scientists and national policy-making a number of scholars have examined major aspects of this subject. The contributing authors differ in their assessments and interpretations of the place of scientists in American politics today, but all agree that that phase of contemporary scientific-governmental relations which began in 1945 is ending, and that the United States is beginning to experience new problems and challenges in this area of national life.

At the close of World War II, three issues of scientific-governmental relations challenged American political leadership: the need to determine the proper place of natural scientists in the making of national policy, the need to develop policy toward basic scientific research, and the need to solve the many problems involved in national security policy, especially with respect to nuclear weapons. At present the great issues *initially* presented by all three issues appear to have been decided. Now, as the essays in this volume reveal, new challenges in each area are emerging as results of decisions taken in the past two decades with respect to these problems.

THE LEGACY OF WORLD WAR II

The roots of the problems of a national policy toward science and of integrating scientists into policy-making are to be found deep in American history.[5] However, it was not until the time of World War II that discussions leading to the present period of concern with these issues were begun by natural scientists serving the war effort as well as by governmental groups interested in forging some postwar links between science and government.

Initially, there were two groups of public officials strongly interested in the future relations of government and the scientific community. In the first place, New Deal Congressmen like Senator Harley Kilgore saw scientific research as a means of promoting full employment after the war. Many politicians believed that by creat-

---

[5] For an excellent historical discussion of the problems of a national policy for science and of integrating science and government prior to 1940, see A. Hunter Dupree, *Science in the Federal Government* (Cambridge, Mass., Harvard University Press, 1957). Professor Dupree, Director of the NSF History Project, is currently writing the history of the post-1940 period.

ing new technologies science could create the jobs which would be needed to absorb the labor force when it was released from defense work. At the same time, these Congressmen believed that "big business monopolies" would suppress new developments arising from research if such developments threatened their traditional markets.[6] Thus Kilgore and others concluded that the federal government rather than business would have to underwrite the research on new technologies which would help provide for full employment in the postwar period.

The military services also became concerned about national policy toward scientific research. The incredible success achieved throughout the war by university scientists-turned-weaponeers convinced many military officers of the need to continue a vigorous postwar liaison with natural scientists and, in particular, with university scientists.[7] Toward this end a committee under the chairmanship of Charles Wilson [8] proposed that after the war the military services contract the National Academy of Sciences-National Research Council (NAS-NRC) to administer research projects of interest to the military. Though such research would be conducted at private institutions such as universities, the military services would determine the object of the research in terms of military requirements.[9]

Both the New Dealers and the military men, therefore, desired governmental support of scientific research principally because of

[6] As Chairman of the Senate "Watchdog" Subcommittee on Technological Mobilization, Kilgore uncovered what he considered to be examples of the failure of American business to develop technologies needed for the war effort; he attributed this to the desire to protect the industry's postwar competitive position.

[7] For accounts of the activities of scientists in the war, see James Phinney Baxter, III, *Scientists Against Time* (Boston, Little, Brown and Co., 1946), and Irvin Stewart, *Organizing Scientific Research for War* (Boston, Little, Brown and Co., 1948). For a discussion of proposed postwar relations between science and the military, see the hearings of U.S. Congress, H.R. Select Committee on Postwar Military Policy (Washington, D.C. USGPO, 1945).

[8] This was Charles Wilson of the General Electric Company and not the Charles Wilson of General Motors who later became Secretary of Defense.

[9] Karl Compton, Frank Jewett, and other spokesmen for scientists argued in the H.R. hearings on postwar military policy that an agency free from military domination ought to be established in the area of applied military research. Such an agency had existed during the war in the form of the Office of Scientific Research and Development (OSRD).

its utility. Science was identified with technological products such as radar, atomic bombs, and synthetic rubber. The idea of support for pure science was, at best, subordinate. Furthermore, the New Dealers wanted a strong federal agency to administer technologically oriented research, and the military took the position that they should determine the nature of the research that the NAS would undertake on their behalf.

Members of the scientific community itself provided a third fertile source of ideas on the postwar relationship of science and government. They, however, introduced into the developing discussion wholly new elements which have come to influence the character of the relations of science and government today. Wartime administrative leaders of science, like Vannevar Bush and James B. Conant, and scientists at the various sites of the Manhattan District Project were stimulated to act principally by the necessity of reaching a decision regarding use of the atomic bomb against Japan and by the implications of nuclear weapons for postwar international politics. Together these natural scientists introduced into the behind-the-scenes discussion the issues which would dominate the postwar discussions of science and government relations: the financial support of *basic* science, the control of atomic energy, and the place of scientists in national policy-making.[10]

After the detonation of the atomic bomb and the surrender of Japan in August, 1945, these issues were brought into the public realm first by nuclear physicists, and shortly thereafter by Vannevar Bush in his now famous report to the President, *Science, The Endless Frontier*.[11] In late 1945 and early 1946, the clamor of scientists

[10] A voluminous amount of literature exists on this early period, particularly on the decision to drop the atomic bomb. The most authoritative history is by Richard G. Hewlett and Oscar E. Anderson, Jr., *The New World, 1939–1946* (Vol. I. of *A History of the Atomic Energy Commission*, University Park, Pa., Pennsylvania State University Press, 1962). The section on sources includes other accounts of this early period. The history of national policy toward basic research and the outcome of Bush's drive for a policy role for scientists in weapons innovation has yet to be written. Hewlett and Anderson tell the early part of the story and later volumes will help fill the gap in public knowledge about scientists in weapons innovation.

[11] Vannevar Bush, *Science, The Endless Frontier* (Washington, D.C., USGPO, 1945). The NSF reprinted this report in 1960 to commemorate its fifteenth anniversary, with an introduction by Alan T. Waterman. A book-length treatment

from the atomic energy laboratories at Oak Ridge, Chicago, and Los Alamos over the domestic and international control of atomic energy focused national attention on the issue of atomic energy. Furthermore, the atomic scientists, and especially Bush, began the education of politicians to the difference between basic, nonutilitarian research and applied, problem-oriented research. Furthermore, the foundation for participation of natural scientists in national policy deliberations established by Bush and others during the war was reinforced by these early postwar political actions of the atomic scientists who were concerned about the international control of atomic energy.

SCIENTISTS AND POLICY-MAKING

The expressed desire of natural scientists in 1945 to be included in national policy formulation has been met; indeed, natural scientists can now be heard to lament that consulting and other responsibilities in Washington demand too much of their time. Recently, for example, as Robert C. Wood points out in his essay in this book, Hans Bethe complained about the "distraction" of national service.[12] Along with many other scientists, Bethe has been called upon to undertake many responsibilities for national leadership. In fact, a notable feature of American government today is the increased variety of public roles played by natural scientists. For although scientists serving the federal government have never been solely researchers, totally divorced from the policy realm, the multiplicity and extensiveness of governmental tasks now undertaken by scien-

of national science policy is Dael Wolfle, *Science and Public Policy* (Lincoln, Neb., University of Nebraska Press, 1959). See also the American Academy of Political and Social Science, "Perspectives on Government and Science," Norman Wengert, special ed., *The Annals*, CCCXXVII (January, 1960). Two further governmental reports on national science policy ought to be mentioned: NSF, *Basic Research: A National Resource* (Washington, D.C., USGPO, 1957) and the President's Scientific Research Board, *Science and Public Policy; A Report to the President*, John R. Steelman, Chairman (Washington, D.C., USGPO, 1947). A more recent analysis of national science policy, is Don K. Price, J. Stefan Dupré, and W. Eric Gustafson, "Current Trends in Science Policy in the United States," *Impact of Science on Society*, X, No. 3 (1960), 187–213.

[12] Center for the Study of Democratic Institutions, *Science: An Interview by Donald McDonald with Hans Bethe* (Santa Barbara, Calif., The Center, 1962), pp. 3–4.

tists signify a near revolution in the relationship between science and government.

The political functions that scientists undertake today range all the way from partisan polemicist to elder statesman. All of these roles are discussed in this volume, although the emphasis throughout is upon the natural scientist as official or quasi-official participant in the actual formulation of public policy. Some of the more important of the functions performed in this connection are discussed in this essay.

Even in his traditional role of the *scientist as researcher,* the scientist is no longer laboring solely in standard fields such as chemistry or even in newer fields such as nuclear physics. He is now bringing his analytical mind to bear on policy matters as well, especially in the realm of national security policy. Whether he works directly for a federal agency [13] such as the Department of Defense or for a contract organization such as the RAND Corporation, the natural scientist now utilizes new tools such as systems analysis and operations research to do research on questions of public policy.[14]

Through their experience in policy-related research and in the development of military hardware for the federal government, natural scientists have acquired an intimate knowledge of many of the government's problems. Because of this and their command of knowledge relevant to the solution of many public problems, natural scientists are increasingly drawn into positions of major political significance. Today natural scientists serve in the federal bureaucracy as policy advisers, public administrators, diplomats, and technological innovators; in these roles they exert a considerable influence on the formulation of many aspects of public policy.

The *scientist as adviser* can be found at practically every level of government and in an increasing number of governmental agencies. At the cabinet level, the secretaries of at least the following departments have scientific advisers: Air Force, Army, Commerce, Defense,

---

[13] For the status of civil service scientists, see Earl W. Lindveit, *Scientists in Government* (Washington, D.C., Public Affairs Press, 1960).

[14] In effect, these natural scientists function as applied social scientists. The best known example of policy research by a natural scientist is Herman Kahn's *On Thermonuclear War* (Princeton, N.J., Princeton University Press, 1960).

Interior, Navy, and State.[15] Also, in many areas of national concern special advisory committees such as the General Advisory Committee to the Atomic Energy Commission (AEC) have been established. Without a doubt, however, the most important scientific advisory group is that which advises the President: the Special Assistant for Science and Technology and the President's Science Advisory Committee (PSAC) under the chairmanship of the Special Assistant. In addition, these scientists are advised by subcommittees or panels of scientists drawn primarily from the academic world. Through this system the President and his immediate advisers have access to the advice of several hundred scientists. The Special Assistant has in fact become a central figure in the management of the nation's scientific program and in the growing network of advisory bodies which assist public officials on technical and scientific matters. These advisory bodies in turn have proliferated so extensively that an auxiliary career as advisers to governmental agencies has been made possible for scientists.

Following the initial use of scientists as advisers by the military services and the AEC, many advisory groups have been appointed to aid public officials on technical and scientific matters. Under the influence of the Special Assistant this trend has been accelerated until it encompasses a great many aspects of national policy, and large numbers of scientists from industries and universities advise and work with public officials on many national problems. Consequently, a pool of competent scientists who possess experience in national affairs but who, for one reason or another, serve government primarily in part-time advisory capacities has been created.[16] Furthermore,

[15] Frequently, the secretary of an executive department will have as his science adviser the head of an office which is responsible for the scientific activities within the department. For example, on September 14, 1962, the Department of State established the position of Director of International Scientific Affairs. This official, who is a scientist, has the responsibility to "participate actively in general foreign policy development" as well as to "advise and assist the Secretary of State . . . on matters having scientific and technological implications." See *Foreign Affairs Manual*, Circ. No. 84 (September 14, 1962).

[16] George B. Kistiakowsky, second Special Assistant to President Eisenhower, stated in November, 1960, that there were over 100 scientists serving on PSAC panels at one time. "Personal Thoughts on Research in the United States," in *Proceedings of a Conference on Academic and Industrial Basic Research* (Washington, D.C., USGPO, 1961), NSF 61-39, p. 49.

a hierarchy of scientific advisory bodies is developing which to some extent parallels the bureaucratic hierarchy of government, and the emerging pattern appears to be that scientist-advisers generally enter the lower rung of this advisory hierarchy and advance through service and experience to its topmost echelon. In short, there is a nascent professionalization of the scientific advisory function.

The Special Assistant plays an important part in this development primarily because of the PSAC panel system. Although he may use his own staff to carry out a study project requested by the President, he frequently employs the device of assigning the problem to a panel of experts working with a PSAC member as chairman.[17] If the problem concerns primarily the scientific community, as did the question of the advisability of the Stanford linear accelerator, scientists drawn from private institutions tend to be used on the panel. On the other hand, if the problem concerns one or more federal agencies, experts who either represent or advise the agencies involved are generally called upon. For example, the Bethe Panel of 1958 which analyzed the potential impact of a nuclear test ban on American military security included representatives from the Atomic Energy Commission, the Central Intelligence Agency, and the Department of Defense.

The PSAC panel system enables the Special Assistant to recruit scientists for governmental service, evaluate their performance, and recommend them for further government service. As former Special Assistant George Kistiakowsky has put it, "A by-product of this panel activity is the identification of younger scientists with a broad-gauged view in addition to usual technical competence" as candidates for higher positions in the advisory network, including membership on the PSAC itself. In short, then, the Special Assistant has to a limited degree become an adviser to the President and other officials on scientific advisory and administrative personnel.

The professionalization of the scientific advisory function, particularly at the higher levels of the federal government, is seen in at least two ways. First, there is a tendency to select scientists for the

---

[17] Unfortunately, the membership lists and even the names of most PSAC panels are classified information; however, information is occasionally released on one panel or another. In November, 1958, James R. Killian, Jr. announced the existence of fifteen panels and identified the membership of five, in *Aviation Week* (November 17, 1958), p. 37.

PSAC panels largely on the basis of past competence as advisers and for the PSAC in turn to recruit its membership from the ranks of panel members. Of greatest significance, however, is the procedure followed thus far by which the President selects his Special Assistant from the membership of the PSAC. In this way, the administration seeks to obtain a highly competent, experienced, and politically neutral body of scientific experts to advise it at all levels of the hierarchy.

The *scientist as administrator* plays a role that is no more novel in American political life than that of the scientist as adviser, but his tasks have changed significantly. Whereas in the past the scientist as administrator tended to be restricted to such scientific service bureaus as the Weather Bureau and the National Bureau of Standards, scientists today occupy administrative positions which cover broad policy areas. In this connection the most notable example is that of the Director of Defense Research and Engineering in the Department of Defense. This highly strategic position in the formulation of national security policy appears to have become one reserved for natural scientists experienced in weaponry like Herbert York and Harold Brown. It is interesting to note that the creation of this important office was the result of the advice of the President's Special Assistant for Science and Technology.

A second important departure to be noted in connection with this role is the recruitment of scientists from private life rather than just from the Civil Service to fill high level policy-making positions. The former pattern has, for example, been employed by the AEC and the Department of Defense while the latter has been more typical of the National Aeronautics and Space Administration (NASA) and the long-established scientific bureaus.

Another role of the scientist in American government is that of initiator and promoter of technological innovation. While the *scientist as technological innovator* has a long tradition in American government, the degree of involvement has developed rapidly.[18] The increasing technological relevance of scientific research, the acceler-

[18] Dupree, for example, in his *Science in the Federal Government,* discussed the public careers of such scientific-political innovators as Alexander Bache, John Wesley Powell, and Gifford Pinchot.

ating cost of technological innovation, and the need for speed in weapons development have all brought both scientists and government more fully into the sphere of technological innovation.

A noteworthy example of scientists as technological innovators is the creation of the atomic bomb. Without their initiative this weapon would never have been developed. Edward Teller's successful campaign for a thermonuclear weapon, J. Robert Oppenheimer's championing of tactical nuclear weapons, and John von Neumann's important contribution to the Air Force missile program are additional examples which point out that on occasion, sometimes against serious opposition, scientists have brought about major innovations in weaponry and even in tactics and strategy.

Closely related to the role as technological innovator is that of the *scientist as strategist*. Beginning with the decision to drop the atomic bomb in 1945 and continuing through the decision to seek a nuclear test ban, scientists have been influential in the formulation of the political and military strategies of the United States. Oppenheimer, for example, was one of the earliest and most forceful advocates of a strategy of graduated response to Soviet pressures.[19] As early as 1948, he stressed the danger of piecemeal Communist aggression once the Soviet Union had achieved nuclear parity with the United States.

It is this role in particular which has brought scientists into political clashes with one another and with other groups such as the military services. Until quite recently, for example, in the national debate over the merits of a nuclear test ban, the principal clash occurred between scientists like Edward Teller who gave precedence to the further development of nuclear weapons and those like Hans Bethe who favored an immediate first step toward arms control.[20] Differences on nuclear strategy have provided the foundation for most of the political clashes among natural scientists since World War II.

Natural scientists in governmental service also now perform many diplomatic functions. Again there are numerous examples of this

---

[19] See Gilpin, *American Scientists and Nuclear Weapons Policy*, chap. 4.
[20] *Ibid.*

responsibility of the *scientist as diplomat.* In October, 1961, President Kennedy sent his Special Assistant for Science and Technology to India to explain America's latest disarmament plan.[21] The scientific attaché program in the State Department utilizes scientists to maintain contact with scientific developments in certain major scientific nations. Scientists such as Isidor I. Rabi and Henry De Wolf Smyth have represented the United States abroad as ambassadors and delegates to international organizations and conferences, and to other nations.

A noteworthy example of scientists' activities in foreign affairs took place in the summer of 1958 when the United States sent a scientific delegation to Geneva to establish the technical basis for an international treaty to outlaw future nuclear weapons tests. On the basis of the agreement reached by the scientists at the Geneva Conference of Experts to Study the Possibility of Detecting Violations of a Possible Agreement on Suspension of Nuclear Tests, political negotiations on a nuclear test ban were initiated by the East and West.

The tendency of political leadership to place so much confidence in the ability of scientists to resolve problems and issues suggests the possibility of a role for the *scientist as witch doctor or priest.* The facetious ascription of this role at least calls attention to the fact that scientists do have access to an esoteric body of knowledge and that in part the salvation of the nation depends upon that knowledge.[22] Not only do they define the nature of physical reality but through their knowledge of it they can change the reality of man's physical and social world. As the past two decades have revealed, these are important powers and constitute the principal claim of natural scientists for a place in the policy-making mechanism.

The place to which natural scientists have risen in American political life and the reasons for this development constitute the principal subject of the initial essays in this volume by Don K. Price, Robert C. Wood, and Harvey Brooks. Price explains this phenomenon principally in terms of the continuity of the relationship between scien-

[21] The New York *Times,* October 11, 1961.
[22] For a version of this theme, see Robert Fitch, "The Scientist as Priest and Savior," *The Christian Century* (March 26, 1958), p. 370.

tists and government in the United States. He is concerned with the historical interaction between American scientific and political institutions and with the impact of one upon the other.

Wood focuses primarily upon the politically relevant characteristics of scientists and the scientific community. He is interested in the individual scientist as a member of a skill group particularly well adapted for American political life and discusses the skills, sources of power, and attitudes of scientists which account for their success in politics.

Brooks analyzes a phenomenon that provides perhaps the most striking example of the natural scientist's magnified place in American political life: the scientist as adviser to policy-makers. A natural scientist himself with long experience in governmental consulting, Brooks discusses a wide range of issues which have been raised with increasing frequency as the number of natural scientists partaking in policy decisions has continued to increase. Among these are the selection of advisers, the responsibilities of the advisers, and possible conflicts of interest.

The next five essays in this volume deal with the political activities of natural scientists in the two policy areas of support for science and science in relation to national security. The two concluding essays consider the proposition that new types of expertise other than those possessed by natural scientists as such are being developed, or must be developed, to cope with the problems created by the interactions of science, technology, and society.

SCIENTISTS AND NATIONAL SCIENCE POLICY

Despite the initial defeat of Vannevar Bush's original conception for a national research foundation, the U.S. government, through a variety of instruments including a modified form of Bush's proposal, has come to assume a major responsibility for the support of basic scientific research. Moreover, as Bush desired, natural scientists have been given almost a free hand in the administration of this research support.

This novel commitment of the national government to underwrite a major portion of American basic research is founded upon a growing appreciation within the executive branch, and to a lesser extent within Congress, that in the long run highly significant technological advances will continue only if preceded by well-supported and extensive—as well as expensive—basic research. No doubt the examples of the atomic bomb, radar, and important wartime medical advances such as penicillin impressed this fact on the minds of many public officials.

Since 1945 the federal government has established institutions and instruments to support basic research within the nation's universities in a manner least offensive to natural scientists. The magnitude of the national commitment is illustrated simply by mentioning the major governmental agencies dedicated in part to this end: the AEC, the National Institutes of Health, the National Science Foundation, and the National Aeronautics and Space Administration. In addition, the military services have agencies such as the Office of Naval Research which have a responsibility to support basic research.

The variety and ingenuity of the ways in which basic research is now supported are as impressive as the proliferation of federal benefactors. An elaborate system of contracted research laboratories,[23] grants to private institutions,[24] and support for particular research projects has evolved in addition to basic research undertaken in government-operated laboratories such as those of the National Institutes of Health. As a consequence, the characteristics of traditional

[23] This development of the administrative contract, or what Don K. Price calls "federalism by contract," is discussed in his essay in this volume. For a more extensive discussion, see chap. 3 of his *Government and Science* (New York, New York University Press, 1954). See also Albert C. Lazure and Andrew P. Murphy, Jr., eds., *Research and Development Procurement Law* (Washington, D.C., *Federal Bar Journal*, 1957), J. Stefan Dupré and W. Eric Gustafson, "Contracting for Defense," *Political Science Quarterly*, LXXVII, No. 2 (June, 1962), 161–77, and U.S. Bureau of the Budget, *Report to the President on Government Contracting for Research and Development* (Washington, D.C., Bureau of the Budget, 1962).

[24] A significant study of this subject is Charles V. Kidd, *American Universities and Federal Research* (Cambridge, Mass., Harvard University Press, 1959). The impact of federal support on higher education has generated considerable interest and study. See, for example, Douglas M. Knight, ed., *The Federal Government and Higher Education*, Background Papers and Final Report of the 17th American Assembly (Englewood Cliffs, N.J., Prentice-Hall, 1960) and Harold Orlans, *The Effects of Federal Programs on Higher Education* (Washington, D.C., The Brookings Institution, 1962).

scientific research institutions are undergoing important alterations.[25]

Along with the institutions and instruments used by government
to support science, certain bodies are evolving within government
and the scientific community itself to assume responsibility for assessing the quality of national policies toward basic research. Both
the Office of Science and Technology (OST) within the Executive
Office of the President [26] and the Federal Council for Science and
Technology (FCST) as well as other agencies of government have
become interested in science as a definitive area for governmental
action in much the same way that government is concerned with
labor, natural resources, and commerce.

As a matter of fact, the ever-accelerating costs of scientific research and the consequently increasing dependence of the scientific
community upon federal financial support necessitate the determination within the federal bureaucracy of major decisions affecting the
American scientific enterprise. In the past, such decisions have been
relatively decentralized since the leadership of each discipline, for
example, physics or biology, has largely controlled the allocation of
its funds. Competing demands on research funds have now increased
to the point where there is a perceptible trend toward centralized
decision-making and the establishment by the federal government,
acting upon the advice of natural scientists, of national research
priorities.

It is presently apparent that basic decisions have been reached
not only on the questions of whether the federal government ought
to support basic research but also on some of the issues regarding
the appropriate conditions for research support such as secrecy
versus freedom of publication, accountability of public funds versus
research flexibility, and internal security versus scientific freedom.
These past decisions, however, only establish the basis for far more

[25] In 1963 the Carnegie Foundation for the Advancement of Teaching released the summary of its study of the impact of federal programs on higher
education. See *The Educational Record*, XLIV, No. 2 (April, 1963).

[26] This office was established by Reorganization Plan No. 2 of 1962. See
U.S. House of Representatives, *Reorganization Plan No. 2 of 1962*, H.R. Doc.
No. 372, 87th Congress, 2d Session (Washington, D.C., USGPO, 1962). The
first director of this office holds simultaneously the position of Special Assistant
to the President for Science and Technology.

crucial decisions on national science policy which scientists and public officials are forced to make with increasing frequency.

The involvement of government in the traditional affairs of scientists and the financial dependence of science upon the public treasury introduces a number of important problems that are brought out by Wallace S. Sayre and Robert N. Kreidler in their essays. Sayre poses a series of questions: Who speaks for science to government? What do they want? How do they try to achieve their goals? He thus seeks to make scientists aware of the limitations that the political process places upon them and to educate the leadership of science to its political responsibilities.

Kreidler discusses the role of the President's science advisers in the making of national science policy. From this perspective he analyzes the problems created for government and the scientific community by the increasing demands of science for financial assistance. Beyond this, however, Kreidler suggests a number of actions that must be taken by scientific leadership if it is to meet the new range of problems and responsibilities created by federal support.

SCIENTISTS AND NATIONAL SECURITY POLICY

The other policy issue which has largely absorbed the energies of natural scientists since 1945 has been that of national policy toward nuclear weapons. While in the area of national policy toward basic research political unity with respect to the proper end of policy has tended to characterize the scientific community, in the realm of nuclear weapons policy disunity has been more typical. Broadly stated, the basic divisive issue has been whether the prime goal of American nuclear policy ought to be to employ the threat of nuclear warfare to deter aggression or to seek the complete elimination of nuclear weapons.

From the decision to bomb Hiroshima in August, 1945 to the nuclear test ban controversy, the deterrence-disarmament issue has divided American natural scientists. It has caused individual scientists to speak out publicly and their concern has motivated many other scientists to undertake positions of public responsibility. It has also inspired many important policy and technical innovations for which natural scientists are largely responsible: the Baruch Plan, tactical nuclear weapons, continental air defense, intercontinental missiles, and the proposal for an inspected nuclear test ban.[27]

On this issue the United States is also at the end of one era and on the threshold of another. The debate over nuclear deterrence versus nuclear disarmament which has dominated so much of the political activity of natural scientists over the past fifteen years appears to have been largely resolved in favor of deterrence.[28] This is not because the ideas of any particular group of natural scientists have prevailed but rather because postwar technological developments such as hydrogen bombs and missiles have made disarmament for the present at least a hopeless cause. Furthermore, those ideas on the purposes and requirements of deterrence which have come to govern strategic thought are as much or more the creation of what Bernard Brodie calls the scientific strategists as of the natural scientists.

It would be erroneous to conclude, however, that natural scientists have lost influence in the making of national security policy. Their responsibilities in this area continue to be major ones and, for this reason, their attitudes and behavior with respect to such matters are important. At the least, as Warner R. Schilling maintains in his essay, these attitudes ought to be appreciated by American political leadership. At the same time, Albert Wohlstetter argues in his essay that the severe limitations of natural scientists in dealing with matters of strategy ought to be more widely understood and that the nation must seek to meet the challenge of preserving nuclear deterrence through reliance upon experts in strategic matters who may or may not be trained as natural scientists.

The emergence in the United States of civilian experts in strategy,

[27] There are numerous writings by scientists and about scientists in this area. See, for example: Robert C. Batchelder, *The Irreversible Decision, 1939–1950* (Boston, Houghton Mifflin, 1962), Donald Brennan, ed., *Arms Control, Disarmament, and National Security* (New York, George Braziller, 1961), Gilpin, *American Scientists and Nuclear Weapons Policy*, Erwin N. Hiebert, *The Impact of Atomic Energy* (Newton, Kansas, Faith and Life Press, 1961), Robert Jungk, *Brighter Than a Thousand Suns* (New York, Harcourt, Brace and Co., 1958), and Edward Teller and Allen Brown, *The Legacy of Hiroshima* (New York, Doubleday, 1962).

[28] Samuel P. Huntington develops this point in *The Common Defense* (New York, Columbia University Press, 1961), see especially chap. 7. The nuclear test ban treaty is no doubt an attempt to stabilize mutual deterrence; whether it is also a first step toward nuclear disarmament remains to be seen.

or "scientific strategists," is the subject of the essay by Bernard Brodie. These applied social scientists have undertaken the responsibility of bridging the gap between the technical and political worlds. Brodie and Wohlstetter both point out that experts in new methods of scientific analysis appropriate to the treatment of social issues are increasingly replacing natural scientists and supplementing military officers in formulating military strategy and assessing the military worth of new technologies. As such, these experts have assumed a responsibility which in the early postwar period was principally that of natural scientists. Whereas, for example, in the early 1950s the United States depended largely upon natural scientists untrained in strategic matters for evaluating the military worth of a thermonuclear weapon, of tactical nuclear weapons, and of continental air defense, the present tendency is to rely upon experts in strategy.

CONCLUSION

In the concluding essay, Christopher Wright analyzes in broad terms the many bridges which have been built between science and society in the postwar period. In reviewing and assessing the different mediating functions scientists have undertaken between the political and scientific realms, he considers the carry-over of the scientists' professional characteristics to this new area of endeavor and inquires whether we have not too freely misused the energies of natural scientists for tasks they may not be ideally qualified to perform. He suggests that there is not only a need—demonstrated by Brodie and Wohlstetter in the national security area—for the development of new skills in those areas of national life where science, technology, and society interact, but also a need to develop professional skills and organizations especially competent at understanding and anticipating the effects of these interactions on the paramount goals and values of the nation and at guiding or otherwise helping to exploit the interactions for the long-range interests of the nation and mankind.

The Scientific Establishment

DON K. PRICE

Dean of the Faculty of Public Administration of Harvard University

This essay is reprinted with the permission of the American Philosophical Society from its *Proceedings*, 106, No. 3 (June, 1962).

Now that the federal government is spending more money on research and development than its total budget before Pearl Harbor,
American scientists find it hard to figure out their new role in society. They used to assume that democracy would never be a patron of
the sciences, and even after the Second World War the Executive
had to urge the support of research on a skeptical Congress. But
even though the last administration started to cut back on expenditures for science, it ended by quadrupling them. And this was by no
means for defense alone; over those eight years the Congress multiplied the budget of the National Institutes of Health more than
nine-fold, giving them each year more than the President recommended. It is almost enough to make one try to apply to politics the
theory of Henry Adams that science, as it becomes more abstract, increases in geometrical progression the power that it produces.[1]

In his farewell message President Eisenhower warned the nation
against the danger that "public policy could itself become the captive of a scientific-technological elite." Even though he quickly explained that he was not talking about science in general, but only
those parts allied with military and industrial power, this was a

[1] Adams predicted that "the future of Thought, and therefore of History, lies
in the hands of the physicists . . . ," and went on to speculate that a rapid
acceleration of thought in the direction of the abstract sciences might "reduce
the forces of the molecule, the atom, and the electron to that costless servitude
to which it has reduced the old elements of earth and air, fire and water. . . ."
His prediction was uncanny, except for the term "costless." Henry Adams, *The
Degradation of the Democratic Dogma* (New York, Capricorn, 1958, first published in 1919), pp. 277, 303.

shock to the scientists.[2] To one who believes that science has helped to liberate man from ancient tyrannies—who in short still takes his political faith from Franklin and Jefferson and the Age of the Enlightenment—it is disconcerting to be told that he is a member of a new priesthood allied with military power.

Yet the plain fact is that science has become the major Establishment in the American political system: the only set of institutions for which tax funds are appropriated almost on faith, and under concordats which protect the autonomy, if not the cloistered calm, of the laboratory. The intellectual problems involved in this new status are likely to trouble scientists almost as much as the fears of the apocalyptic uses to which their discoveries may be put by the politicians.

The scientists are not the first, of course, to find it difficult to adjust their political ideals to the new world of technology. For example, the old corporation executive liked the great power technology had given to industry, but wished to limit the role of government on Jeffersonian principles. But the American scientist has a better right to his political nostalgia. For while the Founding Fathers had very little idea that industrial corporations would ever exist, let alone claim freedom of enterprise as a fundamental of the Constitution, some of them had a strong faith that free science would advance the cause of political freedom.

This faith of the Enlightenment tended to persist in the political thinking of American scientists, even in the period between the two World Wars, when it came to seem naïve to their colleagues abroad. Even to this day they have shown singularly little interest in the conservative political theorists who have been telling them that

---

[2] Quoted in The New York *Times*, January 22, 1961. See also the authorized interpretation of this statement by the President's Special Assistant for Science and Technology, Dr. George B. Kistiakowsky, quoted in "Footnote to History," *Science*, CXXXIII, No. 3450 (February 10, 1961), 355. As Chief of Staff, General Eisenhower had told the Army in 1946: "The future security of the nation demands that all those civilian resources which by conversion or re-direction constitute our main support in time of emergency be associated closely with the activities of the Army in time of peace," and advised the Army to contract extensively for scientific and industrial services. (*Memorandum for . . . General and Special Staff Divisions, etc.*, "Scientific and Technological Resources as Military Assets," April 30, 1946.)

science cannot deal with basic values or solve the major human problems, and the radical theorists who tell them that science can, if it will only join in a political system that will give it real power over society.[3] The conservative theorists have usually supported the conventional views of those in the European parliamentary tradition who believed that major political issues should be dealt with by party leaders and career administrators, with scientists speaking on such matters only when spoken to. And the most important radicals have been the Marxists, who proposed to let science, as they defined it, determine all human values through a disciplined system that would leave no room for the disorder of liberal democracy.

If American scientists generally ignored both the conservative and radical critics of the Enlightenment, it was probably, in the main, because they were simply not interested in political theory, or even in politics. But it may have been also because neither theoretical position seemed very relevant to their practical experience. In disregard of the conservative and conventional theory, American scientists have come to have a much more direct role in high administration and in the making of policy than their counterparts in the parliamentary systems of Western Europe. (This is not to say that they had a more satisfactory role in the performance of scientific functions in the government.) And the more influence the scientists acquire, the more they now seem to work toward the dispersal of government organization and the decentralization of decisions, a trend impossible to explain to technocrats or the theorists of Marxism.

If we wish to understand the nature of our present scientific establishment, and its role in the making of public policy, perhaps we should look at the unusual way in which the role of scientists in public affairs has developed in the United States, and what its in-

[3] Unamuno, Maritain, and Ortega y Gasset represent the conservative critics of the Enlightenment; J. D. Bernal may be taken as a sample on the socialist side. Judith N. Shklar, whose *After Utopia* (Princeton, N.J., Princeton University Press, 1957) begins with the observation that "nothing is quite so dead today as the spirit of optimism that the very word Enlightenment evokes," goes on to admit that "the less reflective public, certainly until 1914, remained cheerfully indifferent to the intellectual currents of despair. . . . [p. 3]" In this optimistic category, I would include most American scientists, and bring the date up to the present.

fluence has been on the governmental system. That influence, I think, has been profound, not because of anything the scientists were seeking to do deliberately, at least until quite recently, but because of the special opportunities that were offered them by the nature of American political institutions. From the Jacksonian period, indeed, American scientists rarely had any distinctive opinion about politics or its relation to science; they were most often inclined to combine the antipolitical prejudices of the business community with an envy of the social status of the European scientist. But while the American scientist lacked the honorific status of a member of a European Academy, he probably found it easier to play a direct role in government policy-making.

Sir Charles Snow has written with great insight of the Two Cultures, of the persisting failure of the humanists to understand the scientists or the changes they are working in the world, and of the scientists' personal and institutional difficulties in their relationship to government administrators and politicians. He has warned Americans most cogently against the naïve belief that their constitutional system protects them against the dangers that face all countries as the result of the terrible weapons that scientists have put at the disposal of politicians who still think in prescientific terms.[4]

But in the United States we need to understand the idiosyncrasies of our institutions not in order to admire them, but to know how to remedy their shortcomings, which were only a minor nuisance a generation ago, but may be a mortal threat today. Our television experts and editorial writers may be addicted to oratorical overconfidence in our peculiar institutions, but our scientists and intellectuals generally—and government reformers in particular—are rather more addicted to applying constitutional cures that do not fit the disease.

I suspect that Sir Charles has a special degree of popularity in the United States for a reason that he would probably disapprove. We enjoy what he writes not only because we see many important ways that it applies to us, but also because of ways in which it does not. We like it much as we like Anthony Trollope; we like to read about

---

[4] See especially C. P. Snow, *Science and Government* (Cambridge, Mass., Harvard University Press, 1961), p. 55.

a scholarly world in which the classicists can still snub the scientists and social scientists hardly exist at all, just as we like to read about the squire and the vicar and the butler. And American scientists like to imagine, as they read about the problems that scientists experience when serving under the career administrators of the United Kingdom, that they can blame their own problems on lack of status in the bureaucracy.

Yet a look at the main outlines of the two systems gives a different picture. In Great Britain, in spite of decades of debate about the basis of recruitment of the Administrative Class, it is still dominated by men trained in the classical and historical studies; not one man in twenty among these guardians of public policy has had a scientific or technical education. In spite of recurrent criticism of its role, it still maintains a professional monopoly (though in a studiously amateur and nonscientific way) over the organization of the government departments, and a major share of influence in the formation of national policy. It thus has no great interest in maintaining easy institutional channels by which scientists could move into its membership, or the universities could work closely with it on its major policy problems.[5]

Now that we are both constitutional democracies, it makes much less difference that Great Britain has a king and the United States a president but a great deal of difference how we set up the professional group of men who actually run the government. Our Jacksonian revolution indeed destroyed the hopes of John Quincy Adams for a continuation of the Jeffersonian alliance between science and republicanism. At the same time, by wiping out the beginnings of a career system, it prevented the development of an elite administrative corps and thus cleared the channels of promotion for the scientists who, decades later, were to begin to move up in the civil service.

---

[5] Edward McCrensky, *Scientific Manpower in Europe* (New York, Pergamon Press, 1958), pp. 27–29, gives the general picture with respect to salaries and personnel policy. For the classic attitude of the Administrative Class regarding its relation to the scientific civil service, see the testimony of Sir Warren Fisher, Permanent Secretary of the Treasury, before the Royal Commission on the Civil Service, 1929–30, *Minutes of Evidence*, pp. 1276, 1282. For its contemporary attitude, see C. H. Sisson, *The Spirit of British Administration* (London, Faber and Faber, 1959).

The frontier radicalism of the day distrusted all forms of Establishment; this was the era in which state constitutions forbade ministers to hold public office and prohibited educational qualifications for admission to the bar. But as the business of government got more complicated, the frontier had to admit that certain skills were necessary. Its essentially pragmatic temper insisted, as it became necessary to hire civil servants for merit rather than patronage, that the requirements be defined in terms of the needs of the specific jobs, rather than by general educational status. It was easiest to prove the need for special skills, of course, in technical fields, partly on account of the objective nature of the problem, partly because scientific societies were determined to raise and maintain their professional standards in the civil service as well as in private practice.[6]

As a result, it was in the scientific and professional fields that the career civil service system was first pushed up to the higher ranks. As we developed our top civil service, we made it something quite different from a career Administrative Class; most of its members are not only nonpolitical, but nonadministrative as well, and they are not career officials in the same sense as a U.S. Navy officer or a British Civil Servant.

In recent years, scientists and engineers, while certainly rare among those in high political office, have done reasonably well in the civil service. The positions of administrative continuity and bureaucratic power in Washington are, in the civil service departments, the bureau chiefs. A study in 1958 of the 63 bureau chiefs showed that 9 of them had advanced degrees in the natural sciences, and 17 others had been trained in lesser ways as engineers or tech-

---

[6] As A. Lawrence Lowell put it: "[T]he great professions, which have secured general recognition in the community, have been strong enough to insist that strictly professional work must not be intrusted to men who have had no professional training or experience." *Public Opinion and Popular Government* (New York, Longmans, 1926), p. 274. Detailed illustrations for specifically scientific fields may be found in the series of "Service Monographs of the United States Government" published by the Institute for Government Research, notably those on the Steamboat Inspection Service, the Office of Experiment Stations, the General Land Office, and the Public Health Service. See also Lewis Mayers, *The Federal Service* (New York, D. Appleton, 1922), p. 21, and Lewis Meriam, *Public Personnel Problems from the Standpoint of the Operating Officers* (Washington, D.C., The Brookings Institution, 1938), p. 317.

nicians. By comparison with these 26 from various branches of technology, there were 9 economists and only 8 lawyers, and 20 from miscellaneous administrative or business careers.[7] Aside from the positions of bureau chief, the top career positions are the so-called "super-grades," which were added above the regular civil service grades to let the government compete for scarce talent.[8] The favorite justification for these positions is the need to employ capable scientists and engineers, notably in the technical branches of the Defense Department and the National Aeronautics and Space Administration. Administrators have ridden along to higher salaries on the political coattails of scientists.

Scientists who become bureau chiefs are, of course, no longer practicing scientists; they are doing work that in the United Kingdom would be done by a member of the Administrative Class educated in history or the classics. But when they are good at their jobs, as some of them are, it is for a reason that would have appealed to Macaulay, who used to argue that he wanted to recruit university graduates in the classics not because they had been studying the classics, but because the classics attracted the best minds, which could adapt themselves to anything.[9] And the American scientist who turns administrator is the equal of his English humanist counterpart in at least one respect: his lack of interest in management as a science, or sometimes at all.

But while the scientists in top civil service posts have not been deeply interested in administration, they have been interested in policy. What chance do they have to make their policy views prevail?

In their influence on policy, as in their advancement in the hierarchy, the scientists in American government had a special opportunity because they did not have to work under a tightly organized

[7] Michael E. Smith, "Bureau Chiefs in the Federal Government," in *Public Policy, 1958,* Yearbook of the Graduate School of Public Administration, Harvard University (Cambridge, Mass., Harvard University Press, 1960), p. 62.

[8] U.S. Civil Service Commission, *The Federal Top Salary Network* (Washington, D.C., USGPO, 1960).

[9] Macaulay put it more pointedly in 1833: "If astrology were taught at our universities, the young man who cast nativities best would generally turn out a superior man." Royal Commission on the Civil Service, *Fourth Report,* Cd. 7338, 1914.

governing elite. After the Civil War, there was no strong conservative tradition based on a landed interest and no national party with a coherent ideology to take control.

As a result, policy tended to develop separately in every field. There was no one to tell the scientific experts that they were on tap but not on top; indeed, they were listened to all the more readily because they were usually not thought of as bureaucrats. There was no one from whom Congress wanted advice less than from the regular career service. But each group of scientists had one foot in government, so to speak, and one outside, and the policy views that the insiders developed would come back to the Congress from the National Academy or the scientific societies.[10] In a government of limited constitutional powers, a research program could be justified in a given field when an action program could not. But the research ultimately seemed to lead to action, in spite of the lawyers' scruples and the lack of interest of the party machines. This was only in part because the politicians were persuaded by objective data; it may have been even more because scientists (and in some fields, the economists) were the major organized communities of professional opinion with a continuous interest in specific public programs. This is a summary of the development of many new federal programs: you can trace it in agriculture, in natural resources, in the regulation of business, in labor and welfare, and we now see its beginnings in the support of education.

The most influential pattern was set in agriculture. Washington and Jefferson had been interested in fostering scientific improvements in agriculture, and in federal support of a national university.

---

[10] "[F]rom the beginning the membership of the Academy included many officers of the Government. . . . On one occasion at least this led to some embarrassment, for the reason that through this double relationship it was thought that the view of subordinate officers might control the action of those higher in authority." Frederick W. True, *A History of the First Half Century of the National Academy of Sciences* (Washington, D.C., USGPO, 1913), p. 202. The same fear, or hope, exists in the present relationship between the Academy and the Federal Council for Science and Technology. F. W. True's history of the Academy, and A. C. True's *History of Agricultural Experimentation and Research in the United States* (Washington, D.C., U.S. Dept. of Agriculture, 1937), Misc. Publ. No. 251, tell a great deal about the role of scientific societies in the development of new federal programs.

They were blocked by the lawyers' scruples about states' rights, until the agricultural scientists found a way to get there by a different route—one that evaded constitutional barriers by merging federal and state interests through the device of federal grants to states in either land or money, and by building a program up on scientific and educational bases. The foundation was, of course, the land-grant college; from it grew the experiment station, the extension program, and the whole system of policy which has let the federal government play a more effective role in the agricultural economy than the government of any supposedly socialized state. In all this development, the land-grant colleges and the associations of various kinds of agricultural scientists maintained an important influence on the Department of Agriculture, supplied most of its career personnel, and generally provided the intellectual leadership for national agricultural policy. They thus in effect greatly weakened the old constitutional distinction between state and federal functions, but without subjecting the field of agriculture to the control of a centralized bureaucracy.

The pattern of grants-in-aid, with its new set of administrative relationships, met two cardinal needs: to provide money, as well as national policy direction, from Washington, and to maintain the autonomy of the states. It accordingly became the basis on which new programs were developed—highways, public health, social security, welfare, housing, and others. This was what political scientists came to call the "New Federalism," which has given the scientists and specialists in each field of policy a chance to work out programs without too much constraint by any party doctrine.

An elite administrative corps may look on scientists as properly subordinate, and science as a way of thinking that should deal with the means to support a policy, a tradition, or an ideology, rather than an end in itself. We can understand this relationship in other countries if we recall how until recent years our military services thought that civilian scientists in military laboratories should conduct their research only pursuant to "requirements" defined by military staff work. This notion was exploded as it became apparent that what scientists discovered by unrestricted research might be of greater military importance than the things the military officers thought they wanted—in short, that the means might determine the ends.

This example provides the extreme (and almost the only conspicuous) example in American politics in which scientists have been faced with difficulties in getting a direct political hearing for their policy ideas. The typical editorial writer may still think in terms borrowed from the experience of parliamentary constitutions with tightly knit administrative elites, but all the habits of American public life run on a different pattern.

Its constitutional peculiarities are typified in one trivial incident: in a recent congressional hearing, a friendly Representative addressed the newly appointed political head of the NASA, to his mild embarrassment, as "Doctor." In a legislature that is supposed to distrust eggheads, a Congressman often wants his advice on a specific program undiluted by either party doctrine or the policy views of general administrators; he is so conditioned to go directly to the scientific expert whenever he can that he sometimes treats his witnesses as experts even when they are not. This constitutional model is worth looking at with more critical sympathy. Its essential parts—none of which exists in the classic parliamentary system—are the standing congressional committee that considers policies without being bound by party doctrine; a chief executive who is elected independently of the legislature on a nonideological platform so that he can tolerate loose coordination and experimentation in policy matters; and a civil service which lets scientists move freely up into top administrative positions, and in and out of government, thus maintaining a continuous interchange of men and ideas between the government and universities. This system makes it impossible to maintain an institutional distinction between ends and means, between policy decisions on the one hand, and on the other hand scientific research or administration. Hence it makes party responsibility in the parliamentary sense impossible, and it greatly complicates the task of coordinating either policy or administration.

On the other hand, to deny the distinction between ends and means is a part of the scientific approach: no scientist likes to feel that his basic values and objectives have been set by others so rigidly that he cannot follow where his research leads him. It was, after all, the purpose of the Enlightenment to free both politics and science from the monarchical and ecclesiastical institutions that defined traditional values.[11] It may be even more necessary to deny the distinction between ends and means, in an institutional sense, in the twentieth century, when it is the requirements of new ideology, rather than old orthodoxy, that threaten freedom. For science itself, by introducing so many complexities into public policy, destroyed the comfortable nineteenth-century notion that public issues could really be determined by the parliamentary competition of two opposing doctrines. At the same time, it made possible, by the development of new techniques of mass communication, the means for producing disciplined support of authoritarian government. If the structure of political institutions does not specifically encourage some social experimentation based on scientific initiative, with some degree of deliberate freedom from the constraints of policy as determined by either partisan theorists or an administrative elite, it will narrow the range of free scientific and political development. Perhaps our eighteenth-century Constitution, with its implied distrust of party discipline, will yet prove to be more adaptable to our scientific era than the classic nineteenth-century parliamentary models of Walter Bagehot or Woodrow Wilson.[12]

At any rate, it is easy to guess why large groups among American scientists—especially in the agricultural sciences—were less pessimistic in the period after the First World War than their European colleagues with respect to the role of science in democratic politics. In

[11] Charles Frankel, *The Case for Modern Man* (Boston, Beacon Press, 1955), p. 58. Ernst Cassirer noted "the almost unlimited power which scientific knowledge gains over all the thought of the Enlightenment. . . . A . . . deeper insight into the spirit of laws, of society, of politics, and even of poetry, seems impossible unless it is pursued in the light of the great model of the natural sciences." *The Philosophy of the Enlightenment* (Boston, Beacon Press, 1955), pp. 45–46.

[12] Walter Bagehot, *The English Constitution* (New York, Oxford University Press, 1936; first published in 1867) and Thomas Woodrow Wilson, "Cabinet Government in the United States," *The International Review* (August, 1879; reprinted in 1947 by The Overbrook Press, Stamford). By the turn of the twentieth century, Wilson had apparently changed his mind in view of the new role of the presidency, especially in international affairs: *Congressional Government* (Boston, Houghton Mifflin, Preface to 15th ed., 1900).

two very practical ways their situation was entirely different; in civil service, their advancement was not blocked by a career bureaucracy, and the constitutional system gave them a chance to advocate policies in comparative freedom from administrative or political discipline. It was no wonder that they had not lost faith in the political approach of the Enlightenment, for they had made it work.

Nevertheless, by the time of the Great Depression this naïve faith was least prevalent in the most important universities and the most advanced fields of science. In them, science was supported more by private corporations and foundations than by government, and its leaders in newer fields like nuclear physics and biochemistry had closer intellectual ties with their European counterparts than with the agronomists or engineers of the land-grant colleges. For the loose American constitutional system had worked best in those aspects of public affairs in which the power of government and the power of the great industrial corporations were not in rivalry. The scientists in institutions that derived their support from industrial wealth and were interested in problems of the industrial urban economy saw the constitutional model in a different political perspective. Among them, accordingly, were to be found both those conservative scientists who were most distrustful of government, and those radicals who tended to take a Marxist view of the role of science in society.

The Depression had thus made it impossible for the American scientist to avoid the second challenge, explicit in Marxism, with respect to the significance of his role in society: does science as it grows in importance lead us away from constitutional liberalism, and require party dictatorship? In a society of growing complexity, is not an increase in the role of government inevitable, and does not that inevitably lead to a centralization of power that will destroy democratic freedom?

These are still troublesome questions, but they are being discussed on a somewhat higher level of sophistication than three decades ago. The change has come about partly because scientists, under the pressure of the Second World War, worked out a new type of contractual relationship that has brought private scientific institutions into a connection with the federal government as intimate and active as that of any land-grant college. And the extension of this system to industrial corporations may now be bringing about a new relationship between government and business following the quarrels of the Depression era, much as the grant-in-aid system transformed federal-state relations after the Civil War.

Before going into the nature of this new system, let us note two peculiarities of American politics that made it possible. The first was the assumption that it was just as appropriate for the voters and legislators to control the administrative organization and procedures of government as its policies, that is to say, the means as well as the ends. This was a radical departure from British or European assumptions. The political progression from conservatives to liberals to socialists never changed the fundamental European assumption that, while governments might be responsible to legislatures for the substance of their policies, it was better for politics and legislation not to meddle with internal administrative organization or the management of the bureaucracy. The socialist political leaders took the unity of the state and its bureaucracy for granted. If anything, they tended to make it all the more monolithic, and to push to its logical conclusion the tendency of Benthamite liberalism to abolish the privileges of guilds and public corporations. But in the United States the current of radicalism ran in the opposite direction; after the age of Jackson, lobbyists and legislators were likely to concern themselves at least as much with the details of administrative organization as with major policies, generally with the purpose of creating centers of independence within government. This tendency was pushed so far that it destroyed the unity of administration, and had disastrous effects on the competence and the political responsibility of government. But it also made it a mistake to assume—as was often assumed both by those who admired and those who feared socialism—that an extension in the scope of governmental business in the United States would automatically involve a corresponding centralization of power.

The second peculiarity of American politics was the extent to which universities and private foundations had a hand in the initiation of new public policies. Private universities as well as the land-grant colleges were drawn into public service functions, partly because they were, in the absence of a career bureaucracy, the main reservoir of expertise on which politicians could draw for advice, and partly in response to the influence of the philanthropic foundations.

By the 1920s, some of the major foundations had lost interest in the charitable alleviation of social problems, and began to hope that science might solve them. This idea led to a strategy of supporting both scientific research and demonstration projects to test the application of such research, which could then be extended by the greater resources of government. Their aid to scientific education and research is a familiar story, in almost every branch of science. But equally important, they went on to help strengthen the professional organizations of scientists,[13] and to pay for the efforts of governments to improve their organization and administration, and to make use of research and research institutions as they did so. By the time of the Second World War, the leading scientists knew that a grant-making agency like a foundation could initiate nationwide programs by working with independent universities and governmental agencies, as the stories of hookworm control, the foundation of public libraries, and the reform of medical education all suggested. And political leaders were inclined to turn to private funds to help them explore future policy opportunities, or experiment with them, as when President Hoover sought foundation financing for his Committee on Social Trends and for a National Science Fund, and the Public Administration Clearing House provided the initial administrative costs for President Roosevelt's Science Advisory Board.[14]

As scientists learned that the organization of government was something that could be influenced from the outside, and that universities and foundations could have a substantial influence on public policy, they were in effect freeing themselves from the assumption

[13] The National Research Council, created by President Wilson to do in the First World War (in a rudimentary way) what the Office of Scientific Research and Development did in the Second, was supported not by appropriations but by the Rockefeller and Carnegie Foundations. Richard G. Axt, *The Federal Government and Financing Higher Education* (New York, Columbia University Press, 1952), p. 78.

[14] *Report of the Science Advisory Board* (Washington, D.C., USGPO, September 20, 1934), p. 15.

that "government and private institutions were sharply different in nature. They were accordingly ready, at the outset of the Second World War, to work out a thoroughly pragmatic set of arrangements for the conduct of weapons research. The approach that they adopted was simply to enlist institutions rather than individuals in the two great scientific programs of the War: the Office of Scientific Research and Development (OSRD) and the Manhattan Project of the Army Engineers.

To those who expect wartime crises and military authority to produce a centralization of authority, this approach must have been as surprising as if the Army had used the war as an excuse to increase, rather than decrease, its reliance on the state militias. But in the hands of Vannevar Bush, James B. Conant, and Karl T. Compton, the government contract became a new type of federalism. Under the OSRD, the Massachusetts Institute of Technology took on the responsibility for developing radar, and California Institute of Technology rockets, and under the Manhattan District, the University of Chicago set up the first sustained nuclear reaction and the University of California fabricated the first atomic bomb, while DuPont, General Electric, Union Carbide, and other industrial giants built the facilities to produce the fissionable materials.[15]

The postwar sequel is a well known story. Through a continuation of this system of administering research and development programs by grant or contract, the Atomic Energy Commission, which was hailed by the draftsmen of the Atomic Energy Act as a triumph of socialism,[16] supports a program in which some nine-tenths of the employees work for private corporations. The adamant argument of many scientific leaders of the 1930s against federal support of science

[15] See the first volume of the official history of the Atomic Energy Commission by Richard G. Hewlett and Oscar E. Anderson, Jr., *The New World, 1939–1946* (Vol. I. of *A History of the Atomic Energy Commission,* University Park, Pa., Pennsylvania State University Press, 1962).

[16] "The field of atomic energy is made an island of socialism in the midst of a free enterprise economy." James R. Newman and Byron S. Miller, *The Control of Atomic Energy* (New York, McGraw-Hill, 1948), p. 4. Mr. Newman, writing the preface to this book a year after the text was completed, noted that "only one major policy formulation, the decision by the Atomic Energy Commission not to conduct research in its own laboratories, departs sharply from the interpretations of the Act set forth in these pages [p. xi]."

now seems as ancient and irrelevant as debates over infra- or supra-lapsarianism; no major university today could carry on its research program without federal money. The Massachusetts Institute of Technology, California Institute of Technology, Chicago, and Johns Hopkins, of course, all administer special military or atomic energy programs and consequently draw from three-fifths to five-sixths of their budgets from government, while Harvard, Yale, and Princeton now get a larger proportion of their operating revenues from federal funds than do land-grant colleges like Illinois, Kentucky, and Maryland.[17]

In dollar volume, the biggest contracts are between the military services and industrial corporations; while most of this money goes for procurement, much of it goes for research and development, and for the kind of systems analysis and the direction and supervision of subcontractors that in a simpler age would have been done by the technical services of the Army and Navy. And even in the business of procurement, the contractual relation is not the traditional market affair: the contract is not let on competitive bids, the product cannot be specified, the price is not fixed, the government supplies much of the plant and capital, and the government may determine or approve the letting of subcontracts, the salaries of key executives, and a host of other managerial matters. A sizable proportion of the government's (and nation's) business is done this way; any one of six industrial corporations spends more federal tax dollars than any of the four smallest executive departments.[18]

But the significance of this development does not turn on the

[17] See the forthcoming study, to be published by the Carnegie Foundation for the Advancement of Teaching in 1963, on the relationship of American universities to the federal government.

[18] For a general discussion of this problem from the legal point of view, see Arthur S. Miller, "Administration by Contract: A New Concern for the Administrative Lawyer," *New York University Law Review*, XXXVI (1961), 957–90. The economic aspects are discussed in a study by Carl Kaysen, *Improving the Efficiency of Military Research and Development*, to be published by the Committee for Economic Development, and the general problems of weapons development and procurement programs in a study by the Harvard Business School: Merton J. Peck and Frederic M. Scherer, *The Weapons Acquisition Process: An Economic Analysis* (Boston, Harvard University Graduate School of Business Administration, Division of Research, 1962).

sheer quantity of money but on the possibilities of institutional development: if a contract can be made with an established academic or industrial corporation, why cannot a new one be set up for the purpose, and if the system will work for scientists and engineers, why not for others? Accordingly we have been seeing not only the splitting off of certain functions that government might have operated directly and their administrative fusion with private institutions, but the creation of entirely new private corporate entities (e.g., the RAND Corporation, the Institute for Defense Analyses, the Aerospace Corporation) for the performance of government business.

As for the kinds of business that can be done under this system, Sir Henry Maine, who believed that progress was measured by the change from status to contract, would be intrigued to note that private corporations have contracts to maintain the Air Force's bombers and its missile ranges, private institutions make strategic studies for the Joint Chiefs of Staff and foreign policy studies for the Senate Foreign Relations Committee, universities administer technical assistance programs for the State Department all over the world, and telephone and radio companies are about to help the National Aeronautics and Space Administration carry our messages through outer space.

This new system is doubtless breaking down the political opposition to federal programs even more effectively than did the system of grants to the states. State and local governments and private corporations used to join in their jealousy of purely federal activities, any extension of which was considered socialistic. The federal grants to states in the field of agriculture, however, were no longer socialistic in the eyes of the governors and the farm bloc; they were a defense of the American way of life, even though they involved more government controls than some avowedly socialistic states have ever managed. And now that the atomic energy and space and military programs support such a large share of the nation's business, and so much of its enterprise and innovation come from research and development financed by federal funds, and so much of that innovation and enterprise spills over quite naturally and properly into related commercial fields, it is no wonder that private business corporations are less jealous of government. More accurately, their jealousy no longer takes the form of fighting socialism, but of haggling over the administrative provisions of contracts. A great deal of private enterprise is now secreted in the interstices of government contracts. In short, what the grant-in-aid programs did to the arguments for states' rights, the new contractual systems are doing to those for pure private enterprise.

But the argument for a measure of independence from central authority still remains valid in either case, and so does the need to recognize that the fundamental responsibility of government cannot be delegated. In a proper sense of the term, "sovereignty" is of course not affected by this type of delegation. Policy decisions remain the responsibility of government. But "policy" here means simply those aspects of the business that government authorities consider it important enough to warrant controlling, either because they think them of major importance, or because they realize that voters or Congressmen think so.

This means that they will consider as policy certain aspects of management (for example, fair employment practices or prevailing wage rates). But, as long as they retain ultimate control, they may act on the advice of contractors with respect to the most momentous new issues, or delegate major segments of the business whenever they can specify the purposes to be accomplished: the complex and costly nature of certain types of military studies, and the sophistication of the new techniques of operations research, make the possibility of such delegation very broad indeed. There is nothing in the nature of the contract itself (or the grant, which differs from it only symbolically and in technical detail) to determine whether in this relationship a central bureacracy will control every detail of the contractor's management, or will leave him free to decide matters in secret that ought to be determined by the President and Congress.

But the general effect of this new system is clear: it has destroyed the notion that the future growth in the functions and expenditures of government, which seems to be made inevitable by the increase in the technological complexity of our civilization, would necessarily take the form of a vast bureaucracy, organized on Max Weber's hierarchical principles, and using the processes of science as Julian Huxley predicted to answer policy questions.[19] To the considerable extent that scientists have shaped this development, its political and administrative patterns have reflected the way scientists actually behaved rather than the way science fiction or Marxist theory would have them behave: they have introduced into the stodgy and responsible channels of bureaucracy the amiable disorder of a university faculty meeting.

Compare, for example, our oldest and least scientific federal agency with a large operational mission with the newest and most scientific—the Post Office with the Air Force or the Space Administration. The Post Office is a relatively self-contained hierarchy. The Air Force develops its policies and runs its program with the advice and cooperation of several dozen of the most influential universities and industrial corporations of the country, whose executives and faculty members consequently have independent bases from which to criticize any policies, strategic plans, or administrative arrangements they dislike—and they can always find a congressional committee to listen to them.

I do not think the role of science in this difference is entirely accidental. This is in part because the pursuit of science itself is a nonhierarchical affair; the best scientists either personally prefer, or are taught by their guilds that they should prefer, the university's combination of research, teaching, and irresponsible administration, and to get the best scientists the government took them on their own terms. But more important, I believe, is the long-range and indirect connection: when the revolution of the Enlightenment proposed that the organization and procedures of government as well as its policies should be open to scientific inquiry and independent criticism, they started a process which has had deep effects on the constitutional system. These effects showed first in the relation of scientific administrators to their executive superiors and to congressional committees, and later in the new structure of federalism and in the new contractual relationships between the federal government and private institutions.

[19] Julian Huxley, *Man in the Modern World* (New York, New American Library, 1948), pp. 120–21. See also his *Religion Without Revelation* (New York, New American Library, 1957), p. 4.

As the story of the President's Science Advisory Committee illustrates, to say nothing of the similar advisory groups to the military services and the Atomic Energy Commission, this type of relationship very greatly reduces the possibility that great issues will be decided by closed scientific politics, or that the increase in importance of scientific staff work will reduce the free play of policy debate. For the institutional bases from which advisers operate give them a measure of independence as public critics, and thus provide something of a counterbalance to the centralizing pressures of wars and rumors of wars.

American scientists, who have tended to be a little disillusioned about their relationship with politicians ever since the Jacksonian period, are now entitled to look with somewhat greater satisfaction on the domestic Establishment that they have helped set up. For to some small extent science has helped the political system of the United States develop along lines quite different from the classic patterns of either parliamentary government and laissez-faire economics on the one hand, or socialism and one-party rule on the other. Among its essential institutional features are universities that are concerned with applied as well as basic sciences, and continuously exchange personnel with the government at all age levels; a personnel system which puts up no barrier against the administrative promotion of men with scientific training; and grants-in-aid and contracts through which federal agencies may influence or guide the policies, but not direct the detailed management, of certain aspects of local governments, business corporations, and universities. Among these institutions, the connecting links are strongest in scientific and technical fields. And the peculiar looseness of the constitutional system enables the scientists in each field to take the initiative in developing policies—just as their innovations are providing the greatest impetus to industrial enterprise. Most important, science is not restrained in its impact on policy by any rigid distinction between ends and means, imposed by institutionalized systems of traditional or ideological values. The key to this is the freedom to influence or determine the organization and procedures of government from the outside, not conceding control over them to professional administrators or party leaders.

But there are some good reasons why scientists should not be too self-satisfied about their new status. A good many of them already think that science has been corrupted by this new system, and the wealth that it has brought.[20] They tend to look back on prewar science as the Reformers looked back to the Primitive Church: a period of austere purity, an era in which no vows were needed to guarantee the poverty of the professor, no scientist was seduced by a government contract, and teaching fellows were obedient. One may well be a little skeptical about this point of view, and suspect that poverty probably brought its distractions no less troublesome than those of riches. But even if we discount such dangers so far, the worst may be yet to come. The public and members of Appropriations Committees are being led to think of science in terms of spectacular results like a space satellite or a cancer cure, and the political pressure to pass miracles may lead to some major distortions in our national policy and put some uncomfortable pressures on the independence of scientific institutions. We probably have less reason to fear that major governmental decisions involving science will be secret than they will be popular.

For while our new system of administration by contract temporarily avoids the political problems that come with the growth of bureaucracy, it encounters them again in more subtle and difficult forms. We do well to recognize that a government bureau is tempted to be more concerned with its own status and power than with the purposes of national policy. But if we entrust those purposes to industrialists or even scientists, we do not sterilize that political temptation. We only let it begin to work directly on the industrialists and scientists. If public ownership is no guarantee of unselfishness, neither is private ownership. And it is ironic, in view of the general public image of his political ideas, that it was President Eisenhower who presented most forcefully to the country the danger that, having hired private corporations to further specific public ends, we will see them use the public means for private profit, or even in political efforts to control the policy decisions of the government.

Government policy, like science itself, needs to be conceived and

[20] Merle A. Tuve, "Basic Research in Private Research Institutes," in Dael Wolfle, ed., *Symposium on Basic Research* (Washington, D.C., AAAS, 1959), p. 178.

pursued with some regard for its totality as well as its parts. By giving priority to the parts—by turning over the administration of public functions to private institutions—we have strengthened our ability to do a great many separate things, but not our ability to give integrity and discipline and direction to our total effort. Indeed, by relying too much on the contracting method we have probably weakened the quality of the scientists within the civil service, whose help is needed by the executive who seeks to manage our scientific programs as a coherent system.[21]

In the dimensions of its financial support and in the breadth of its influence, science has indeed become a national Establishment. Politicians are more likely to abuse it by calling on it to advance their special causes than they are to ignore it. In this predicament, scientists cannot protect their essential interests in government by setting themselves apart in a separate status or separate department. They used to be content with the control of particular bureaus or programs. Today, in the White House Office or the lobbies of the Capitol, they are obliged by the nature of the system they helped create to play a responsible role in all aspects of national policy, and in the development of a new pattern of relationships between public and private institutions in our society.

[21] Harold Brown, "Research and Engineering in the Defense Laboratories," an address by the Director of Defense Research and Engineering in Washington, D.C., on October 19, 1961.

Scientists and Politics: The Rise of an Apolitical Elite

ROBERT C. WOOD

*Professor of Political Science at the
Massachusetts Institute of Technology*

If the war years of the 1940s gave formal recognition to science as a national resource, to be used systematically and extensively for security purposes, the late 1950s marked the emergence of American scientists as genuine political influentials. Gone are the days, surely, when many eminent scientists lived the life J. Robert Oppenheimer describes as his in the early 1930s in Berkeley.

I have never read a newspaper or a current magazine like Time or Harpers; I had no radio, no telephone; I learned of the stock-market crash [sic] in the fall of 1929 only long after the event; the first time I ever voted was in the presidential election of 1936. . . . I was interested in man and his experience; I was deeply interested in my science; but I had no understanding of the relations of man and his society.[1]

Today, Hans Bethe's account of his activities describes what seems to be the more typical relation of many distinguished scientists to public affairs.

I would say I spent about half of my time on things that do not have any direct connection with my science. This is somewhat worse for older people like me, but even the young people feel the external pressures to do things other than their scientific work. . . . I used to be a member of the President's Science Advisory Committee. That committee has been assigned and has also made for itself great responsibility, particularly in the field of military technology. I sit on a large number of its subcommittees and they take a great deal of my time. Many of my

---

[1] Atomic Energy Commission, transcript of hearing before the Personnel Security Board, *In the Matter of J. Robert Oppenheimer* (Washington, D.C., USGPO, 1954), p. 8.

colleagues here in this department and in other departments sit on committees that must advise on funds from, say, the National Science Foundation. And there are many committees on scholarships. . . .[2]

Some of the forces which help account for this transformation in the workaday world of science are now familiar: the exponential rise in public research and development funds, the establishment of new governmental agencies and enterprises with predominantly scientific and technological missions, and the rapid evolution of mechanisms for the provision of scientific advice on policy. A less emphasized but perhaps more important factor has been the scientists' own participation in the political arena while these new arrangements were being fashioned.

Since the days of the Office of Scientific Research and Development (OSRD), scientists have articulated and fought for their political goals. Sometimes they have lost, sometimes they have compromised, but often they have achieved political goals which they conceived to be in the interest of their profession. Their struggle in Congress for civilian dominance of the Atomic Energy Commission (AEC) can be interpreted in this light, as can the matter of Dr. Oppenheimer, the long drawn out wrangle over the organization and management of the National Science Foundation (NSF), and, more recently, the triumphant revitalization of the President's Science Advisory Committee (PSAC) and establishment of the National Aeronautics and Space Administration (NASA). Scientists have demonstrated in these instances as well as in the continuing negotiations between government and universities over terms and conditions of sponsored research and in their heavy involvement in disarmament policy that they possess both political influence and, on occasion, the capacity to use it effectively.

The rise of scientists in political visibility has been so rapid that observers disagree on the nature and scope of their influence and the bases of their power. One prevalent interpretation, often advanced by the scientists themselves, amounts to an "orphan theory" of the scientists' political status. Thus, Sir Charles Snow and Gerald

---

[2] Center for the Study of Democratic Institutions, *Science: An Interview by Donald McDonald with Hans Bethe* (Santa Barbara, Calif., The Center, 1962), pp. 3–4. Hereinafter referred to as *Bethe Interview*.

Holton would have us believe that although the potential of their profession for constructive contributions to public policy-making is enormous, their counsel is misunderstood, misused, feared, and neglected. In this view, scientists bear the burden of men possessed with the capacity to solve the burning issues of the day, who are nevertheless excluded from counseling the great by reason of popular ignorance and cynical political manipulation.

A sharply contrasting view that is usually advanced by nonscientists asserts that in many major policy areas the scientific community bids fair to dominate the political scene. President Eisenhower is not alone in his concern for the "scientific-technological elite." It is common practice for nonscientist participants in high policy circles to refer, rather ruefully, to the cult of "doctor worship," to the conspiratorial atmosphere of the Cosmos Club, and to the uninhibited disposition of some scientists to take policy positions unrelated to their fields of expert knowledge. Indeed, a substantial body of scholarly and popular commentary now takes the natural scientist to task for his failure to "join the team" in the federal establishment and impose some measure of self-discipline in his advice-giving capacity.[3]

The divergence of these views is intriguing because of the great differences in the estimated nature and amount of influence of natural scientists, and in the normative evaluation of the proper role of the scientists as a group. Yet our present knowledge of civil-scientific relations is so limited that we should not take either of these views as an approximation of reality. We should reserve judgment until we have established a frame of reference for observing the political behavior of natural scientists and engineers and have collected some hard data with which to characterize our model.[4]

[3] See Don K. Price, *Government and Science* (New York, New York University Press, 1954) and James L. McCamy, *Science and Public Administration* (University, Ala., University of Alabama Press, 1960). This point was also elaborated during the Columbia University Civil-Science Relations Seminar held in the Winter of 1961–62. For an unbridled condemnation, see Frank Gibney, "The Missile Mess," *Harper's* (January, 1960).

[4] The empirical basis for the study of civil-science relations is still small and much of the data remain under security classification. Aside from the general literature in the field, this analysis rests on approximately 100 tentative probes conducted over the past five years at M.I.T. This material includes professional

As a first venture along these lines, we shall attempt to identify the distinguishing characteristics of the scientific and engineering profession and explore the process by which these characteristics might be transformed into political resources. The limited empirical evidence available indicates that if the scientist in politics is a little less than a leader of a snowballing political crusade, he is a good deal more than another expert performing tricks of virtuosity at the command of politicians, bureaucrats, or soldiers. He is instead a member of a still small and untutored elite which has entered an inhospitable political system but which possesses such valuable assets that it bids fair to displace entrenched skill groups in certain parts of the system and to establish an over-all new equilibrium in the competition for power among the professions.

It is especially important that the influence of this group apparently does not come about by conscious adaptation to the political world, that is, by learning the skills of other elite groups, but by continuing its own sharply differentiated behavior pattern. The group is an apolitical elite, triumphing in the political arena to the extent to which it disavows political objectives and refuses to behave according to conventional political practice.

IN QUEST OF A MODEL

In a field still imprecisely defined and with few substantial empirical investigations to its credit, there are, admittedly, many appropriate observation posts. Some students prefer to treat the majestic sweep of science as a force transforming almost every aspect of polit-

---

case studies and student field investigations of political conflicts involving scientists and engineers. On the local level, these studies are concerned principally with educational and public health matters, and in particular with fluoridation. On the state level, they deal with highway and natural resources controversies. On the federal level, they range from atomic energy and space matters to regulations respecting the marketing of cranberries.

The studies varied enormously in reliability and quality, of course, and cannot be interpreted as systematic and exhaustive explorations closely correlated to the total population of these conflicts. But they are something more than episodic histories since they deal with scientists in their several roles. These studies thus serve the classic function of case analysis by overturning simplistic notions of how scientists behave in politics, and by indicating where further inquiry is required.

ical behavior and requiring radical readjustments in our public institutions and processes if our knowledge of the universe is to be used for the benefit of mankind. Other students see the scientist's role as comparable to that of the military or administrative technician, speculating that characteristics of expertise, social responsibility, and corporateness apply to him in much the same way as Samuel P. Huntington has viewed the professional role of the soldier. Still other students look upon the scientific community as a pressure group, more loosely organized and with less formal obligations to the state than the military but capable of cohesive, effective political action on matters which directly touch their occupational and public interests. There are also those who prefer to deal with the "scientific enterprise" in structural terms by focusing on that complex of public agencies, advisory bodies, and contractual relations among government, universities, and industry in which scientists work for public purposes, and evaluating these arrangements in terms of more or less conventional organizational and operational criteria.[5]

Yet, if our principal concern is to comprehend the influence of scientists active in politics, we need a frame of reference somewhat less lofty than that which regards science as an impersonal historical force and begs the question of who directs and mobilizes that force. We require a model more comprehensive than that which deals piecemeal with a scientist in his various capacities as an expert, adviser, and private citizen in varied situations and structures and assigns him roles by the technique of analogy. We need a model which permits us to account for the scientist's notable achievements as expert and adviser, his spotty record as lobbyist, and his apparently inconsequential efforts to provoke the public to action. The middle-range theory which suggests itself as especially appropriate to the scientists in America is the "skill commonwealth" of Harold Lasswell, since this analysis organizes groups of influentials not on

[5] James B. Conant, C. P. Snow, Gerald Holton, Vannevar Bush, Pendleton Herring, Lewis Mumford, and Walter A. Rosenblith are examples of individuals with the scientist-philosopher or philosopher-scientist view. Wallace S. Sayre has dealt with the possibilities of the pressure-group analogy in an essay in this volume. J. Stefan Dupré and Sanford A. Lakoff stress the enterprise model in their *Science and the Nation: Policy and Politics* (Englewood Cliffs, N.J., Prentice-Hall, 1962).

the bases of geography and class, but according to the exercise of a common set of skills which can be taught and learned.[6]

"Skill politics," as first used by Lasswell, was a term designed to distinguish among specialists in bargaining, organizational, propagandistic, and violence activities of classic political relevance. It provided a perspective for studying the rise of, and competition among, elites and decision-makers separate from those based on differences in social status, personality, race, ethnic origin, or occupation, when treated as productive of common political outlooks and ideology.[7] It coupled the possession of particular skills with major political issues and events; with the "redirection of culture" as Lasswell phrased it. It linked the emergence of particular skill groups in politics with long-run developmental tendencies in economic and social organization.

We shall not adopt the skill commonwealth in the fullest sense in which Lasswell has employed the concept, but shall modify its components in several important respects. For example, no claim is made that a scientific skill group enjoys an elite status which dominates all parts of the political process or makes it a prime contender for filling major decision-maker positions in the society. This analysis first seeks to establish the relevance of scientific and engineering skills to what seems to be a recent but vital new function of the modern state—the assurance of a high quality and an accelerating rate of technological innovation. Given that basic point of departure, the model takes on the familiar characteristics of contemporary political analysis. We inquire as to (1) what political significance the skills have, that is, how they may be used in the bargaining process, (2) how the political utility of these skills is augmented by other groups' perceptions of them, (3) what group disposition exists to spend the political resources possessed, and (4) where within the existing political structure these resources are maximized.

We proceed to study skill politics within the framework of a decision-making process which has been transformed rapidly since

[6] Harold D. Lasswell, *The Analysis of Political Behavior: An Empirical Approach* (New York, Oxford University Press, 1948), p. 134.

[7] For an excellent summary of elite analysis, including that of skill groups, see Donald R. Matthews, *The Social Background of Political Decision-Makers* (Garden City, N.Y.. Doubleday, 1954).

World War II as major outputs contain more technical and less normative components, as the executive assumes predominance over the legislative, as the issues in a campaign bear less and less relevance to the issues which preoccupy those in authority between elections, and as the utility of different skill groups changes accordingly. It is this simultaneous consideration of the scientists' skills, their political uses, and the evolving political system which leads us to specify how and why a skill group traditionally aloof from political activity is now emerging to influence policy on crucial issues at key places of leverage.

PROPERTIES OF THE SCIENTIFIC SKILL GROUP

Identification of the scientific skill group is the starting point for tracing its political emergence. If we take the broadest possible interpretation of scientific skills, those required (in Bethe's words) for an understanding of nature, and add to them the companion skills of technology, those involved in the mastery of nature, we can identify a group of considerable magnitude whether reference is being made to the approximately 100,000 individuals listed in the *American Men of Science* or the more than 2,000,000 membership in the American Association for the Advancement of Science (AAAS).[8] Yet these are not the relevant characteristics for the politically active scientific skill group. At best they indicate the manpower pool from which the elite can be recruited with its members still having some claim of knowing about or speaking for science. Although attempts have been made to attribute to this expansive group and its members properties of cohesiveness, uniformity of personality, and common norms, incentives, and audiences, these attempts still appear to rest on shaky empirical foundations.[9] At least as far as political attitudes

[8] A systematic effort to assemble and compare various estimates of the size of the scientific community was made by Vernon Fladager, "The Size and Nature of the U.S. Scientific Community," in *Science and Public Policy* (Cambridge, Mass., M.I.T. Industrial Liaison Program, January 22–23, 1961).

[9] One of the most provocative theoretical analyses of science as a social system resting on identifiable membership, shared values, and incentives has been advanced by Norman W. Storer in his "Some Sociological Aspects of Federal Science Policy," *The American Behavioral Scientist*, VI, No. 4 (December, 1962), 27–30.

are concerned, the so-called scientific community is known to be divided by fields of specialization, geographical location, blocks in communication between government and university bases, positions on matters of public moment, and institutional environments. It lacks any overarching structure of professional associations or established procedures for determining membership attitudes and interests. Its engineering component in particular is cross-pressured by an industrial orientation and ideology and by the frequency with which the final career patterns of engineers bear little relation to their formally acquired occupational skills. The common ideology which members of this community are often presumed to share resembles the occupational analogue for God and motherhood—a belief in progress through experimentation and the accumulation and systematic application of knowledge.

The politically relevant scientists constitute only a small sliver of the larger group. For federal issues, Christopher Wright has estimated that there are between 200 and 1,000 men and women who significantly and directly influence the availability of scientific knowledge and ideas and their technical application. James Killian is inclined to fix the number of the consistently influential at 200— the lowest point of Wright's estimate. In an initial empirical exploration, Howard Rosenthal screened names from the *American Men of Science* according to five measures of elite participation in advisory posts, professional associations, and mass media recognition to arrive at a core group of approximately 900 members. But Rosenthal's calculation of an "active elite"—participation in at least two elite capacities—resulted in a group numbering only 392.[10]

Reduced to these proportions, the scientific skill group tends to acquire characteristics of considerable cohesion. In reviewing their backgrounds, Rosenthal found that in comparison to his total population the active elite displayed a high propensity to be native-born, living in the New England and Middle Atlantic regions of the coun-

[10] For the Wright estimate see his essay in this volume. Killian's estimate was given in the course of his graduate seminar on Science and Public Policy at M.I.T., and Rosenthal's is contained in his "The American Scientific Elite" (mimeographed, May, 1961).

try, between forty and fifty years of age, university-employed, and engaged in professional fields other than engineering. Killian identifies as further characteristics a widely shared goal among members of the group to protect the "integrity" of science or assure respect for scientific knowledge and the means and institutions through which we acquire it and a highly efficient, though informal, communication network within the group. Wright concurs in these characterizations, emphasizing the further property of self-selection. He suggests that particular environments—notably eastern universities where contacts between scientists and nonscientists are likely to occur—and special intellectual traits, notably "virtuoso manipulation of facts and arguments," impel the elite members into political activities.

The group is not politically united in the partisan sense and is wracked with controversies in their judgment on technical issues. Moreover, below the national level the scientific expert often works without contact with his peers. But, granted these differences, a convergence of forces—basic skills, basic goals, shared backgrounds and environments, ease of communication, personal dispositions as to how issues are raised and resolved—operates to make this small, mutually respecting and respectable group a meaningful entity.

SCIENTISTS IN AN ALIEN CLIME

To identify the politically relevant scientific skill group—the vocal and effective scientists, as Robert Gilpin has termed them—is not to demonstrate that they have become influential or to explain how this status was achieved. Indeed, the protest against the "doctor cult" seems at first to reflect the hypersensitivity of other participants in national policy-making to the entry of a handful of scientists into positions of limited scope and responsibility. In terms of the history of the American commonwealth of skills, the scientist-activists are only a tiny minority among the occupants of key decision-making posts in the federal government. Clearly, they fail to fit the broad skill classifications used by Lasswell to distinguish among decision-makers: bargaining skills acquired through business experience, propagandist skills of manipulating symbols having mass appeals, political skills involved in the negotiation of favors, and administrative or military skills applicable in the direction of large organizations or the use of violence.

If we shift our attention from political to occupational skills, the scientists still seem overwhelmed by sharply contrasting skill groups. Aside from the two occupations confronting the scientist in his advisory capacity—the soldier and the administrator—it is the lawyer who has claimed near-monopoly in supplying the participants in public life. Traditionally, the legal profession in the United States has provided both the incumbents of high posts and their expert advisers including 70 percent of American presidents, vice-presidents, cabinet members, and a large portion of state governors and representatives. Of course, lawyers comprise the overwhelming majority in state and federal judicial systems. On the whole, lawyers seem to have fair claim to the title "high priests of American politics." [11]

With respect to the specific role of adviser, the role in which scientists have generally been assigned most influence:

[T]he lawyer is today . . . the one indispensable adviser of every responsible policy-maker of our society—whether we speak of the head of a government department or agency, of the executive of a corporation or labor union, of the secretary of a trade or other private association, or even of the humble independent enterpriser or professional man. As such an adviser the lawyer, when informing his policy-maker, is in an unassailably strategic position to influence, if not create policy . . . for better or worse our decision-makers and our lawyers are bound together in a relation of dependence or identity.[12]

The typical reasons offered for the preeminence of the legal profession as the source of supply for decision-makers and their advisers are straightforward. The lawyer's training in interpersonal mediation and conciliation and his facility with words in debate and oratory seems obviously useful in the American system. The lawyer also finds it relatively easy to enter politics and subsequently return from politics to a private law firm, with the assurance that the practice of law has not been revolutionized in the interval. Most impor-

---

[11] Matthews, *The Social Background of Political Decision-Makers*, pp. 30–31.
[12] Lasswell, *The Analysis of Political Behavior*, p. 27.

tant of all, perhaps, is the fact that government service and professional advancement are inseparably intertwined since so much of the
successful practice of law revolves around familiarity, contact, and
influence with the political process.[13]

The scientific skill group is not only overwhelmingly outnumbered
by the legal skill group in its various roles, but appears at first to be
exceptionally ill-equipped to do battle with the lawyer in any policy
conflict. To use Lasswell's terms, men skilled in the manipulation of
symbols of things confront men skilled in the manipulation of symbols of interpersonal relations. Men who are unaccustomed to reflective consideration of values and their allocation argue with men
whose stock in trade is the clarification of value choices and their
rationalization to secure acceptance. Men steeped in the tradition of
empirical investigation undertake to compete with men versed in the
dialectic, whose scholarship is heavy with syntax and virtually barren
of the scientific perspective of even the social sciences. Men oriented
toward the concept of change face men who by tradition are history-
oriented. They do so in a process that apparently appeals to values,
and is responsive to historical analogy and the regularization of political and social behavior by prescription and enforcement rather
than by an empirical understanding of trends and probabilities.
While almost all decision-makers can be expected to be familiar
with, and sensitive to, the lawyer's reasoning and behavior, few communicate easily with the scientific skill group.

This characterization of the political environment, more often in-
stinctively felt than explicitly identified by spokesmen of scientists,
is frequently used to belittle the influence of the new skill group.
Yet those who detect and protest against the rise of the influential
scientist also base their indictment on this characterization. The
one despairs at the "noise," the "nonsense," the endless disputation
in which the legal, the historic, the value-laden approach enfolds

---

[13] See for example, Esther L. Brown, *Lawyers, Law Schools and the Public
Service* (New York, Russell Sage Foundation, 1948); John T. Doby, "The
Lawyer as a Political Leader," *Wisconsin Law Review*, MCM, No. 2 (March,
1950), 308–13; William Miller, "American Lawyers in Business and Politics,"
Yale Law Journal, LX, No. 1 (January, 1951), 66–76; David R. Derge, "The
Lawyer as Decision-Maker in American State Legislatures," *Journal of Politics*,
XXI, No. 3 (August, 1959), 408–33.

questions of policy. The other fears that these criteria are poorly understood or cavalierly ignored when scientists undertake to decide public issues of moment.

On an empirical basis, the judgments of either are irrelevant. What counts are the rapid transformations taking place in the established political system and the drastic alterations in the channels for advice giving and receiving. Political scientists who have contributed to the description of the new circumstances of policy-making have yet to make a corresponding descriptive evaluation of the new skill group. Still protesting the insensitivity of the new breed to their established rules of conduct, these political scientists overlook the fitness of new functions and new duties of the state to the scientists' present talents, whether leavened by an awareness of ancient wisdom or not. Although scientists do not yet run for public office, exercise demagogic appeal over the masses, communicate easily with legislators, mobilize their ordinary members into smooth-functioning and hard-bitten lobbies, they are, nevertheless, occupying critical positions of strength in the evolving new process with increasing frequency while other occupations are not occupying comparable positions.

SOURCES OF INFLUENCE

The technological responsibilities of the modern state. The present eminence of the scientific skill group rests upon the frequently emphasized but not always accurately understood fact that since World War II major powers in the nation-state system live by their wits. Brainpower more than firepower is the crucial element from which national strength evolves. Every modern political system must have the capacity to translate basic scientific knowledge into workable, effectively engineered design and structure. Hence, its decision-makers must have the assurance that the society it directs maintains technological innovation at least on a par with major competitors.

The need for scientific quality extends beyond consideration of national security. In determining the availability of natural and human resources, the modern state needs assurance of first-rate technology across a wide spectrum of organized activity, civil and domestic as well as military and international. Thus, relative technological conditions in agriculture, in other resource development, medicine, and industry become as much a matter of moment to imaginative decision-makers as the scientific sophistication present in weapons systems. And all imply a concern for the quality of the national education and research enterprise—an assurance that curiosity and the expectation of change are deeply embedded characteristics of a national style.

In the period of a generation there has been a massive shift in the functional responsibilities of the private and public sectors of our nation. Twenty years ago, when the United States first assumed the role of arsenal of democracy, few would have assigned to Washington the task of underwriting the rate of technological innovation or establishing priorities among scientific fields. "Progress" in the industrial-business-oriented state took care of itself, was reinvigorated, strengthened, and accelerated by the invisible workings of the market place and the genius of individual effort. Except for the stimulation provided by the patent laws and the protection granted by trade regulations, the understanding and mastery of nature occurred without conscious and comprehensive public design. In the Western world, what a government "could do" was a matter for judicial deliberation, not the laboratory.[14]

In this context, a political decision-maker's overriding responsibility as far as the innovative force was concerned was to determine the impact of the force on the prevailing balance of political and social interests. There were, to be sure, serious problems of equilibrium: how to distribute the fruits of progress, what ideology best rationalized the allocation of increased material well-being, what weight to give to conflicting claims of property and labor, and what industrial structures to encourage or inhibit. One need only reflect on the tight grip which the English Poor Laws maintained on welfare philosophy for 400 years to recognize the elaborate rationalizations required of nations in the midst of industrial revolutions to accommodate an ex-

---

[14] This is not to ignore the frequently cited instances of governmental sponsorship and use of science in the eighteenth and nineteenth centuries from the census to steamboat-boiler inspections. It is simply to emphasize that these activities were sporadic, unsystematic, and relatively inconsequential in the process of technological development.

ponential increase in innovation. But it was the distributive, rather than the innovative, problems of industrialization and the technological bases that triggered radical philosophies and stout defenses of the existing order and consumed the attention of the political system. Thus, bargaining skills, propaganda skills, and violence skills all assumed great importance. The political order obviously required leaders and advisers with the lawyer's special skill in value clarification, his verbal capacity, and his experience as an intellectual jobber and contractor who could make a strong case wherever one was required.

Today, no national political system can afford to concentrate on distributive and allocative problems. Indeed, the decline of ideological conflict, the gross simplification of value alternatives engendered by the Cold War, the growing constraints upon applying the techniques of violence, and the continued pace of innovation with its accompanying increases in material well-being suggest a steady decline in the urgency of value-oriented decisions. A government can support farm programs made obsolete by increased agricultural productivity, countenance shorter work weeks, and hold out the promise of more business profits on the expectation that new technological break-throughs can provide more products for everyone. It can project its international image in the relatively simple, though not necessarily effective, terms of an open society. It must limit the use of force to extend value acceptance. What a political system cannot ignore, in either a domestic or international sense, is the quality of the scientific enterprise—the public policy adopted for science and the caliber of scientific advice in public policy-making.

This transformation of the functional responsibility of the modern state drastically alters the position of the scientist from that of a benevolent outsider occasionally affecting the affairs of state to one of a valuable insider possessing information vital to the continued survival of the system. It subtly shifts the emphasis of the persistent political question "Can we do this?" from the consideration of legal constraints to consideration of physical constraints. In these circumstances, it is not surprising that the ranks of senior career personnel of the federal government, executives, advisers, and specialists have been increasingly filled by the scientific skill group.

Analyzing the 1,354 supergrade positions of GS-16 to GS-18 in 1957, David and Pollock observed: "A considerable number are lawyers, an even greater number are engineers and natural scientists. . . . Most of these individuals act frequently as advisers to executives and most of them probably have limited executive responsibilities." [15]

The increased number of decisions about science or having scientific components and the corresponding rise of the skill group to positions of influence within government agencies is naturally accompanied by opportunities for influence. But of more significance is the fact that in many instances these opportunities equip the skill group with special political advantages not possessed by other experts in the bargaining process.

One advantage arises from the fact that the possession of technical know-how about physical matters gives the scientist direct initiative in proposing action which is not available to other experts. Military, legal, and administrative advisers can speak to the decision-maker in strategic and procedural terms. Once provided with a statement of objectives—a given set of resources available from a given state of nature—they can suggest alternative courses of action, different mixtures of components, and new methods of application. Still they cannot seriously propose to change the state of nature itself.

Actually manipulating nature is the scientist's stock in trade. From Einstein's letter to Roosevelt, to Teller's proposal for Super, and the Lincoln Study Group's recommendations for the Distant Early Warning Line (DEW), the scientific skill group is in the position of generating new policy issues. Its judgment as to value implications may be neither sophisticated nor seriously considered, but in fields as far apart as disarmament and water desalination, no program can seriously be considered until the technological potential is discovered and articulated.

It is true that the decision-maker does not always have to wait for the scientist to come forward with his innovations. As Walter Rosenblith has pointed out, the presumption exists that in an age of forced-draft technology "a massive national (even industrial) effort will

---

[15] Paul T. David and Ross Pollock, *Executives for Government* (Washington, D.C., The Brookings Institution, 1957), p. 92.

produce almost any technological goal once the necessary basic facts are known." [16] Given the reliance of scientists on government support for the provision of the complex facilities and organization now required in research and development, the alert administrator, general, or politician can indicate the kinds of areas in which the national interest requires concerted scientific activity. He can organize projects, authorize special studies, and specify public policy needs for more intensified research. Thus, his decisions can powerfully affect the rate at which innovation goes forward in particular disciplines and fields of inquiry.

Nonetheless, the fundamental inability of a decision-maker to command specific results suggests a second source of influence dependent on the possession of scientific knowledge. The scientist's allegiance, interest, and loyalty to particular endeavors has to be secured. He must be persuaded that he ought to become associated with a venture. He is in a position to bargain over terms and conditions. He can choose to participate or not. In short, the scientist has recourse to behavior not usually available to other professionals in government. He may participate in a mutiny or strike.

It may be argued that these are not real alternatives, that ultimately the scientific skill group can be brought along. Appeals to basic loyalties have been persuasive in times of great emergency. Yet, in particular situations, scientific attitudes about prevailing governmental policies and programs can result in behavior very close to disassociation. At the height of the AD-X2 battery additive controversy between the Secretary of Commerce and the Director of the National Bureau of Standards, 400 scientists, or over 10 percent of the Bureau's technical complement, told newspaper reporters that they planned to resign in protest. The companion actions of the Federation of American Scientists, both public and private, made plain the disposition of the elite to treat the Secretary's proposed dismissal of the Director as an issue involving the integrity of the scientific effort.[17] On a broader front, the Oppenheimer hearings, coming

---

[16] Walter A. Rosenblith, "The Federal Government and Science" (unpublished memorandum, August, 1960).
[17] Samuel A. Lawrence, "The Battery Additive Controversy," in *Inter-*

after years of security investigations which had increasingly irritated and enraged scientists, diminished the disposition of numbers of the most distinguished members of the elite to participate in governmental programs.

These incidents have generally led decision-makers to treat respectfully the claims of the scientific skill group for special working arrangements, new institutions, and new concepts of administration. As their experience in governmental affairs has grown, the group has exchanged its initial organizational preference embodied in the independent, self-selecting, self-perpetuating board of directors which managed the National Advisory Committee for Aeronautics (NACA) for access to the Presidency instead. But the institutionalization of the first *ad hoc* think groups into permanent corporations, the perpetuation of the great governmental laboratories, and the continued preference for a university environment in which to conduct sponsored research attest to the substantial modifications which scientists have made in conventional concepts of administrative theory. In the name of protecting scientific integrity, they have secured for themselves conditions of administrative discretion which contradict ancient principles of hierarchy, chain of command, and span of control. With powerful ideological assistance from the American free enterprise tradition, scientists and engineers in universities and defense industries have contributed mightily to the destruction of the governmental agency and the business corporation as meaningful entities in the development and execution of public programs. The present array of research and development half-way houses born of systems analysis are monuments to their ingenuity and to their success in escaping the established modes of organization. The growing concern with conflicts-of-interests of members of the skill group is evidence of the preference for "loose" administration and indicative of the problems raised thereby.

Media support—scientist as disinterested party. The core of the scientists' strength rests in the decision-maker's need to understand and manipulate the physical world as well as words and symbols.

University Case Program, No. 68 (University, Ala., University of Alabama Press, 1962).

This resource is powerfully enhanced by the perceptions of the scientists' value accorded by other political influentials and the alliances developed on this basis. One valuable alliance is based on the favorable and deferential treatment accorded the skill group by the communication enterprises. No comprehensive content analysis presently exists to demonstrate how frequently and how favorably the scientist is treated by the press, radio, and television. In the M.I.T. explorations, however, the scientific expert was clearly assured sympathetic interpretation.

The most striking examples of respect for scientists from the communications media attach to issues of fluoridation, matters of school curriculum, and transportation policy at the local and state levels. Each example involved severe controversy and in many instances the professional qualifications of the experts involved would be suspect to the national peer group. Nonetheless, the media treatment was almost uniformly on the side of the "expert" who was depicted as "objective, disinterested, uncorruptible," and an "impartial searcher for the truth." Dentists, highway engineers, and doctors are laudable figures in the eyes of many local newspapers in these cases because their participation tends "to take the problem out of politics," a goal apparently devotedly, though illogically, coveted by many of the fourth estate.

Similar support has been evident in national cases where the skill group has become embroiled in open disputes. In the Oppenheimer case, the most influential of columnists came to the defense of the scientist. In the AD-X2 controversy, Drew Pearson led the attack against the Secretary of Commerce, and was joined by national radio and television commentators and most of the metropolitan dailies in defending the right of scientists to "find the truth." Again, in the DEW line case, the press was instrumental in supporting the scientist-advocates of continental air defense. Steven Rivkin has written that the Alsops "kept up a drumfire of articles in favor of air defense proposals. . . . As the controversy developed, the newspaper columnists and reporters themselves became an important element in the policy-making process. The scientist-participants could think of the press as a useful aid to their arguments." Such comment as the Alsops' characterization of the continental defense problem as "whether to gamble . . . vast sums and perhaps the health of the economy on the scientists' being right, or to gamble the survival of America on the scientists' being wrong," sustained the scientists' cause.[18]

It is true that the press is not unanimously and consistently on the side of the scientists. Powerful counterarguments were launched both in newspapers and magazines against the DEW line decision and against Oppenheimer, and even in the AD-X2 controversy editorial opinion was divided. Nonetheless, on major incidences to date, the bulk of support seems to have been with the "expert."

This support is not surprising. The scientist's conception of the vital role of public opinion in a democracy corresponds to that of the media skill group, and may even be held more sincerely. Both emphasize the dangers of secret decisions by a handful of men, the essential need for public awareness of the vital issues of the day, and public participation in their resolution. Hence, Oppenheimer's conviction:

We do not operate well when the important facts, the essential conditions, which limit and determine our choices are unknown. We do not operate well when they are known in secrecy and in fear, only to a few men. I believe that until we have looked the citizen in the eye, we shall be in the worst of all possible dangers, which is that we may back into him. More generally, I do not think that a country like ours can in any real sense survive if we are afraid of our own people.[19]

For instance, in the 1958 Conference on Science and Public Policy held at M.I.T., the scientist-participants time and again voiced their conviction that the public was a critical factor in decision-making: it "had to be assisted so that it could make wise choices," it "must be brought along," and the educational process should be devoted to the objective of allowing the layman to "understand and appreciate science" so that in a modern world the public could be re-equipped with Jeffersonian characteristics.[20]

[18] Steven R. Rivkin, "The Quest for Air Defense," in *M.I.T. Falk Cases in Science and Government* (mimeographed, 1959).

[19] J. Robert Oppenheimer, "Atomic Weapons and American Policy," *Foreign Affairs*, XXXI, No. 4 (July, 1953), 532.

[20] M.I.T. Endicott House Conference, "Science and Public Policy: A Range of Issues" (mimeographed, 1959).

Whether these common perspectives about the public promote an affinity between scientists and media, or whether the bond is one of convenience—the scientists seeking an escape from secret decisions and the journalist finding a ready source of news—may be a moot question. But in contrast to the politician, the businessman, the labor leader, and the lawyer, the scientist in these examples enjoyed a privileged position in the eyes of most editorial writers. Although the "doctors" might be naïve in the political jungle, or even silly, they have been deemed well-intentioned, while members of other occupations have been fair game for press attacks.

The public image—the scientist as miracle worker. Not only the press but the general public as well is likely to offer comfort and support to the scientists' political objectives, even while it misunderstands them. Most polls designed to rate professional prestige put the scientist close to the top, although interlaced with sentiments of respect are expressions of doubt concerning the benefits of science and the personal characteristics of scientists. Mead and Metraux found a double image of the scientific career among high school students—one strongly positive and the other negative. As portrayed in popular literature, the Frankenstein potential of unrelieved destructiveness and unsanctioned tampering with nature's mysteries vie with the power of science to bring health, prosperity, and contentment to the masses. In instances where scientists have been involved as neighbors and friends in local controversies, the public's respect for their judgment is more likely to hinge on evaluations of personalities than on deference to specialized knowledge.[21]

Coupled with doubts as to the ultimate effects of science is a gross lack of information about the skill group and its work. Limited interviews conducted under M.I.T. direction of students, businessmen, and housewives indicate that neither the scientists active in political affairs nor major contemporary scientific accomplishments are visible to the public. On the contrary, the "sensational" scientists (Teller, von Braun, Salk) or the "oddities" (Pauling and Oppen-

---

[21] Margaret Mead and Rhoda Metraux, "Image of the Scientist Among High School Students," *Science*, CXXVI, No. 3270 (August 30, 1957), 384–90. On the dual image among adults see Gerald Holton, "Technological and Scientific Society," an address to the Carolina Symposium, March, 1960. On the scientist at home among friends and neighbors, M.I.T.'s power-structure analysis of Lexington, Massachusetts, has been revealing.

heimer) are most familiar. Our samples all revealed chronic difficulties in naming distinguished scientists, their achievements, or
their associations with public life.

The ambivalence and ignorance of the public concerning scientific
affairs may be less important than its conviction that science may
offer the "way out." Whether the popular concept of the scientist is
good or bad, or accurate or distorted, it at least provides the skill
group with respect and often with considerable support, if and
when it chooses to make use of it. What the public learns of science
is essentially related to its spectaculars, where payoffs seem clear:
medical discoveries, moon shoots, satellites, missiles, new educational
techniques, and new gadgets. These images may miss the mark from
the point of view of what science is really about or the need for basic
research. Killian has deplored the fact that "it is the technological
spectaculars which the public at large and, often, the press tend to
use as the sole measure of scientific as well as technological prowess,
and thus, of military power as well." [22] Whether or not this emphasis on the dramatic is a burlesque, it assigns to the scientists the
fundamental attribute of power.

In the same address in which he scored the public's misconception
of science, Killian acknowledged: "Since World War II the status-
seekers in the community of nations have relied increasingly on
science and technology to build their prestige." The very inability of
the public to understand the scientific mind or its work, the lack of
communication which scientists deplore, the aura of magic about
their investigations, and the faith in research augment their position,
at least in the minds of the Washington community where the scientists are most visible.

Contrasted with the shopworn image of the lawyer, where the
public may easily be as ill-informed, but much more negatively persuaded, the scientist's position seems stronger. He is not yet identified
with big business, notorious crimes, shabby practices, sharp tricks,
unpopular court decisions, and unsettled convictions so as to earn
the aphorism "to be a good lawyer is to be a poor Christian." [23] To
be viewed as an oddity, as naïve in political affairs, or as inexpert in

[22] James R. Killian, Jr., "Making Science a Vital Force in Foreign Policy,"
address to the M.I.T. Club of New York, December 13, 1960.
[23] Doby, "The Lawyer as a Political Leader," pp. 308–13.

compromise in a nation traditionally suspicious of its public leaders may well be preferable to being regarded as members of the profession from which all politicians are naturally recruited.

The scientist's self-image as "nature's agent." The possession of skills critically needed for national development and strength, access to, and perhaps rapport with the national communications networks, and public prestige are valuable political assets only if the skill group is disposed to use them. If scientists were plagued by self-doubts as to the utility of their calling and its effects on social and political affairs, they might operate under considerable restraints in the political arena. However, since Hiroshima, scientists have "known sin," and there is little evidence that their faith in the essentially benign effects of expanding knowledge or the enobling nature of their calling has been shaken. What James McCamy has called the "myth of science" has served to assure the skill group that its substantive work is not related to unfortunate political consequences, and that its participation in policy-making brings much needed qualities of reason and objectivity to the political process.

In this generation, spokesmen for science have articulated at least three versions of the scientific enterprise designed to establish its social value and public usefulness. The first version emphasizes the innocence of scientific inquiry. Compton insisted that science contains no moral imperatives in that the use of discoveries for good or evil is not determined by the discoverers. Bethe has asserted that science provides "a true picture of the world of living things so far as they are physical entities" but excluding "those things which man puts into the world." [24] The second version asserts the beneficial sweep of science: Vannevar Bush's classic statement of science's contribution to three great public goals—national security, conquest of disease, and increase in public welfare.[25] The third version expresses the conviction that scientists are specially endowed to bring order and sense to the political process: Snow's lyrical characterization of the scientific community as "tough and good men determined to fight it out at the side of their brother men," prepared to accept individual tragedy but not the tragedy of the human race, or Dean

[24] *Bethe Interview*, p. 8.
[25] Vannevar Bush, *Science, the Endless Frontier* (Washington, D.C., USGPO, 1945).

George Harrison's call in the M.I.T. Conference for the triumph of the scientific attitude over mysticism, inertia, and political disorganization.[26]

To the degree that these attitudes toward science are general within the skill group, a better impetus for unfettered political activity can scarcely be imagined. Not responsible for past errors in public policy, carrying the keys which will unlock the doors to a better way of life for all, and capable of bringing order out of political chaos, the scientists can enter the decision-making process secure in the knowledge that their activities are not impelled by personal ambition and the thirst for power. Reluctantly, they emerge from the laboratory at the time of a great emergency to save the nation or the world or, as at Pugwash, to use "the international community of science" as a basis for improved political understanding. They sacrifice professional careers in the interests of an informed debate on great public issues. Their function in the controversies over space, missile systems, or education is not to find new glory or power for their peer group, to promote new funds for a pet project, or to protect a vested interest. Rather, their mission is to assure that the wellsprings of creative achievement continue to flow, and that the same characteristics of reason, logic, respect for individualism, and objectivity are brought to bear on problems of human relations. Compared to the self-seeking, the parochialism, and the limited knowledge of other participants, the scientists offer the welcome contrast of prescient men concerned only with explaining and using the powers of nature. As Gilpin has explained, their higher duty is to their profession, in contrast to the lawyer's cynical willingness to forget his search for justice and serve only the interest of his clients.[27]

The issue is not whether the scientist's view of his political self is an accurate one. Nor is it relevant that a careful reading of public controversies involving scientists leads to a conclusion that personal ambition, avarice, and egotism can characterize the members of the scientific skill group as much as members of other groups. What is important is the fact that the view of science serves as an operative

[26] M.I.T. Endicott House Conference, "Science and Public Policy."
[27] Robert Gilpin, "Civil-Science Relations in the United States: The Example of the President's Science Advisory Committee," unpublished paper presented to the American Political Science Association Convention, September, 1961, p. 8.

ideology sustaining the evaluation of the group's activity in time of stress. To believe simultaneously, as Bethe does, "that science has nothing to say or little to contribute to these human values" but that you "don't need much formal training in this [value choices]" is at once a reassurance of the fitness of one's work and an invitation to extend its sphere of influence because the mingling of technical and political advice is "unavoidable." [28] Secure in the conviction that the twentieth century is the age of Big Science, with the acceleration of innovation as its major theme, scientists can easily take the next step of extending the approach and spirit of scientific inquiry to human affairs. Problems of defense, of resources development, education, and space are not to be approached in an atmosphere of emotion, conflict, and controversy. Rather, effective policy-making requires objective sifting of the facts, balanced vision, thoughtful reflection, and "the mobilization of the best wisdom and highest competence available to a nation." [29] These work habits, presumably possessed by scientists, serve the larger purposes of human endeavor. Therefore, the presence of scientists in high policy councils is more likely to result in "better policy" than if they were to function in strictly technical and informational roles.

The disposition for action. Closely akin to the scientist's conception of the special benefits he brings to decision-making is his conviction that something can be done to resolve major public issues. That is, an analysis of a problem by his skill group is not only likely to proceed without the distortion of emotions and special interests but will also result in more definitive solutions. The participation of the group will make a difference. In Bethe's words:

One major problem which one faces as a scientist lies in the difference in approach to the problem-solving process between scientists and many non-scientists. For instance, when one testifies before a Congressional committee one often has the impression that the purpose of the hearing is not to search out the facts and then reason a solution, but that the solution has been determined and the hearing will now put such facts on the record as will support the solution.[30]

[28] *Bethe Interview*, p. 15.
[29] James R. Killian, Jr., and Albert G. Hill, "For a Continental Defense," *The Atlantic Monthly*, CXCII, No. 5 (November, 1953), 41.
[30] *Bethe Interview*, p. 27.

Throughout the M.I.T. inquiries there is evidence of the scientists' instinct to rely on rationality and creativity as capable of bringing profound changes in an existing state of affairs, the urge to bring together a "think group" for a one-shot onslaught on a problem, and the preference for searching for bold, imaginative new approaches and deprecating the importance of obstacles and inpediments. Warner Schilling contrasts the scientist's perspective to that of the diplomat inclined to believe there are no solutions to his problem, or the politician desirous of finding the lowest common denominator of many approaches.[31] It also contrasts with the military attitude that although action is often required no ultimate change in a world of violence or conflict is to be expected; or with C. Wright Mills' administrator who listens intently to all sides in a dispute before suggesting soberly and cautiously that no action is warrented for the time being.

Just as the scientist's faith in his role as an agent of nature can be questioned, so his disposition for quick far-reaching solutions may be suspect. Albert Wohlstetter has suggested that the solutions of the skill group represent drastic oversimplifications of the issues, an apparent reliance on reason mixed with heavy doses of intuition that are never explicitly recognized, with solemnity, and with an unwarranted deprecation of politicians and generals.[32] Others have termed the scientist's posture "naïve utopianism or naïve belligerency," "intellectual arrogance," or the compulsions of a latent "social conscience." [33]

Once again, the correctness of the scientist's position in the political labyrinth is beside the point. In a context where urgent problems are piled one on top of another, where there are constant crises, and where progress is necessary, the scientist's disposition for action can be appealing. It can be especially appealing in a political system where conventional ideologies stress rationality, creativity, and ingenuity as important elements in the national style. It is most important to realize that when innovation and change is a public function, it

[31] See the essay by Schilling in this volume. See also E. B. Skolnikoff, "Science, Scientists and National Policy in the United States," unpublished paper presented to the American Political Science Association Convention, September, 1962.

[32] See the essay by Wohlstetter in this volume.

[33] See the essay by Schilling in this volume.

may be difficult for even the most skeptical decision-maker to contain the proposals of the scientists. Men who see a way out in desperate situations, who have grand designs and bold new schemes, and who promise relief from age-old torments have political advantages not enjoyed by those intent on making marginal adjustments in a going system. The results of the proposals may be disastrous but they may still be politically potent. After all, the Women's Christian Temperance Union achieved the goal of prohibition for a time.

The arena of the executive branch. If one simply counts the noses of persons in formal positions of authority or traces the sweep of politics from nominations and campaigns through final administrative action, scientists do not appear frequently enough to seem significant. This is simply to say that the talents of the skill group are not marketable political commodities everywhere in the political system. What is important is that the arena in which the skill group demonstrates competence is precisely the one where the public decisions that touch scientific concerns and, in fact, the long-run fate of the political system, are made. In the modern age of the executive and bureaucratic state, contemporary political analysis fixes the locus of policy-making away from the legislative halls and great public deliberations. Decisions on military strategy, space explorations, budgetary allocations, foreign policy, medical research, and transportation facilities are in the first instance almost always formulated within the executive branch, and are frequently conclusively determined there. If a small number of key legislators can be brought in, a few prominent members of the press briefed, and an advisory committee established for prestige purposes, then the "cardinal choices" are made in executive chambers. The legislative process, the prevailing public sentiment, and the articulate opinion of organized interest groups operate as constraints, reduce the number of feasible alternatives, and sometimes upset the calculations of the policy-makers. They do not, however, alter the prevailing concentration of power to propose, persuade, and establish the critical policy positions which the insiders now possess. So, at the height of the DEW line controversy the Alsops could write from the normative vantage point of established democratic ideology:

It was ludicrous and it was also pretty shocking to listen to the windy public debates of the last campaign, and meanwhile to have a general notion of the topics of secret debate . . . [the leaders of government] were privately arguing about the increasing danger of a full scale catastrophe in South Asia; the increasing Chinese Communist threat on the approaches of Formosa . . . the desperate need for an American air defense . . . the urgent need for a mighty effort to overtake the Soviet lead in guided missiles . . . and other such grim matters. You could almost say in truth that while the politicians were solemnly discussing the President's multi-billion highway construction program, those with Q-clearance were discussing whether there would be any Americans left to ride the highways.[34]

Spokesmen for science often protest against this structure of decision-making as secret choices made by a handful of men. Yet, from the point of view of maximizing their own influence, it is difficult to conceive of a more advantageous location for policy-making. The skill group is not required to possess the personality attributes needed for election to public office, or to observe the stylized dialectic ritual of legislative or judicial proceedings. Rather, its participation is confined to a process of conferences, interviews, committees, task forces, memoranda, and close personal communications where technical and reasoned arguments are permitted, where the capacity to articulate a particular position lucidly or to summarize data in comprehensive terms and extract their logical implications persuasively are important assets. In this arena, consensus may be achieved precisely on the basis of the performance for which scientists are best equipped or through coalitions built in terms of a relatively few personalities, the marriage of interests among a limited number of agencies and departments, or the impact of a well-executed briefing. With the line between technical advice-giving and policy-making obscure, and the emphasis on documents, consultations, proposals, and counterproposals continuing, the scientific skill group works in an atmosphere which reflects their best personalities to fullest advantage.

The ideology and work habits of the scientist in bureaucracy can lead to special advantages. Other occupations can also argue, reason,

---

[34] Joseph and Stuart Alsop, "That Washington Security Curtain," *Saturday Evening Post,* CCXXVII, No. 34 (February 19, 1955), 33.

and, to a limited extent, propose, but they are likely to be constrained by the shibboleths of adminstrative doctrine: notions of responsibility and loyalty in the case of the general administrator; respect for procedures, processes, and the position of his client in the case of the lawyer; and at least formal acknowledgment of the concept of civilian supremacy in the case of the military officer.

The scientist often has no such inhibitions. His higher loyalty is to the scientific community and the preservation of its integrity and vitality. In the executive setting, it is a help rather than a hindrance that this community is not organized and lacks clear channels of communications. The natural base for the scientist is the university, and he is fond of pointing out that he would return there happily, not reluctantly as the lawyer might return to private practice. His disposition is to value individual, unorganized activity. Hence, the scientist is often prepared to ignore established channels, cut red tape, minimize the importance of touching base, make strategic contacts with press and public, and fume at delay and procedural "nonsense." As a "wild man" that must be handled with kid gloves he can secure the advantages of his executive environment while ignoring the traditional limitations of action in a large organization. A predilection for violating the rules of the game often leads to greater opportunities for winning the game. In McCamy's words:

Scientists, whether they think so or not, still have a favored status now in the emotions of public administrators. They walk into a room where lay administrators still stand in awe of imagined mystery. That myth of science, the picture of the infallible specialist in immutable fact, lingers on in the minds of administrators.[35]

In an institutional framework undergoing rapid transformations, where the lines between public and private activities are increasingly blurred, contractual relations replace hierarchical relations, and notions of authority and responsibility become more and more difficult to implement, the freewheeling perspective of the scientific skill group may be a more accurate appraisal of the reality of administrative influence than that of other skill groups still carrying more conventional models of political strategy in their heads.

[35] McCamy, *Science and Public Administration*, pp. 204, 208.

The scientist may not as yet understand how he wins the day and what the sources of his strength are, but his instinctive behavior and natural predilections fit the circumstances. He possesses technical information critically required by top decision-makers, he forecasts the effectiveness of innovation, and he can articulate his conviction with few restraints. As he comes to participate in executive politics, he may play the game with zest and even ruthlessness, and still disclaim any understanding or involvement in it. In short, as Wohlstetter suggests, he may practice the politics of Mr. Dooley while remaining innocent of the precepts of Aristotle. No wonder other participants view his emergence with some discomfiture.

THE APOLITICAL ELITE

We have speculated that the study of civil-scientific relations can fruitfully proceed from a model of skill politics which treats the scientists as an emerging elite with influence based upon, but not limited to, its particular type of technical competence. We have suggested that analyses which see the scientist simply as another expert, or part of a poorly organized pressure group or an amorphous community, are likely to underestimate his potential. The relevant measures of scientists' present influence are not visibility in the public eye, cohesions within the scientific community at large, accurate impressions of scientific personalities and their contributions by the media, or even the degree to which scientists attain the goals they profess they wish to attain. What matters is their important role in the expanding set of decisions which resolve around the new public responsibility for innovative excellence and the need for both technical and political judgment.

There are those who counsel now that the prime deficiencies in the pattern of civil-scientific relations is the failure of the scientific skill group to recognize the true character of the political process, including the demands it makes on general knowledge and the compulsions it contains for seat-of-the-pants decisions made with a sensitivity for competing values. The scientist is scored for carrying in his head at the same time the simplified version of the democratic system born in the Age of Reason and a self-image akin to the Platonic navigator. The ideal arrangement for science within the federal government is seen as one in which the general administrator serves, in Don Price's words, "as a useful layer in the pyramid of policy between the peak of political power and the base of science and technology." [36] In this view, the scientific skill group would be admitted to positions of influence only after its members had been steeped in the humanities and social sciences so that they "can appreciate the problems faced by the administrator and the politician." [37]

In terms of skill politics analysis, these proposals seem to miss the mark on two counts. First, they fail to recognize that the scientist's greatest possibility for enhancing his influence lies in the continued differentiation of his skills from those of other experts. It is the maintenance of his magic, the continuation of his separate expertise, the preservation of his independent base in a university, and the admiration and respect he can evoke from press and public and apply within executive confines and the social order that have moved the scientist ahead in politics and created the special agencies and offices for him against the opposition of general administrators. It is asking a great deal to require even a skill group which disavows conscious and personal political ambition to surrender its major instruments of influence.

Second, those who would "regularize" the scientific skill group in the executive arena where they are most preeminent miss the particular affinity that group has to American political ideology. They fail to acknowledge the acceptable theoretical posture which the scientist's apolitical behavior achieves. It may well be that contemporary students of our politics correctly describe our political process pluralistically as multiple "whirlpools of influence," a web of subgovernments, a tortuous path of conflict, bargaining, negotiation, and compromise in which the ultimate end is to "muddle through." As Price has pointed out, superimposed over that reality is a set of myths and symbols conceived in the Age of Reason, paying deference to individuals, not groups, expecting rational behavior, and giving due weight to strokes of genius such as the "invention" of the Constitution that is devoted to a government so carefully balanced

---

[36] Price, *Government and Science*, p. 186.   [37] *Ibid.*, p. 203.

in its distribution of powers and procedures that it might be expected to function according to some version of Newtonian physics.

This ideology is doubtless a fiction for it expects no fundamental conflicts and looks forward to the almost automatic resolution of momentary disagreements through the process of sweet reason, sanctified by custom and law, and embedded in folklore. It is, nevertheless, a persuasive fiction and an operative one, and the scientists' espousal of it places them in the mainstream of American political thought. At the same time, those who "know" or work in the real world of politics with its irrationality, repetitiousness, and deep divisions gain no lustre by their greater wisdom. They lose status and influence in conventional philosophy by their very pragmatism.

Of course, the power and appeal of the scientific skill group may bode ill for the Republic. Misconceiving the complexities and intractability of the real world of politics, the scientists may be just another band of Niebuhr's "foolish children of light." All the criticism of their naïveté, arrogance, and irresponsibility may be justified.

But it may also be that the scientists' greatest failing has been that to date they have not actually applied their skills competently and seriously to an analysis and manipulation of the political process. They have not paused to become versed in new types of data or bothered to observe seriously the phenomenon with which they are now concerned. They have encountered trouble by being casual or careless, or even diffident, in their study of the political world not because they function as poor politicians, but because they function as poor scientists. Perhaps those who now best represent the scientific and the revolutionary tradition in policy-making are that small but growing number of experts variously dubbed civilian strategists or operations and systems analysts. These are social scientists working seriously at the business of applying the techniques of empirical investigation and controlled experimentation to political aspects of human behavior.

If the actual state of affairs is that we are only at the threshold of the application to public problems of science, broadly conceived, then an accurate evaluation of the function of the present skill group is not that its members should learn new skills or limit their advice to physical matters. On the contrary, the prudent political decision-maker would invite members of this group to exercise their curiosity in the solution of political puzzles and extend their scope of inquiry in the manner which they would employ in their investigations of less complex subjects. He would not seek to beat them in the political arena by the exercise of his instinct, intuition, common sense, or incompletely understood experience—he would seek to join them.

The Scientific Adviser

HARVEY BROOKS

*Dean of the Division of Engineering and Applied Physics of Harvard University
and member of the National Science Board,
the President's Advisory Committee, and the
Naval Research Advisory Committee*

Throughout American history the federal government has used scientific advisory committees made up of part-time outside consultants. Since World War II this practice has flourished, and has even become institutionalized in the form of statutory scientific advisory committees. The function of giving scientific advice to the federal government has begun to assume a professional status, and, as Gilpin points out,[1] a hierarchy of part-time advisory groups has emerged that parallels the bureaucratic hierarchy within the structure of government. This interesting development has accompanied the rapid increase in the use of contracts and grants by federal agencies to support research and development in the private sector—in industry, universities, and research institutes. It is difficult to decide which is cause and which is effect, but there is little doubt that federal support for private research and development and scientific advising have gone hand in hand.

Government scientific advisory committees form a complex interlocking network and many scientists and engineers are members of committees at several different levels in the hierarchical structure. In some cases this overlap is deliberate; for example, in the Department of Defense the chairmen of the advisory committees to the three military services are automatically members of the Defense Science Board, which advises the Secretary of Defense. In other cases the overlap is accidental; the same individual is co-opted for different committees on the basis of his individual talents and ex-

---

[1] See essay by Gilpin in this volume.

perience. In both instances, this overlap forms a parallel communication network within the federal government which to a very considerable extent circumvents the customary bureaucratic channels. This bypassing of the bureaucracy is probably one of the most important and useful functions of scientific advisory committees. In science and engineering no level of the bureaucracy has a monopoly on new ideas, and the loose nature of the advisory system provides one means by which ideas originating at a low level in the bureaucratic structure can be brought directly to the point of decision without going through regular channels, and new ideas from outside the federal structure can be introduced quickly into governmental operations.

We shall begin with an examination of some functions of scientific advisers, and will then examine the roles of scientists in the advisory process, the qualities and skills of scientists that are called upon when they give advice. Finally, we shall discuss a number of problems and conflicts which arise in scientific advising.

FUNCTIONS OF SCIENTIFIC ADVISORY COMMITTEES

The term "scientific advisory committee" is used generally although such committees are often as concerned with technology and engineering as with science and include many engineers or other applied scientists among their members. The role of the adviser varies greatly, depending upon the level in the federal hierarchy at which his advice is sought and implemented. In general, the lower the level, the more strictly technical the nature of the advice sought, although this is not always the case.

We may distinguish five advisory functions:

1. To analyze the technical aspects of major policy issues and interpret them for policy-makers, frequently with recommendations for decision or action. At the highest levels this often involves the analysis of political issues to determine which issues are political and which can be resolved on a technical or scientific basis. It also involves interpreting the policy implications of technical facts, opinions, or judgments. Familiar examples of this type of advice are such questions as whether to seek a nuclear test ban or whether to resume nuclear testing and, if so, when.

2. To evaluate specific scientific or technological programs for the purpose of aiding budgetary decisions or providing advice on matters affecting public welfare or safety. Many important decisions involving choice between alternate weapons systems, or determinations of whether to proceed with major technological developments such as civilian nuclear power are of this nature. The review function of the Advisory Committee on Reactor Safeguards of the Atomic Energy Commission (AEC) is an example of such use of scientists in the area of public safety.

3. To study specific areas of science or technology for the purpose of identifying new opportunities for research or development in the public interest, or of developing coherent national scientific programs. Such studies may be science-oriented, that is, concerned with specific scientific disciplines as in the work of the Committee on Oceanography of the National Academy of Sciences (NAS) [2] or the Panel on High Energy Physics of the President's Science Advisory Committee (PSAC). They may also be need-oriented, that is, concerned with the use of science for a specific social purpose, as in the case of the recent study on natural resources made by the National Academy.[3] These studies may be conducted either on a continuous or *ad hoc* basis.

4. To advise on organizational matters affecting science, or a particular mission of an agency involving the use of science or scientific resources. The continuing advisory boards of the military services and the Defense Science Board serve mainly this function. A recent example is the recommendation of a PSAC panel which led to the establishment of the National Aeronautics and Space Administration (NASA), or the recommendation of another panel for the creation of the Federal Council on Science and Technology (FCST).[4]

5. To advise in the selection of individual research proposals for support, as in the so-called "study sections" of the National Institutes of Health, or the Advisory Panels of the National Science Foundation.

[2] NAS-NRC, Committee on Oceanography, *Oceanography 1960 to 1970* (Washington, D.C., NAS-NRC, 1959).
[3] NAS-NRC, Committee on National Resources, *Natural Resources; A Summary Report* (Washington, D.C., NAS-NRC, 1962), Publ. No. 1000.
[4] PSAC, *Strengthening American Science* (Washington, D.C., USGPO, 1958)

With the possible exception of the fifth designation, none of these functions is purely scientific in nature or depends purely on technical knowledge or expertise. All recommendations involve nontechnical assumptions or judgments in varying degrees. In some cases the nontechnical premises are provided by the policy-maker seeking the advice, but more often they have to be at least partly supplied by the scientist himself. For instance, in the judgment as to the safety of a nuclear reactor installation, "safety" itself is a relative term. In a sense the only truly safe reactor is the one which is never built. Every technical judgment on safety is actually a subtle balancing of risk against opportunity—the tiny risk of injury to the public against the advantages of nuclear power. Yet the administrator seldom makes clear to the adviser just how this balance between advantage and risk is to be achieved. Much of the apparent disagreement among scientists over the danger of fallout from bomb tests stems not from a conflict as to actual technical facts, but rather from a difference of views as to the relative weight to be assigned, on the one hand, to the political and military risks of test cessation and, on the other hand, to the possible threat to human welfare resulting from the continuation of testing in view of the large uncertainties in our knowledge about radiation effects.

In a somewhat oversimplified way, the functions of the scientific adviser may be divided into those concerned with science in policy and those concerned with policy for science. The first is concerned with matters that are basically political or administrative but are significantly dependent upon technical factors—such as the nuclear test ban, disarmament policy, or the use of science in international relations. The second is concerned with the development of policies for the management and support of the national scientific enterprise and with the selection and evaluation of substantive scientific programs. It is not possible to draw a sharp line between these two aspects. For example, the negotiations over a nuclear test ban—which certainly involved science in policy—led directly to recommendations for a greatly expanded program of federally supported research in seismology, with quite specific suggestions as to the particular areas of promise—which is obviously policy for science. Conversely, the proposal for an International Geophysical Year, which was essentially a very interesting and exciting scientific proposal, involved highly significant political considerations and in many ways became an important tool of U.S. foreign policy.

ROLES OF SCIENTIFIC ADVISERS

What are the particular qualities and skills demanded of scientific advisers? What kind of knowledge and experience do they bring to bear? Although the public image of the scientific adviser is primarily that of expert or specialist, the way in which he is actually used is much broader. One may distinguish at least seven different roles which closely relate to the above five functions.

The scientist or engineer is used for his expert knowledge of particular technical subject matter, as in the study sections of the National Institutes of Health whose function it is to rate research proposals.

He makes use of his general "connoisseurship" of science and scientific ways of thinking. In this role he is required to transfer his scientific experience from fields in which he is expert to fields of science and technology with which he is only generally familiar. He is used for his ability to understand and interpret quickly what other experts say, to formulate general policy questions involving scientific considerations in terms suitable for presentation to a group of experts, and to detect specious or self-serving arguments in the advice of other experts.

He makes use of his wide acquaintance within the scientific community and his knowledge of scientific institutions and their manner of operation. In this role he often helps by suggesting key technical people to serve in full-time government positions, and even in persuading the preferred candidate to accept the appointment. He may also predict the effects of government policies or actions on scientific institutions, and serve the ends of both government and science by defending the scientific community against ill-advised or inappropriate administrative procedures of government affecting the conduct of research and development.

The public administrator often makes use of the confidence and prestige enjoyed by scientists in order to obtain backing for projects or policies which he has already decided to undertake. While this particular use of scientific advisers is not necessarily to be deplored, it is subject to abuse. In many cases the administrator may "stack" his committee to obtain the advice he wants, or to obtain a "whitewash" for doubtful decisions. On the other hand, an advisory committee may often legitimately be used to help an administrator rescind an unwise decision without humiliation or embarrassment. A famous example is the appointment of an advisory committee of the NAS to investigate the National Bureau of Standards at the time of the battery additive controversy.

The scientist is increasingly being used as a specialist in policy research. This practice began during World War II with the development of the science of operations research, mainly by physicists in Great Britain and the United States. It involves the construction of mathematical models of varied military situations and the quantitative prediction of the military results of the use of varied weapons systems and strategies. During the postwar period this methodology was extensively elaborated by mathematicians, economists, and theoretical physicists, and has been institutionalized in such organizations as the RAND Corporation, or the Weapons System Evaluation Group which serves the Joint Chiefs of Staff. A number of amateur and professional groups have also developed to carry on policy research in the field of disarmament or arms control. In all these examples natural and social scientists collaborated in order to bring to policy problems the methods of analyzing problems which are characteristic of the physical sciences.

Scientists are often sought for policy advice merely because the scientific community provides a convenient and efficient process for selecting able and intelligent people. One is reminded of Macaulay's dictum that he wanted "to recruit university graduates in the classics not because they had been studying the classics, but because the classics attracted the best minds, who could adapt themselves to anything."[5] If one substitutes nuclear physics for classics in this quotation, one has a basis for the selection of certain kinds of advisory committees. It is also probably true that physicists have a way

[5] See reference to this in the essay by Price in this volume.

of simplifying problems which is especially useful to harassed administrators—a capacity which has its pitfalls, since the temptation to oversimplify is always present.

According to C. P. Snow, science is more oriented toward the future than most other disciplines, and scientists are animated by a belief that problems are soluble.[6] Such natural optimism, even when unjustified, is an asset in attacking disarmament problems which have resisted solution for such a long time. It is undoubtedly a characteristic which has brought scientists into policy advisory roles even in areas where they are not especially qualified. Similarly, science forms the most truly international culture in our divided world, and scientists probably enjoy better communication with their counterparts throughout the world than members of any other discipline. Consequently, it was natural that scientists should lead in the cultural penetration behind the iron curtain, and in organizing and promoting joint international activities and exchanges.

PROBLEMS IN SCIENTIFIC ADVISING

The preceding discussion demonstrates that specific expertise is only a small part of the scientist's role as adviser. It is this very fact that is responsible for much of the controversy surrounding the present role of scientists in government and especially their role in the White House and the Executive Office of the President. The criticism of scientists is epitomized by Harold Laski's stricture on expertise:

It is one thing to urge the need for expert consultation at every stage in making policy; it is another thing, and a very different thing, to insist that the expert's judgment must be final. For special knowledge and the highly trained mind produce their own limitations which, in the realm of statesmanship, are of decisive importance. Expertise, it may be argued, sacrifices the insight of common sense to intensity of experience. It breeds an inability to accept new views from the very depth of its preoccupation with its own conclusions. It too often fails to see round its subject. It sees its results out of perspective by making them the centre of relevance to which all other results must be related. Too often, also, it lacks

[6] C. P. Snow, *Science and Government* (Cambridge, Mass., Harvard University Press, 1961). See also essay by Schilling in this volume.

humility; and this breeds in its possessors a failure in proportion which makes them fail to see the obvious which is before their very noses. It has also a certain caste spirit about it, so that experts tend to neglect all evidence which does not come from those who belong to their own ranks. Above all, perhaps, and this most urgently where human problems are concerned, the expert fails to see that every judgment he makes not purely factual in nature brings with it a scheme of values which has no special validity about it. He tends to confuse the importance of his facts with the importance of what he proposes to do about them.[7]

The view so eloquently expressed by Laski is sometimes echoed by political scientists and government administrators in referring to the present influence of scientists in the high councils of government. While it is a valid warning against the uncritical acceptance of scientific advice, particularly where tacit ethical and political judgments are involved, it is not exactly a fair description of the way in which the senior scientific advisers have exercised their responsibilities. Scientists in government have not claimed that their advice should be overriding, but they do insist on the value and importance of this advice in reaching a balanced decision in matters involving the use of scientific results. This is true even when the scientist is speaking primarily as a citizen outside his area of special competence. Especially on matters of military technology, scientists are often in a position to exercise their political and ethical judgments as citizens in a more realistic and balanced manner than other citizens. Precisely because they are so familiar with the technological aspects, they are able to concentrate more on the other issues involved without becoming bemused by mere technical complexities. While scientific advice is not free of bias, or even of special pleading, it is probably more free of prejudice than much other professional advice, and at least has the virtue of providing a fresh perspective unprecedented in government councils.

A number of problems arise in scientific advising which are, in one way or another, related to the type of problem raised by Laski in the above quotation. Discussion of these problems can be organized under eight topical headings: (1) the selection of advisers, (2) the

---

[7] Quoted by I. L. Horowitz, "Arms, Policies, and Games," *American Scholar,* XXXI, No. 1 (January, 1962), 94. The original source of the quote is Harold Laski, "The Limitations of the Expert," *Fabian Tract* No. 235.

scientific adviser as the representative of science, (3) communication between the scientist and the policy-maker, (4) the relation between advice and decision, (5) the responsibility of the adviser, (6) the resolution of conflicting viewpoints, (7) executive privilege, and (8) conflict of interest.

SELECTION OF ADVISERS

Although the method of selecting members of a scientific advisory committee depends strongly on the function of the committee, the usual procedures are rather informal and based, for the most part, on personal acquaintance. This is especially true of committees that operate at the higher levels of policy discussion. The final selection is made by the executive to whom the committee is responsible, but usually the executive accepts the suggestions of present members of the committee or of other advisory committees. Thus the advisory role tends to become self-perpetuating, and constitutes a kind of subprofession within the scientific professions. Certainly administrative skills and some degree of political sophistication are factors almost as vital as scientific competence and reputation in the selection of members for the top committees. Experience in one of the major wartime laboratories, especially the M.I.T. Radiation Laboratory and the laboratories of the Manhattan Project, or an apprenticeship on one or more of the military "summer studies," still appears to be a useful qualification for scientific advising. There is as yet little sign of a change of generations that would affect this pattern. Even the relatively few younger scientists who have filtered into the higher-level advisory committees are often students of one of the wartime giants like Rabi, Teller, Oppenheimer, or Fermi. Full-time administrative experience in the federal government or long experience on lower-level advisory committees or panels are also important qualifications. One of the most common methods of evaluating possible candidates for membership on the PSAC is a tryout on one of its numerous specialized panels. In this process of selection for advisory committees the characteristics deplored by Laski often tend to be weeded out.

REPRESENTATION OF THE SCIENTIFIC COMMUNITY

The higher-level committees are often criticized for inadequately representing some particular disciplines, certain kinds of institutions, or some points of view on major national questions such as disarmament. For example, the PSAC has been criticized for having too many physicists and not enough engineers, too many academic scientists and too few industrial scientists, too many scientists from the east and west coasts and too few from the central areas of the nation, too many scientists who are prepared to negotiate with the Soviets and too few representing the school of thought of which Professor Edward Teller is the most articulate spokesman. All of these criticisms have some factual basis and yet it is essential to remember that scientific advisory committees are not legislative bodies, that the ability to reach a large measure of consensus and settle matters by a good deal of give and take in rational argument is much more important to the policy-maker than assurance of equal representation for all the "estates" of science and technology. People with very strong viewpoints which are impervious to rational argument or compromise merely tend to lead to a hung jury which does not help the decision-maker. A majority vote is much less useful than a well-reasoned consensus in providing scientific advice.

Many of the criticisms regarding lack of representation are either untrue or grossly exaggerated. For instance, there have always been industrial scientists on the PSAC. Although a majority of the Committee are physicists, it also consists of engineers, life scientists, and members of the medical profession. A high representation of academic scientists on the presidential committees and panels is balanced by a predominant representation of industrial scientists and research directors on the Defense Science Board and the top advisory committees of the military services. Yet to some extent this is beside the point. The members of the Committee are supposed to be selected for their ability to look at problems in broader terms than those of their own corner of science. The advice of a committee is not the sum of the individual expertise of its members, but a synthesis of viewpoints of people accustomed to looking at problems in the broadest terms. The high proportion of physicists stems from their wartime experience and their subsequent military advisory experience, for it must be remembered that scientists came into the top advisory role in government via their contributions in the national security field, and it was only later that they became concerned with the broader problems of basic science policy and the impact of science on international affairs.

It is important to bear in mind that on any given problem it is the practice of most scientific advisory committees to delegate much of the groundwork to panels whose memberships are carefully chosen to reflect the scientific and engineering skills required in the solution of particular problems. Furthermore, if the issue to be resolved is politically controversial, a special effort is made to ensure representation of a wide spectrum of viewpoints on the panel even though such a variety may not be represented on the parent committee. At the same time it is important to avoid people who are so committed to one view that a discussion of real significance is impossible. A surprising measure of agreement can be reached by a group of scientists of divergent views when they are partially protected by individual anonymity and not constrained by the need to be consistent with previously voiced public positions.

The Special Assistant to the President for Science and Technology, as well as the PSAC, is often thought of as the "spokesman" of science. It is sometimes said by both scientists and nonscientists that the members of the PSAC should be lobbyists for the interests of the scientific community and promoters of science. This feeling came about partly because the creation of the Office of Special Assistant was the result of public concern over inadequate national attention to the cultivation of national scientific strength. An important part of the task initially facing the Special Assistant was to promote the support of science, particularly basic science, in every way possible.[8] Actually, the PSAC and the Special Assistant are not, and should not be, official spokesmen for science but are organs of government. They regard themselves not as advocates of science, but as mediators between science and government. In this function they feel an obli-

[8] See essay by Kreidler in this volume.

gation to take into account the needs and interests of the government as a whole and not just the needs of the scientific community. It is the NAS and its committees which are and should be the advocates of science. The enthusiasts for a particular field of science are represented on these committees, but their reports are criticized and reviewed by the Special Assistant, by the PSAC and its special panels, and by panels of the FCST. This process is an attempt to balance the demands of a special field against the over-all requirements of science, and to adjust the requirements of a special program to the fiscal and administrative limitations of the federal government. It is still an imperfect process which has not yet been fully tested. In recent years science budgets have been rising so rapidly that the problems of maintaining balance between fields of science within the confines of severely limited resources have not had to be faced.

COMMUNICATION WITH THE POLICY-MAKER

Scientific advisers are frequently criticized for their tendency to expand their role beyond that of purely technical advice into the political, financial, and organizational spheres. The point is a valid one, but this tendency is inherent in the nature of scientific advising rather than a deliberate effort at usurpation on the part of scientists. Science makes progress largely by redefining the key questions and problems. The scientist approaching a policy problem wants to begin by understanding the whole problem, in order that he can break it down into its components in his own way. This habit, learned from his experience as a scientist, has been strongly reinforced by his wartime experience in solving military-technical problems. As Rabi puts it: "[T]he military man who doesn't come clean on the *whole* problem is like a patient who doesn't tell his doctor all the symptoms." An important part of the task of a scientific adviser is to define just what the technical issues are that have a bearing on a given policy decision. The policy-maker who tries to define the technical issues himself will not obtain the best advice from his scientific advisers. Similarly, the scientific adviser has an obligation to interpret his advice in terms of its policy implications, while at the same time trying to make explicit the nontechnical assumptions which necessarily underlie his recommendations. The policy-maker and the adviser together have the obligation to differentiate between technical and political questions, as well as between what is actually known and what is a matter of professional judgment.

The science adviser cannot always be blamed when he steps outside the technical area. Too often the politician or administrator is tempted to throw the onus of difficult or controversial political decisions onto his scientific advisers. An important decision may be much more palatable to the public and to Congress if it is made to appear to have been taken on technical grounds. In the early days of the negotiations on a nuclear test ban, both scientists and diplomats fell into the trap of believing that the basic issues were primarily technical ones which could be resolved by discussions among experts, if not at the time, then later on as new scientific knowledge became available. Subsequently, it became increasingly clear that the really difficult issues were related to the degree of assurance which the United States felt it must have against the conduct of clandestine underground tests, and to the Soviet judgments as to what would be the acceptable degree of penetration of their military security. The importance of detecting clandestine underground tests has been differently estimated by the United States, depending on judgment as to the military decisiveness of tactical nuclear weapons. The winds of public and governmental opinion appear to be too much influenced by day-to-day changes in technical developments and ideas such as the "Latter hole" or the Tamm "black boxes." [9]

The nonscientist often has an exaggerated faith in the exactness of physical science, and has great difficulty in distinguishing between what is known with a high degree of certainty and what is only a matter of reasonable probability or scientific hunch. Under pressure to make concrete recommendations, the scientist has often tended to exaggerate the validity of his data and to permit the administrator to erect an elaborate superstructure of policy on a very flimsy technical base. Something of this sort happened twice in the nuclear test

[9] U.S. Disarmament Agency, State Department, *Geneva Conference on the Discontinuance of Nuclear Weapons Tests; History and Analysis of Negotiations* (Washington, D.C., USGPO, 1961), Publ. No. 7258.

ban negotiations when much too general conclusions were drawn from fragmentary data obtained from one particular U.S. underground test. As in military decisions, policy decisions can seldom be made with all the necessary information available, and the scientist who refuses to commit himself until he considers his data completely adequate is not very useful to the administrator. He does, however, have an obligation to explain the areas of uncertainty to his political master and to prepare him as best he can for technical surprises.

ADVICE VERSUS DECISION

Political scientists writing about the PSAC and other advisory groups have often tended to confuse advice with decision, thereby investing the PSAC with a power and responsibility which it does not in fact possess. It is true that the scientist's public prestige occasionally gives his advice an influence and authority with decision-makers. He thus has power which is in some respects equivalent to, though not identical with, political power. Ultimately the scientific adviser recognizes that his influence in government rests solely on the degree to which his views are verified by subsequent events. He has no true constituency to give his advice political force, and perhaps to a greater degree than in the case of any other type of adviser his influence must rest with the persuasiveness of his arguments. Professor Bethe's prestige as an adviser was, perhaps unjustifiably, dimmed by his failure to anticipate the possibility of decoupling in underground nuclear explosions. At the same time, his prestige would have suffered much more if he had not been so quick to accept the new technical suggestion and examine it on its own merits without reference to its effect on his own deeply held political convictions regarding the desirability of a test ban.

Congressman Melvin Price has publicly attacked the PSAC for its role in the decision to abandon the aircraft nuclear propulsion program (ANP),[10] implying that it alone was responsible for this decision and that its recommendation was based on political and

[10] Melvin Price, "Atomic Science and Government—U.S. Variety," an address delivered to the American Nuclear Society in Washington, D.C., on June 14, 1961.

budgetary grounds. While there is no doubt that nontechnical considerations played an important role in the actual decision, the PSAC's part was to give advice on primarily technical grounds, as has been clearly stated by Kistiakowsky.[11] Contrary to Congressman Price's implications, the responsibility for the ANP decision was shared by many administrators and advisers; the voice of the PSAC was only one among many voices, and this voice was probably not decisive. Such decisions within the executive branch are seldom reached through the advice of a single group or individual but are the result of a gradually evolving consensus among many advisers.

THE PROBLEM OF RESPONSIBILITY

The scientific adviser differs from the military adviser in government in that he is seldom responsible for carrying out his own advice, or even for the consequences of the advice he has given. This situation has both advantages and disadvantages. It can lead to the particular type of irresponsibility which Laski describes above so graphically, or it can permit a degree of detachment and objectivity which would be difficult to achieve if the adviser were more deeply concerned with the consequences of his advice. The advice given by the Joint Chiefs of Staff has always been plagued by parochial service interests.

The problem of the responsibility of advice comes to the fore in the field of budgetary decisions affecting science. Unfortunately, advisory committees of scientists are seldom presented with the hard choices between attractive alternatives which usually concern the budgetary officer or administrator. The competing claims of different fields of science have yet to be squarely presented to a scientific advisory committee. When confronted with the virtually unlimited opportunities in a scientific field, the advisory committee is tempted to recommend expansion without much reference to other alternatives. The balance between scientific fields in the past has been determined by the somewhat accidental resultant of many pressures,

---

[11] George B. Kistiakowsky, "Personal Thoughts on Research in the United States," in *Proceedings of a Conference on Academic and Industrial Basic Research* (Washington, D.C., USGPO, 1960), NSF 61-39, pp. 49–53.

both political and scientific. The committees that recommend expansion, while not achieving all they hoped for, generally see enough effect from their recommendations to be reasonably satisfied. In an era of expanding scientific budgets this has worked fairly successfully, and the general balance of scientific effort seems to have been preserved. The scientific adviser may find himself faced with an entirely different responsibility when the time comes, as it inevitably will, that scientific budgets level off. The scientist who has to live with his professional colleagues outside government, especially in universities, will find himself torn between his natural inclination to appear as the champion and promoter of science on every occasion and his sense of responsibility as a government adviser.

RESOLUTION OF CONFLICT

In controversial issues the ideal advisory committee is one which succeeds in enlarging the area of agreement and reaching as wide a consensus as possible. A wise committee or panel can often succeed in narrowing the disagreements on a complex issue to a few technical issues which might be resolved by further research or to a clean-cut set of political alternatives which can then be resolved by the administrator. The committee which strives for consensus at all costs usually ends up with a series of pious platitudes which are useless to the policy-maker—and useless in a peculiarly irritating and frustrating way. Having reached the widest possible area of agreement the committee should then attempt to formulate the disagreements as clearly and objectively as possible. Recommendations should generally be formulated in terms of forecasts of the probable consequences of alternative actions rather than in terms of exhortation. The responsibility for these tasks rests, for the most part, with the chairman, on whom usually falls the further duty of interpreting both the agreements and the disagreements to the policy-maker. This calls for unusual objectivity and detachment on the part of the chairman. In some cases it is wise for the policy-maker himself to hear the arguments of both sides directly from the proponents rather than filtered through the chairman.

It has sometimes been suggested that major issues involving technical advice should be resolved by a sort of adversary procedure, as in a court of law. There are instances when this is desirable, as, for example, when the rights or interests of individuals or groups may be in jeopardy as a result of the decision to be made. However, on broader policy issues the advisory process should be designed to encourage convergence rather than divergence of views. An adversary procedure tends to produce a polarization of viewpoints which then must be resolved by the policy-maker himself. The administrator would be forced to immerse himself in the technical details of every decision as does a judge in patent litigation. Given the many decisions which have to be made by every administrator, and especially by the President, such a process would be ludicrously cumbersome and would paralyze decision-making.

The alternative suggestion that every advisory committee should include a devil's advocate, is probably a good one. There are times when the chairman should deliberately assume this role. Sometimes it is the only way that the strongest arguments for the committee's final position can be brought out and potential objections to its recommendations anticipated.

On the whole the greatest occupational hazard of advisory committees is not conflict but platitudinous consensus.

EXECUTIVE PRIVILEGE

No aspect of the PSAC has received as much criticism as the sheltering of its deliberations and recommendations under executive privilege. Other scientific advisory committees enjoy varying degrees of privilege, but never to the extent of those operating directly under the aegis of the White House. Of course, this is only a part of a more general source of irritation between the executive and legislative branches. The irritation has been directed at the PSAC only because its advice has frequently been followed, and has sometimes been against important agencies or congressional positions and projects. In practice, Congress, and for that matter, the public, have seldom been denied access to the technical and nontechnical considerations on which the PSAC advice was based; only questions of who said what are withheld. In some instances the PSAC panels have actually been reconstituted as panels of other agencies in order that their views could be made public without revealing the advice precisely as it was given to the President. In the early days of the PSAC, the Special Assistant, Dr. Killian, frequently advised the heads of agencies about the recommendations he intended to make to the President, and this has remained a common practice.[12] The decision to drop the ANP project, for example, was actually concurred in by the Director of Defense Research and Engineering and a panel of the General Advisory Committee of the AEC. Most of the technical and military considerations involved in that decision were covered in testimony before Congress by Dr. Herbert York and others.

There is a general feeling in the scientific community that J. Robert Oppenheimer was persecuted because of the unpopularity of his advice, supposedly given in private. The protection of executive privilege is sometimes necessary to induce scientists to join panels. They feel, rightly or wrongly, that their private interests may be vulnerable to reprisal by Congress or by powerful agencies which may be adversely affected by their recommendations.

A different type of problem has arisen when scientific advisers have chosen to speak out publicly on issues with which they have also been concerned as scientific advisers under the mantle of executive privilege. People opposed to their views feel that advisers who take public stands on controversial issues are trying to have their cake and eat it too. These advisers have, however, been willing and even eager to testify before Congress, with the exception of specifics like who recommended what to the President. The suspicion may remain that their testimony is filtered or distorted by the omission of privileged matter, but it is hard to see how this problem is any different for a presidential adviser than for an agency or department head who also gives privileged advice to the President. Perhaps the principal difference is that the part-time adviser does not consider himself under political or administrative discipline, and so may feel more free to volunteer a public statement at variance with the official line of the moment. The administrator who differs from the official line is constrained from expressing his difference except when called upon to do so while testifying under oath.

[12] See essay by Gilpin in this volume.

This is a complex question, but its facets are not peculiar to scientific advisers, except insofar as scientists may enjoy greater public prestige than other experts. Because of their relative newness in the higher government councils, the reputation of scientists is less tarnished by special pleading or self-serving, and it is hoped that in their public statements scientific advisers will bear in mind their responsibility to preserve the reputation for objectivity which scientists generally enjoy, and which is their greatest asset in the political arena.

Speaking out on public issues should not in itself be considered an abuse of executive privilege. Under the Eisenhower administration, the Special Assistant often felt hampered by the rigidity of the practice of executive privilege, which is even more enforced when the Executive and Congress are controlled by different parties. There were times when the Special Assistant was unable to testify although it would have been to the interest of the government for him to do so. Reorganization Plan No. 2, which became effective in June, 1962, created the Office of Science and Technology and gave the Special Assistant two hats—one as a confidential White House adviser and the other as statutory Director of the Office, subject to Senate confirmation. One of the purposes of providing such statutory underpinning to the science advisory role was to permit the Director to testify before Congress and thereby formally defend administration positions on new science legislation, on budgetary matters affecting basic science, and on the coordination of federal scientific programs. As a result of this reorganization, the area which we have called "policy for science" can become the subject for congressional testimony, while the area which we have called "science in policy" remained under executive privilege.

In the reorganization, the PSAC remained in the White House and continued to enjoy the protection of executive privilege. It is possible that if all the PSAC members had been made subject to Senate confirmation, this might ultimately have led to political control of science and to a serious threat to the independent and apolitical nature of the Committee. This nonpartisan character was explicit in the PSAC's original charter from President Eisenhower, and was recognized by President Kennedy through his continuation of the membership after the change in administration. Offsetting the fear of partisan control is the historical fact that there has so far been no problem of partisan politics with respect to the National Science Board, whose membership is subject to Senate confirmation.

A possibly more serious problem resulting from the new status of the Special Assistant is the amount of time involved in congressional relations that must now be added to that required for all the other responsibilities of the office. A major part of the past effectiveness of the whole presidential science advisory operation has been due to its compactness and lack of bureaucratization. The Special Assistant and the PSAC were able to be highly selective in the problems undertaken for study. With greater congressional visibility the Special Assistant may find himself forced to know less and less about more and more, and to depend increasingly on staff work rather than first-hand study for his expression of views. Since he has no decision-making or executive responsibility, other than for his own small staff, he can, I believe, avoid this dilemma by proper selectivity with respect to the type of things on which he chooses to testify. The Director of the Bureau of the Budget is in an analogous situation, and has so far lived with it successfully by delimiting his areas of testimony.

The preservation of executive privilege is clearly essential if the President is to get honest and independent advice. Too frequently the violently unpopular position of today becomes government policy tomorrow. If the adviser could not look ahead without fear of political crucifixion, policy would soon become frozen in a static mold. Furthermore, it would be ossified at the very moment of generation, when it should be most fluid and dynamic.

CONFLICT OF INTEREST

Nearly two-thirds of all the nation's research and development is financed by the federal government, and 55 percent of the work is carried out through contracts and grants from the government to the private sector. Much of this work is of a nature that is unique to government financing. It is usually impossible to recruit advisers in these fields unless they are closely associated with institutions whose work is heavily financed by the federal government. In its modern guise, the problem of conflict of interest is much more subtle and complicated than envisioned in the conflict of interest statutes, which were designed originally to prevent government officials from directly and personally benefiting from their official position.

Until recently the law was not very clear on the extent to which it was applicable to part-time advisers. By a strict interpretation, most of the complex advisory structure in the federal agencies would have been made illegal. The best that could be done from a practical standpoint was to avoid situations in which government consultants were in positions to affect directly a specific contract or grant with an institution in which they had a substantial interest, or to which they owed an allegiance. Many government consultants, and especially scientific advisers, have acted on the assumption that the statutes applied only to employees or stockholders of profit-making institutions, arguing that as long as a government contract could not affect their personal compensation or financial status there was no possibility of conflict or even impropriety. Few advisers were more than vaguely aware of the conflict of interest statutes; they could be excused for not taking them very seriously since there had been no prosecution under these statutes against a part-time adviser, and therefore the law had never been tested or interpreted in the courts. Most scientists feel that the best protection for the government lies in full and public disclosure of all the outside interests of the advisers together with sufficient technical competence and general sophistication on the part of the administrator receiving the advice to enable him to make allowance for possible bias and discount it in his own mind. In many instances the loyalties of a scientist or engineer are much more closely identified with his professional community than with the institution which pays his salary. Most scientific advisers would assert their ability to be objective even when the interests of their own institution are involved, though they may recognize the undesirability from the standpoint of public relations of having a potential conflict of interest.

Recent legislation and legal interpretation have clarified the concept of conflict of interest, especially as it pertains to part-time consultants. While this legislation does not fully embody the principles enumerated above, it does permit the government to retain the services of its advisers, and to operate with advisory boards and panels much as in the past, though with greater circumspection as to the public record.

No government adviser can be free of bias. Although no statute recognizes the possibility of a conflict of interest within government, every administrator is well aware of the agency biases harbored by federal employees who give scientific advice. The scientists of the three military services tend to favor strategies and weapons systems which lead to the aggrandizement of their service, and the professional military scientist can seldom be depended on for unbiased advice on disarmament.

In fact it is often to counteract the effects of conflicts of interest within government that administrators have sought advice from the private scientific community. This community, in turn, has its own bias toward contracting out as much research as possible rather than doing it within government. Government scientists generally favor government laboratories and are opposed to the practice of contracting out either research or development. University scientists have a bias favoring basic research. These biases are seldom consciously self-serving; they are merely a part of human nature. "What's good for General Motors is good for the country" is not a sentiment unique to a famous Secretary of Defense; there is a little bit of it in every institution and profession. Some advisers are more able than others to recognize this sentiment in themselves and consciously strive to discount it in formulating their advice. These are generally the people that make good advisers. There is also an opposite danger of leaning over backwards, of failing to defend the interests and values of science because of a fear of the appearance of pleading the cause of a special interest.

Issues of the kind described above are much more important in scientific advising than are the obvious conflicts of interest involving personal profit. Yet it is basically impossible to resolve such issues by any legislative prescription. As long as the federal government retains the necessary competence within its own full-time administrative and technical staff, it has less to fear from advice subtly or overtly biased by self-interest than it does from loss of the benefit of a perspective from outside government. The answer to the conflict of interest problem in scientific advice is not restrictive and negative legislation but positive legislation and administrative action to improve working conditions within government so that it can continue to attract people capable of properly using outside scientific advice. With respect to scientific advisers acting at the higher policy levels, it is important to develop a professional code of ethics connected with the advisory function. Fortunately, among basic scientists there is a stern ethical code associated with the question of scientific credit and priority which is powerfully sanctioned by public opinion within the scientific community. It provides a model for a similarly sanctioned, though unwritten, code with respect to the objectivity of scientific advice.

CONCLUSION

The reader may conclude that this essay has presented an unduly rosy picture of the beneficial effect of scientific advisers in government, and particularly of the operation and influence of the PSAC. There are certainly many critics, especially among those who have disagreed with the influence exerted by the PSAC in the field of disarmament and weapons policy, who would emphatically and sincerely disagree concerning the beneficial effects. Only history will tell who was right with respect to policy.

A major criticism would be of the tendency toward self-perpetuation among the most influential committees, and especially the consequent preservation through two administrations of a single viewpoint on many questions of policy. Furthermore, critics would argue, the presidential advisers have, through their influence on major appointments, gradually imposed their policy viewpoints throughout the upper levels of the scientific agencies and in the Bureau of the Budget. Although there may be superficial evidence for such an analysis, it will scarcely stand historical examination. The diversity of viewpoints and institutions represented on high-level advisory committees has been much broader than the critics claim. If it can be said that any policy viewpoints have become dominant in government, this has been imposed more by the logic of events than by any particular group of advisers. The advisers merely foreshadowed what would probably have been brought about by events anyway: the creation of an invulnerable retaliatory force; the inadequacy of the policy of massive retaliation; the importance of limited and guerrilla warfare and of conventional arms; the creation of the NASA, the Arms Control and Disarmament Agency, and a research and development section in the foreign-aid program; the centralization of research and development responsibility in the Department of Defense; increased support for basic research and graduate education; the fostering of international scientific activities and of scientific exchanges with the Soviet bloc; the creation of the FCST and its interagency committees; and the creation of the Office of Science and Technology by reorganization plan.

In matters of armament policy the critics have had their day in court and indeed have spoken from a much more firm base of power and influence than the various scientific advisers. Perhaps where the advisers have won out they have done so because their case was more persuasive, rather than because of illegitimate pressures or some sort of inside track to policy.

The scientific community and its influence in government is in a politically exposed position if only because of the magnitude of the scientific enterprise and the success of scientists, especially university scientists, in influencing policy despite their lack of a true constituency or base of power. To an increasing degree the country is looking to the Special Assistant and his supporting advisory staff, and, rightly or wrongly, there will be a growing tendency for Congress to blame his office for everything that goes wrong in the manifold scientific activities of the government. Whether the office can maintain its ability to concentrate on the key issues and not become lost in a rash of bureaucratic brush fires is the crucial question for its future success. It seems probable that the test of the political viability of the present network of advisory committees, and particularly of the presidential advisory structure, will come during the next few years, when budgetary ceilings may put a greater strain than ever before on the advisory committee's task of judging, and when the accountability of scientists to Congress and to the public will be more carefully probed than it has been in the past.

Scientists and

American Science Policy

WALLACE S. SAYRE

*Eaton Professor of Public Administration and Chairman of the
Department of Public Law and Government of Columbia University*

This essay is reprinted, with permission, from *Science*, XXXIII, No. 3456
(March 24, 1961)

The phrase "scientists and American science policy" suggests other
comparable formulations: soldiers and American military policy,
farmers and American farm policy, businessmen and American business policy, educators and American education policy, labor and
American labor policy, and a host of other variations. These parallels
serve to remind us sharply of the limitations which a democratic
order places upon the role of experts as well as upon special interests
in the shaping of public policy. If it can be said, for example, that
war is too important to be entrusted to the generals and peace too
important to be left to the diplomats, then it may be asked whether
science policy is not too important to be delegated wholly to the
scientists. In a democratic order all policies of significance must
secure a wide range of consent, not merely from the general public
but also from the many organized groups and institutions that see
their interests importantly involved. Scientists do have a special involvement in science policy, but under the rules of a democratic
society they have no monopoly in its development or maintenance,
nor have they inherently any greater legitimacy or relevance as
participants than all the other claimants who aspire to influence the
content of science policy.

Scientists, we may assume, aspire to be influential as a group in
the determination of public policy over a wide range, especially
those elements of public policy which may be described as science
policy. To exercise such influence the scientists must enter the politi-

cal arena. Scientists in politics encounter the questions posed by the political process to all those who enter: Who are they? Who speaks for them? What are their goals? What are their strategies?

WHO ARE THE SCIENTISTS?

If scientists are to be influential participants in constructing an American science policy, they will need to be self-conscious participants, that is, they must have a visible and concrete identity. That identity is now vague and elusive—to many scientists as well as to the other groups involved in the policy process. "The scientific community," a phrase often submitted as an identification, is a world of uncertain boundaries.

Who are the members of the scientific community? Is it an open community, hospitable to all who desire to enter, or is it open only to those who meet severe tests of eligibility? More specifically, are there "hard scientists," whose membership is taken for granted, and "soft scientists," whose credentials are dubious? Are physicists and chemists members of the scientific community by right, while other natural scientists must submit additional claims for admission? Do all engineers qualify, or only certain types of engineers? Do doctors of medicine have entry, or only research scientists in medicine? Are social scientists full members of the scientific community? The answer of the moment appears to be that the natural scientists are the most fully accredited members of the science community but that the life scientists and the social scientists regard this as a transient condition of affairs.

The difficulties raised by these questions suggest that the scientific community is most often used as a strategic phrase, intended by the user to imply a large number of experts where only a few may in fact exist, or to imply unity of view where disagreement may in fact prevail. The phrase may thus belong in that class of invocations, so familiar to the political process, which summon up numbers and legitimacy for a point of view by asserting that "the American people," or "the public," or "all informed observers," or "the experts" demand this or reject that. There is nothing especially astonishing about this, since all participants in the political process indulge in the stratagem, and each participant learns to discount the claims of others, but there may be grounds for mild surprise that the code of science permits its extensive use by scientists either as deliberate strategy or in genuine innocence.

If scientists are themselves uncertain as to who all their fellow scientists are, then some ambiguities attend their relationship to American science policy. Are they a small elite group (for example, the approximately 96,000 named in *American Men of Science* for the physical and biological sciences), or do they number several million (as they do if the engineers, the social scientists, and the medical profession are included)? If scientists want to be among the shapers of American science policy rather than simply the objects of that policy, then they must expect these and similar questions from the other participants in the making of science policy. The spokesmen of science will be asked: For whom do you speak? The scientists themselves confront a prior question: Who are to be the accredited spokesmen for the scientists?

WHO SPEAKS FOR THE SCIENTISTS?

The notion of an American science policy, a policy with which the scientists are to be influentially identified, requires the scientists to have leaders who can act as their representatives in that bargaining with public officials and other groups which accompanies the policy-making process. Not every scientist can participate directly in this process; there is not room enough, nor time enough, for a town meeting of all the scientists with all the other groups that have equally legitimate claims to be present. Some few scientists must be selected to speak for the many, but the scientists may choose these few in many different ways. They may let the science spokesmen nominate themselves, they may let nonscientists select the leaders of science, they may develop nominating and electoral devices for choosing their leaders through the votes of all scientists in a single scientist constituency, they may choose their leaders in numerous specialized constituencies, or they may combine these methods in various ways, or invent still other methods.

Tradition and recent practice have already provided some important patterns of choice. The history of American science is rich with examples of the articulate, self-directing, individual scientist of high prestige who felt it his obligation to speak often and boldly in behalf of science and the scientists. Few scientists, and fewer nonscientists, have been inclined to question his representative role, although his peers in prestige and self-confidence have often publicly challenged his advice. Another pattern has been provided by the habit which high-ranking government science officials have of speaking, from their position of special eminence and authority, for the interests of science as they perceive them; this would seem to be, for example, the primary function of some government science advisers and advisory committees. If these advisers are the spokesmen of the scientists, it is relevant to ask: What role did which scientists have in choosing them? Still another pattern has been demonstrated by the role of the National Academy of Sciences (NAS) since 1863. This quasi-governmental body of scientists, its membership small and its new members elected on the basis of scientific eminence by those who are already members, has for many decades acted upon the assumption that it could and should speak for the scientists in the realm of public policy. The scientists who are not members of the Academy have not invariably agreed that the Academy spoke for them, or that its silence was to be taken as neutrality on their part on contemporary issues of science policy.

These patterns of individuals and small, elite groups, some self-nominated and some the designees of government officials, speaking for the scientists have been accompanied by several efforts to establish more comprehensive scientists' constituencies from which spokesmen might be chosen. The American Association for the Advancement of Science (AAAS) is the most durable of these constituencies. Its own membership is large, and its affiliated societies enlarge its base. Its officials, and especially its committees and its journal *Science*, often speak eloquently for the values and priorities of science and scientists. One of the most dramatic assertions of its representative role as spokesman for the scientists was its 1958 Parliament of Science, assembled in Washington, D.C., to consider the proposal for a government department of science and other issues. Some privacy surrounded the identity of the delegates to this parliament, the method of their selection as representatives of the scientists, the record of their deliberations, and the extent of their agreement upon the terms of the published report of the parliament. The sense in which the AAAS and its parliament are authentic spokesmen for the scientists as a scientific community thus cannot be easily determined, either by scientists or nonscientists. The Federation of American Scientists provides still another variation—an association of scientists quite explicitly committed to participation in the political process.

But the most prevalent pattern for choosing the spokesmen of the scientists is provided by the specialized associations of scientists. The officers and committees and journals of the American Physical Society, the American Chemical Society, the American Institute of Biological Sciences, the Federation of American Scientists, the Engineers' Council, the Association of American Geologists, and perhaps a thousand other specialized societies provide the scientists with hundreds of spokesmen in their specialized areas of interest. These spokesmen do not often speak with one voice upon a given aspect of science policy, nor do they often if ever concern themselves with the elements of a comprehensive science policy. Instead, the leaders of each specialized society tend to express their views upon that segment of science policy which touches significantly the interests of the society's own members. As spokesmen for the scientists, their voices are often competitive, emphasizing separate priorities, asserting specialized rather than general goals. In this characteristic the associations of the scientists share the pluralistic, fragmented, and internally competitive attributes of the other group participants in the American political process—whether political parties, business, labor, agriculture, the professions, nationality groups, or the governmental bureaucracies.

The leaders of still other groups often speak confidently in policy discussions as surrogates for scientists. The Association of Land Grant Colleges and Universities, the American Association of University Presidents, science laboratories and institutes, and the science communication media are prominent among these groups. Do they, too, hold a watching brief for scientists by the scientists' own choice?

Who, then, speaks for the scientists? The answer would seem to lie somewhere in a broad zone of ambiguity. Only the scientists themselves can identify their authentic spokesmen. If they have already done so, it would seem to have been done privately and to have been kept confidential. When and if the scientists undertake an explicit identification of their spokesmen, it is not improbable that they will conclude that no one can speak for all of them, and that in a democratic society we will all, perforce, continue to be confronted by numerous, competing spokesmen for science, each often claiming to speak for more of the scientific community than he in fact represents.

AN AMERICAN SCIENCE POLICY

Uncertainty thus surrounds the questions: Who are the scientists and who speaks for them? Ambiguity also characterizes the phrase American science policy. It is not difficult to cite examples of particular science policies, these exist in abundance—from the patents clause of the Constitution to yesterday's progress reports of the National Science Foundation (NSF). But the unity and comprehensiveness implied by the phrase American science policy are not achieved by merely consolidating and codifying all these separate items of science policy. Something more than this is quite clearly implied and evidently desired by many of those who speak for the scientists. It may be assumed, then, that an American science policy is something aspired to but not yet achieved by the scientists: a unified, comprehensive, coherent, rational statement of goals and methods for science in the United States, accepted by and binding upon all the participants in the policy process, and including agreement upon the rules by which the policy may be changed.

The main elements of such a policy might include the following:

1. A preamble, asserting the values of science to society and the nation; a statement defining the boundary line between the governmental and the private sectors in science.

2. A statement of the priorities for science in each of these sectors.

3. A ranking of the competing claims of science education, basic research, and applied research, as well as an assignment of priorities

among the fields of science—chemistry, engineering, physics, biology, psychology, economics, and perhaps a score of others.

4. A statement of agreement and action upon the structure, location, and assignments of the science agencies in the executive branch —for example, a unified science department (or, alternatively, decentralized science agencies) and the relation of such a department or such agencies to the President and Congress.

5. Explicit statements of governmental procedures intended to reflect the values of scientists in such matters as secrecy, personnel loyalty and security, government contracts and grants for research, definitions of basic research, and provisions concerning the chain-of-command in science activities, including protection for the autonomy of individual scientists.

If such a body of public policy existed, accepted by the scientists and legitimatized by the President and Congress in a statute, thus attesting the consent of the nation, then an American science policy in the fullest implications of that phrase would have been established.

Is such a unified and comprehensive policy a feasible goal for American scientists? Do they in fact desire it?

If a 1963 Town Meeting of Science were to be assembled, despite the problems of deciding which scientists were eligible to attend, agreement could no doubt be reached on the preamble to an American science policy. Preambles, like political party platforms, are usually triumphs in ambiguity. A viable consensus could probably also be reached on the last item—the "working conditions" for scientists—although ambiguity would overshadow precision here, too. But beyond these two items the available evidence suggests that there are no other major elements of an American science policy upon which one could expect unanimity, or even a clear majority agreement, among the scientists themselves. The document which might emerge from the work of such an assembly of science would most likely be an unstable mixture of vague agreement and sharp minority dissents, a testament to the pluralism of science and the scientists. And if the scientists are not likely to agree upon a unified science policy, the prospects that the nonscientist participants might develop such a policy are even less convincing. There are no apparent powerful incentives for any other great interest group in the American society to develop a unified, comprehensive science policy. And even if agreement were possible among the scientists, there is no persuasive evidence that they could win consent without major concessions to the competing claims of all the other interests that must, in a democratic order, agree to such a significant allocation of social values and resources.

Unity and comprehensiveness are thus not likely to be the hallmarks of American science policy. Talk of a single, comprehensive American science policy has an essentially fictitious quality. There will be many science policies, rather than a master science policy. Diversity, inconsistency, compromise, experimentation, pulling and hauling, competition, and continuous revision in science policies are more predictable continuing characteristics than their antonyms. This has been the history of American science policies and this describes their present state. We are accustomed to view this state of affairs as deplorable. But to live with diversity and accommodations of policy, and yet to be impatient of them, may be the process by which a democratic society achieves progress in science as well as in other fields. In any event, the future seems to offer American scientists more dilemmas than unequivocal answers in science policy.

PERSISTING DILEMMAS FOR SCIENTISTS

Some of these dilemmas may be illustrated by a brief exploration of a few of the choices concerning governmental arrangements for science—choices which some scientists have helped to make in the past, or which nonscientists have made for them, and still other choices which must yet be made.

Science advisers. One of these choices involves the aspirations of scientists to give advice to officials at the highest levels of the national government—advice not simply in an area defined as science policy but also concerning those elements of foreign policy, defense policy, and domestic policy to which many scientists believe their specialized knowledge is relevant. These aspirations of scientists were reflected in the establishment of the NAS a hundred years ago and in the creation of the National Research Council almost fifty years ago. They are reflected today in the existence of the Office of Special Assistant to the President for Science and Technology, the President's Science Advisory Committee, the office of Science Adviser to the Secretary of State, and the General Advisory Committee of the Atomic Energy Commission (AEC). The Council of Economic Advisers is still another example.

Attempts to define the role of these advisory institutions raise several important questions. Is their primary responsibility to advise the officials as an autonomous voice of the scientists, or are they, as agents or colleagues of the officials, to explain official policies to the scientists, or are they to participate in working out those accommodations in policy which will build a bridge of collaboration between scientists and officialdom? The history of these institutions of advice reveals the tensions, as well as the temporary adjustments, between these inherently competitive conceptions of the advisory role. For the scientists the dilemma remains unresolved: an autonomous science adviser is soon at the periphery rather than at the center of policy-making; an involved adviser is soon the advocate of all official policy rather than its critic, an ambassador from the officials to the scientists rather than the scientists' spokesman, or at best a broker between the scientists and the officials. The scientists who are dismayed by these hard choices may perhaps find some consolation in knowing that all other groups in a democratic order confront similar frustrations.

A department of science. Another choice involves the recommendation for a unified department of science, or for a department of science and technology. This proposal to concentrate most of the talents and other resources of the scientists in a single agency, and "to give Science a voice at the Cabinet table," is a strategy supported by the precedents of comparable aspirations in agriculture, business, and labor. But the proposal encounters today, as it has since John Wesley Powell advocated it before the Allison Commission in the 1880s, the stubborn pluralism of the scientists themselves, the uncertainties of the scientists about the boundaries of their interests, and the opposition of government scientists more willing to endure their existing, familiar organizational environment than to risk the unknowns of a new and untested arrangement. With the scientists thus embattled among themselves, neither the nonscientist interest groups nor the public officials now seem likely to take a determined initiative on a question the scientists, as such, cannot decide. A department of science, then, waits upon the unlikely event that the scientists will soon be able, and will find it desirable, to decide who they are, who their accredited spokesmen are, what their common goals are, and, most important, able to conclude that they are sufficiently unified to risk their separate interests to the leadership and fortunes of a single government institution.

An autonomous science agency. An alternative choice—the creation of an autonomous science agency, but with a limited assignment —has been at least temporarily decided upon. The NSF has completed its first decade; its durability now appears convincingly demonstrated. The independence of the agency from the supervision of officialdom is not as great as was hoped for by those spokesmen for the scientists who piloted the proposal through the hearings, the amendments, the debates, and the votes of the 79th and 80th Congresses, past the shock of a presidential veto indicting excessive autonomy, to the eventual compromise enacted by the 81st Congress. Some of the form, and more than a little of the substance, of autonomy was lost along the way. Annual budgets and annual appropriations are continuing reminders that autonomy is limited, even in decisions about kinds and amount of basic research, and even after Sputniks gave the agency higher priorities and the scientists greater authority.

A close look at the composition of the National Science Board since 1950 also raises the question of whether the agency does not more nearly reflect the autonomous voice of university and other administrators of science, alumni from the ranks of scientists though they be, than it does the voice of scientists in the classrooms and laboratories. The task of representing the scientists on the Board has apparently, with the passage of time and with the entry of presidential and other preferences, been entrusted more to surrogates for scientists than was the expressed expectation of the sponsors and the officials in the discussions accompanying the passage of the National Science Foundation Act of 1950. Surrogates perhaps provide "virtual" or "existential" representation for the scientists; other groups in American society must often accept a similar settlement.

Specialized science agencies. Most existing government science organizations represent a different kind of choice for scientists. These science agencies are immersed in the political system of a large department or independent agency, the degree of autonomy of the science unit in that system varying widely. The life scientists, for example, occupy many special units in Agriculture, in Health, Education, and Welfare, and in Interior; the nuclear scientists are found in the AEC, and other physicists and chemists in the Bureau of Standards; meteorologists staff the Weather Bureau; scientists of many varieties inhabit Department of Defense units; while the geologists have their sanctuary in the Geological Survey, the space scientists have theirs in the National Aeronautics and Space Administration (NASA), and the economists have theirs in the Council of Economic Advisers. The other social sciences are less visibly accommodated, but they do staff numerous units in Agriculture, Commerce, Health, Education, and Welfare, and Labor.

The leaders of all these science units have links, strong or attenuated as the case may be, to the associations and institutions of scientists outside the government, but inside the departmental or agency system they share the powers of decision and compete for priorities with other members of the executive hierarchy, and they report to congressional committees whose concerns are not confined to questions of science or the preferences of scientists. In these many science enterprises the scientists are partners with nonscientists rather than autonomous decision-makers. They may employ the mystique and the expertise of science as strategies to maximize their autonomous role, but they cannot realistically expect to be more than senior partners. Most frequently they will be compelled to accept the status of equal partner with nonscientist officials; not infrequently they will find they are actually junior partners. Their hopes for autonomy are, in practice, curbed not only by nonscientist officials in the executive hierarchy and by congressional committees but also by the activities of the interest-group associations in the science bureau's own special constituency. Thus, the Bureau of Mines must listen attentively to the American Mining Congress and the United Mine Workers; the Bureau of Standards, to many industry associations; the Weather Bureau, to the Air Transport Association and the Farm Bureau Federation; the Public Health Service, to the American Medical Association and the American Cancer Society; the NASA, to the aviation industry associations; the AEC, to the electric power associations and many contractor groups; and agricultural research bureaus, to the Cotton Council and numerous other commodity associations. Rare is the science bureau which is not required by its political environment to bargain continuously with, and accommodate its aims and its priorities to, the interest groups in its constituency.

Advice to Congress. Science agencies in the executive branch have occupied most of the attention of scientists. If they are to pursue their aspirations for a more distinctive and influential role in science policy, the scientists will find it necessary to formulate a general strategy concerning advice to Congress from scientists. No congressional committee is now organized and staffed to give exclusive and comprehensive attention to science policy and to listen continuously to scientists, although the House Committee on Science and Astronautics takes a broad view of its science role, and its Senate counterpart may follow suit. Most scientists must pursue their congressional interests across almost the whole range of committees and subcommittees in both Senate and House. If unity and comprehensiveness in congressional action on science are desired—unity such as is sometimes proposed for science in the executive branch—scientists will be required to choose among several apparent alternatives: they can propose a joint committee on science and technology, with a wide-ranging jurisdiction over all the concerns of scientists; or they can propose a comprehensive committee on science and technology in each House, rather than a joint committee; or they can aim at the creation of a joint committee on science policy with a more limited assignment, or of such a committee on science policy in each House. If changes like these were to be made in congressional science committees (an event to be anticipated only after long and determined effort), the scientists still could not expect to enjoy a monopoly of attention from the new committees.

Those other groups who now share power with the scientists'

spokesmen in the numerous specialized committees and subcommittees would follow the scientists into the new arenas of influence. The scientists might, however, hope to have, at least for a time, higher status and legitimacy as spokesmen before such new committees, and they might also hope that their competitors in the new setting might compete with each other as well as with the scientists. The question which would soon confront the scientists, however, would be: Could they establish and maintain their own unity of goals and priorities before the new committees? The odds in favor of an affirmative answer do not seem to be high.

POLITICS INESCAPABLE

Scientists influential in the creation, maintenance, and modification of American science policy are scientists in politics. The spokesmen for the scientists need not be party officials or candidates for, or occupants of, elective public office, but they will have to be active participants in other phases of the political process—as high government science officials, as science advisers to executive officials, as spokesmen for science policies before committees of Congress, as organizers of opinion through the communication media, or as officials and leaders of science associations and institutions. The leaders of the scientists cannot escape politics and remain leaders in science; since their leaders cannot escape politics, the scientists as a whole are in politics too, even their silence being interpreted as acquiescence.

Leading American scientists have long entered the political arena with boldness and success. Convincing examples are provided by the zeal and skill with which the Scientific Lazzaroni piloted the NAS through Congress and secured Lincoln's signature in 1863; by the subtlety and determination with which Powell secured the establishment of the Geological Survey in 1879 through an appropriation bill rider (a technique that is of the essence of politics); by the frequency with which the Cosmos Club has served as the meeting place of an informal caucus of scientists' *coups d'état* in the public interest; by the magisterial role of Vannevar Bush in national science policy; and by the sophistication of the Federation of the Atomic Scientists in their 1946 attack upon the May-Johnson bill and their shaping of the terms of the McMahon Act.

Scientists in politics share the problems of other participants in the political process. No special dispensation exempts the scientists from the hard choices and continuing difficulties which the political process imposes upon all those who aspire to shape public policy. One course is to seek to maximize the unity of all scientists and to establish legitimacy for the spokesmen of a unified science community. An alternative is to accept diversity and competitive priorities among scientists and to establish the identity of the separate groups of scientists, establishing the legitimacy of their respective spokesmen. Whichever of these two main roads is chosen, the united or the separated scientists will face the necessity of recruiting allies from among organized groups of nonscientists; the scientists cannot exercise a unilateral dominance in the making of science policy. Alliances are created and maintained at a price; the price takes the form of mutually acceptable accommodations in policy or priorities.

Scientists in politics meet with varying fortunes in the process of bargaining with allies and opponents: in the Bureau of Agricultural Economics they find an environment too severe for survival; in the National Institutes of Health, an embarrassment of riches; in the Weather Bureau, high-velocity cross-winds of pressure; in the Geological Survey, an atmosphere of quiet and modest benevolence which has existed for a half-century, since the belligerent initial decades; in the Bureau of Standards, a favorable equilibrium of forces, but in the Public Health Service, an unsteady equilibrium. Such variations are the common experiences of most participants in the political process. The conditions which determine the range of variation are best understood, anticipated, and managed by those who are politicians, that is, by those who are expert in the political process.

The 1958 Parliament of Science states the scientists' hopes and fears in persuasive terms:

The scientific revolution will totally dwarf the Industrial Revolution and the other historical instances of great social change. It will be more compelling, and will pose more urgent problems, because of both the pace and the magnitude of the changes which now impend.

What faces man is not, in any restricted sense, a scientific problem. The problem is one of the relation of science to public policy. Scientific issues are vitally and almost universally involved. The special knowledge of the scientist is necessary, to be sure; but that knowledge would be powerless or dangerous if it did not include all areas of science and if it were not effectively pooled with the contributions of humanists, statesmen, and philosophers and brought to the service of all segments of society.

What is to be done? Scientists certainly have no arrogant illusion that they have the answers. But they do want to help. They are, moreover, convinced that the time is overripe for a more understanding collaboration between their special profession and the rest of society. [AAAS, 1958]

The scientists are now inescapably committed to politics if they hope to exercise influence in the shaping of public policy, including science policies. The leaders of the scientists, then, are perforce politicians. As politicians in a democratic order, they are effective in the degree to which they understand the political process, accept its rules, and play their part in the process with more candor than piety, accepting gladly the fact that they are in the battle rather than above it. The spokesmen for science have occasionally lectured the nonscientists, sometimes sternly, upon their obligation to understand science. Perhaps the advice may be reversed: the scientist has an obligation to understand and to play his significant role forthrightly in the polity.[1]

BIBLIOGRAPHY

American Academy of Political and Social Science. *The Annals,* CCCXXVII (January, 1960).
American Association for the Advancement of Science, "1958 Parliament of Science," *Science,* CXXVII, No. 3303 (April 18, 1958), 852–58.

[1] In the preparation of this essay, I have referred to the publications listed in the Bibliography, to data developed through an extensive series of interviews with science officials in Washington, D.C., during 1959–60, and to pertinent official and unofficial documents.

American Association for the Advancement of Science, Committee on Science in the Promotion of Human Welfare, "Science and Welfare," *Science*, CXXXII, No. 3419 (July 9, 1960), 68–73.

Barber, Bernard. *Science and the Social Order*. Glencoe, Ill., Free Press, 1952.

Brode, Wallace R. "Development of a Science Policy," *Science*, CXXXI, No. 3392 (January 1, 1960), 9–15.

Dupree, A. Hunter. *Science in the Federal Government*. Cambridge, Mass., Harvard University Press, 1957.

President's Science Advisory Committee. *Strengthening American Science*. Washington, D.C., USGPO, 1958, and subsequent reports. President's Scientific Research Board. *Science and Public Policy*. Washington, D.C., USGPO, 1947. Vols. 1–3.

Price, Don K. *Government and Science*. New York, New York University Press, 1954.

U.S. Senate Committee on Interstate and Foreign Commerce. *Hearings on National Science Foundation Act*, 79th, 80th, 81st, 83rd, 85th, and 86th Congresses.

U.S. Senate Committee on Government Operations. *Hearings and Reports on Science and Technology Act of 1958*, 85th Congress; Hearings on a Department of Science and Technology, 86th Congress.

Waterman, Alan T., "National Science Foundation: A Ten Year Resume," *Science*, CXXXI, No. 3410 (May 6, 1960), 1341–54.

Wolfle, Dael, "Government Organization for Science," *Science*, CXXXI, No. 3411 (May 13, 1960), 1407–17.

The President's Science Advisers and National Science Policy

ROBERT N. KREIDLER

*Director of Educational Affairs at the Alfred P. Sloan Foundation
and former member of the staff of the Office of the
Special Assistant to the President for Science and Technology*

In the late fall of 1957, President Eisenhower summoned leading American scientists to help make science policy at the very summit of government. This act, as seen from today's perspective, may well have been historic, for it ratified a wholly new relationship that had been developing between science and public policy in the United States. Earlier presidents, notably Franklin D. Roosevelt, had called upon scientists to mobilize science for war, but it was only after Sputnik that the President personally asked scientists for advice on large decisions that were likely to affect the health and future progress of science itself.

Throughout the history of the Republic, American presidents have regarded science as useful and have lent it their support. With the onset of World War II the decisive importance of science to national security was recognized, and scientists were welcomed to the inner councils of government. Following the War, their new position was preserved and extended. With increasing frequency, scientists appeared at meetings in Washington, D.C., to advise on a wide range of national programs. As a rule their main concern at all these meetings was not with national science policy but with advising the government on the uses of science for other national purposes, usually defense and the development of atomic energy. As in the past, the decisions most affecting the direction and progress of science—the ultimate budgetary decisions concerning such matters as government support of basic and applied research—were largely being made outside the scientific community by nonscientist administrators. It was only after President Eisenhower appointed a full-time Special Assistant for Science and Technology and established his science advisory committee, that members of the scientific community were given direct access to the President and an established means of expressing themselves on matters of science policy.

The President's appointment of his own science advisers has established a direct line of communication between science and government at the level of the presidency. While both the President's Science Advisory Committee (PSAC) and the Special Assistant are actively engaged in developing policies for science, most of their energies are devoted to questions troubling the President on the uses of science and technology for a host of practical objectives ranging from air defense systems to arms control measures. They are not restricting themselves to science policy, but, on the contrary, are becoming active molders of national security policy, foreign policy, and domestic policy. They are concerned with public policy where they believe scientific factors have relevance.

The President's science advisers are, however, making themselves heard on the two crucial matters that most affect the progress of science: the allocation of resources for the support of science and the possible effects of other government programs on the direction and strength of the scientific enterprise.

Recognizing that important decisions affecting science were often being surrendered by default to nonscientist administrators, these advisers are now undertaking to furnish scientific advice where none existed before. In doing so, they have found it necessary to depart from the traditional reluctance of scientists to plan for the support of science for fear of risking their freedom of action. They have also found it necessary to speak to the American people on the importance of science to our national life and on the needs and interests of science. The public reports issued by the PSAC reveal how much these advisers are aware that government support of basic research, of expensive research tools, and of science education depends upon public support and understanding.

The President's science advisers have thus taken a firm hand in relating science to policy and in developing specific policies for the promotion of science. To accomplish this they first had to organize themselves. The responsibilities given and assumed in the initial months still exist, despite the development of newer arrangements such as the Federal Council for Science and Technology (FCST) and the more recently established Office of Science and Technology. An examination of the initial organization is illuminating because the Special Assistant and the PSAC have somewhat different roles to play in the formulation of science policies. The Special Assistant, in every sense, is a member of the administration and of the President's official family, whereas the scientists on the PSAC are not even full-time government employees. Regardless of these differences their ability to shoulder a combined responsiblity is dependent on the close relationship between them.

THE PRESIDENT'S SCIENCE ADVISERS

The Special Assistant is first and foremost a member of the President's personal staff. As such he has no operating responsibilities for the conduct of research and development; nor does he decide policy. He serves principally as an adviser to the President. In this capacity he keeps himself informed about major developments in the scientific programs of government agencies, reports his findings and evaluations to the President, and presents his own recommendations. His contributions rest fundamentally on his ability to convince the President and others through persuasion and argument rather than through the exercise of specific authority. Because of his closeness to the President and his detachment from operational programs, he is in a unique position to expose the self-serving or parochial arguments of agencies and prevent the President from being overwhelmed by impressive displays of technological sophistry. In these ways his position is remarkably close to other staff officers in the Executive Office of the President, but there are subtle differences. In the first place, he does not have a career staff as do those other advisers, and, in the second place, he is institutionally a part of the White House.

In common with most presidential advisers, the Special Assistant also does more than monitor federal activities and respond when advice has been sought. He has the more active role of identifying technical issues that impinge on national policy and of mapping out a strategy for their study and for relating the conclusions of these studies to policy decisions. He tries in this way to anticipate future problems or trends and to formulate alternative courses of action involving science in a form suitable for political decision. Although he works closely with the heads of federal agencies and departments and makes himself available to them as an adviser, he does not serve as a substitute for their own direct access to the President. The unique contributions of the Special Assistant stem from his staff position, from which he can view scientific and technical problems broadly, across jurisdictional and along functional lines, free from departmental prejudices. In this way the Special Assistant occupies an especially advantageous position to serve the President as a source of independent advice and to inform him on the interaction of science and policy as it affects both government and private institutions.

The major task of the PSAC is to advise the President on a wide range of issues in which science is an important component. It, like the Special Assistant, has no operating responsibilities, but because of this task it is heavily engaged in technical studies of national security problems. Often in considering these and other problems the Committee serves as a personal review board for the President. It undertakes technical evaluations and assessments of proposed projects awaiting presidential approval and renders an independent opinion. This demanding task is steadily increasing because major technical programs are increasing in number and they vary greatly in their nature and technical complexity. Projects where the PSAC has made technical reviews have ranged from consideration of air defense systems to technical assessments of various space projects. As the number of such projects increases, and as it becomes necessary to devote more attention to policies for the support of science, it seems clear that the demands on the Committee will, likewise, grow considerably.

The PSAC frequently takes the initiative in identifying problems and presenting new proposals to the President. Because neither the Committee nor the Special Assistant need wait for a presidential request or an agency sponsor, they have sometimes found fresh approaches to problems that were long studied elsewhere in government with little success or at least with little of the same enthusiasm. In this spirit the Committee suggested a number of ways to use science more effectively to aid underdeveloped countries, and ways to improve government-university relationships involved in the conduct of research and development by private institutions. It has also developed new ideas about problems that other parts of the government had either overlooked or ignored because they did not fall within the traditional boundaries (such as the nuclear test ban proposals and suggestions for employing new technologies to add vigor to the civilian economy) of an agency's mission. In all these areas, the most creative part of the Committee's work and the source of some of its greatest satisfaction has been the study of problems of its own choosing.

Nevertheless, one of the PSAC's more important responsibilities, and perhaps the one most keenly felt, is the responsibility for advising the President "in regard to ways by which United States' science and technology can be advanced, especially in regard to ways by which they can be advanced by the Federal Government. . . ."[1] This responsibility constitutes the Committee's mandate to build a national policy for science. Because of the demands on the Committee to render advice to the President on costly technological developments, the fraction of effort devoted to this responsibility is undoubtedly less than each member would prefer. But it is still high on the agenda, not merely because the PSAC members are scientists, but because they believe that the health and progress of science are indispensable to the nation's future strength and security.

In some ways the Committee is better able to develop policies for science than is the Special Assistant, who shares this responsibility but who serves as a full-time adviser. The PSAC members are scientists and engineers drawn from private life who spend only a fraction of their time serving the government. The rest of the time they are working in science or with scientists in private institutions. Because of their dual occupation, they have both the scientist's understanding of science and considerable government experience which enables

[1] See address of Dr. James R. Killian, Jr., "Science and Public Policy," to the American Association for the Advancement of Science in Washington, D.C., on December 29, 1958.

them to form both a bridge of understanding and a strong link facilitating communication between government and the private scientific community.

The link with the scientific community is enhanced by the rotation of members and by the PSAC's subcommittee or panel system. Rotation of members brings to the Committee scientists with different points of view as well as scientists from different disciplines, while the panel structure permits the Committee to draw upon a wider range of scientific experience and undertake intensive study of a larger number of problems than would be possible using only the talent and expertise of its own members. The use of *ad hoc* panels permits "the policy-making agencies of government to have roots deep in the creative non-government community of science." [2] Other advisory committees in scientific fields have made use of expert panels, but the PSAC panel system may be unique in the degree to which "old" panels are continually being abolished as they complete a particular task and "new" ones created. It is this *ad hoc* nature of the system that brings to the government fresh scientific talent and diverse points of view.

It is not possible to understand the role of either the Committee or the Special Assistant without understanding the close relationship between them. In many ways the Special Assistant appears to dominate the whole scene, and in some ways he does. He establishes most of the work schedule for the Committee and its panels by raising the issues that his daily contact with the administration leads him to believe will be of concern to the President. He appoints the panel chairmen, selects panel members, and decides, largely as a matter of his own choice, whether or not to take a panel report to the President, lay it before the PSAC, or return it to the panel for further study and refinement. As chairman of the PSAC his judgments frequently carry the weight of a broad consensus which adds greatly to his influence and prestige. As the employer of the small, full-time staff that also serves as staff to the Committee and its panels, he also holds the reins of administration that enable him to manage the com-

---

[2] James R. Killian, Jr., "Foreword," J. Stefan Dupré and Sanford A. Lakoff, *Science and the Nation: Policy and Politics* (Englewood Cliffs, N.J., Prentice-Hall, 1962), p. iv.

bined enterprise. Yet the main source of his power and leadership does not devolve from his administrative authority; rather it stems from his confidential relationship with the President. As a member of the President's political family he has an enormous influence with cabinet officers and with heads of independent agencies.

The PSAC is not without authority of its own. It can choose to report directly to the President, a privilege which could assume special importance were the Committee to disagree with the Special Assistant on major questions of policy. The Committee also selects its own chairman. Dr. James R. Killian, Jr., the first Special Assistant, reports that "when the committee was first established, some of the President's advisers, both political and scientific, urged that the Special Assistant be made ineligible to serve as its chairman in order to avoid any possibility of hindering independent decisions." [3] While the Committee so far has always selected the Special Assistant as chairman, it has done so on its own initiative. Whether or not this situation will continue to prevail, however, is a matter of speculation. On the one hand, a tradition has now been established. On the other hand, it is not likely that this formal power of the Committee could be exercised in opposition to a President's own choice.

It is not the powers of the Special Assistant or of the Committee that is the key to their combined effectiveness, but how well they work together. No Special Assistant could recruit the range and quality of expertise now represented on the PSAC and its panels if the scientists believed that the integrity and independence of their views would be compromised. The Special Assistant is dependent upon the Committee for thorough study and analysis of specific issues. He needs the Committee, for the "committee has brought to [him]—and to the President—a range of views, an objectivity, and an uninhibited freedom of comment that no single science adviser could hope to match." [4] The Committee, likewise, needs the Special Assistant. Its members are well aware of the directness of the channel to the President provided by the Special Assistant. This gives all of them the feeling they are talking to someone who can act on their advice, while the "national" character of advice rendered at the pres-

---

[3] *Ibid.*, pp. iii–iv.   [4] *Ibid.*, p. iv.

idential level gives them a free-ranging opportunity to move beyond the narrow technical limits often imposed by highly mission-oriented agencies to consideration of broad policy issues. The Special Assistant and the Committee thus respond together to their mutual obligation to the President and share a highly developed sense of opportunity.

The establishment in the spring of 1962 of an Office of Science and Technology (OST) as an independent unit in the Executive Office of the President provided the Special Assistant with a new "hat"[5] as its Director. He remains on the White House staff as a personal adviser to the President. The PSAC retains its position as a White House committee and has chosen, as before, to have the Special Assistant serve as chairman.

The principal advantages of this reorganization can be stated simply: the organization of science at the top level of government is given statutory underpinnings and legislative permanence; provision is made for Congress, as well as the President, to have "authoritative commentary on the government's scientific activities from an overall rather than a departmental point of view";[6] and a needed increase in staff, always politically difficult in the White House, is now permitted.[7]

There are also potential pitfalls which are not obvious but are nonetheless real. The most serious hinges on the degree to which the President's science advisers, meaning both the Special Assistant and the PSAC, can withstand congressional and departmental pressures and still retain the initiative of choosing their own problems. In the past they planned their work subject to one overriding criterion—the needs of the President as they saw them—and, in defining those needs, they enjoyed a great deal of latitude. The President, of course,

---

[5] In addition, it should be appreciated that the Special Assistant also serves as Chairman of the FCST.

[6] U.S. Congress, Senate Committee on Government Operations, *Organizing for National Security—Science Organization and the President's Office*, 87th Congress, 1st Session (Washington, D.C., USGPO, 1961), p. 5.

[7] Since the appointment of the first Special Assistant to the President for Science and Technology, there have never been more than eight full-time professionals serving as staff for the Special Assistant, for the PSAC and its panels, and for the FCST.

sometimes "directed" their work by asking the questions to which they responded; but more often than not, they chose problems which they thought ought to be matters of presidential concern and focused their efforts on self-defined "targets of opportunity." Under the new arrangements, Congress can now be expected to relay its pressures to the President's Special Assistant who may find these pressures difficult, if not impossible, to avoid and will have to rely on the help of the Committee, as before. As a consequence, the Office and the Committee may find themselves involved in seeking solutions to problems that should be solved by government agencies or in answering congressional complaints about operations over which they have no managerial responsibility. The extent to which the President's science advisers become absorbed in these affairs will diminish the extent to which they can help the President. And it would certainly be ironic if the President, in his desire to enhance communications with Congress, were to find his own advisers less able to serve him.

The roles of the Special Assistant and the PSAC have been altered only slightly by the establishment of the OST, and a number of options have been left open by this minimal change in organization. For example, all the functions of the Special Assistant could be assumed by the Director of the new Office who would then serve the President in much the same way as does the Director of the Bureau of the Budget or the Chairman of the Council of Economic Advisers. Should the President find it necessary to have a personal science adviser, an independent Chairman of the PSAC could possibly serve in that capacity. Only time and experience can dictate what further changes, if any, need to be made by the President. Meanwhile, wisdom and restraint on the part of Congress in placing new demands will allow the Office to demonstrate its full effectiveness.

NATIONAL POLICIES TOWARD SCIENCE

The installation of science in the White House, it will be recalled, was born of crisis—the successful launching by the Soviet Union of the world's first artificial satellite in the fall of 1957. This spectacular technological achievement had an inevitable effect on the initial work of the President's science advisers. Whereas scientists could for the first time express themselves directly to the President on the needs and interests of science, his immediate needs required the scientists to devote most of their energies to the problems of technology, to the uses of science for the nation's military and space programs. How was the government to organize and accelerate its program for outer space? How could the Department of Defense strengthen its planning and management to deal more effectively with problems of technological complexity? How was the best missile system to be selected, and when should it be taken out of research and development and put into production? These and many similar questions to which the President's science advisers have had to respond, confirmed their preponderant involvement in relating science to national security policy rather than in formulating policies for science.

Many of the projects of military technology evaluated by the President's science advisers required heavy commitments of scientific resources, yet they were often studied with little attention to their pervasive effects on the health of American science as a whole. These effects have been and still are exceedingly difficult to determine, because the facts are not readily available. It is virtually impossible, for example, to project the number and kinds of technical specialists needed to develop a new weapons system composed of a staggering number of components or the effects of this development on a host of other research programs from which these specialists may have to be drawn. It needs to be recognized, however, that if advice is to be useful, it must be put forward in a usable form when it is needed. In times of urgency, the immediate issues take precedence over many considerations of longer-range importance. Thus the attention given by the President's science advisers to these problems of pressing presidential concern—while it undoubtedly resulted in the neglect of some fundamental long-range issues—greatly advanced the President's confidence in his advisers, and he has increasingly turned to them for advice on an astonishingly wide range of problems. As Dr. Killian said of President Eisenhower: "If his science advisers at any time have not advised, it was not because he failed to afford them the opportunity." [8]

Despite the demands of technology, the President's science advisers have nevertheless directed some substantial part of their attention to the strengthening of science and its uses on the part of the federal government. With the development of new organizations, such as the National Aeronautical and Space Administration (NASA) and the Office of Defense Research and Engineering in the Department of Defense, it has been possible for them to assign a greater fraction of their total effort to the formulation of science policies.

Among the first reports of the PSAC was a study published in 1958 by its panel on research policy entitled, "Strengthening American Science," which attempted to set forth the responsibilities of government for this area of national life and which thereby signified the willingness of the President's science advisers to give expression to the needs and interests of American science. This study was the beginning of a continuing effort to develop national policies for the support and promotion of science.

Policies directed to this end have, generally, been more concerned with the development of scientific resources than with the more difficult task of allocating these resources. Although problems of allocation have not been ignored, the President's science advisers have been mainly concerned with the development of policies and recommendations in three main areas: more support for scientists engaged in basic research, financing and planning the large and expensive research instruments and facilities of modern science, and federal support for the education and training of qualified new scientists as well as for improved science education of all citizens.

Basic research. The President's science advisers have sought from the beginning to obtain and implement a policy decision that basic

---

[8] Remarks addressed to the National Press Club in Washington, D.C., on July 7, 1959. On the same occasion, Dr. Killian described President Eisenhower as "an enthusiasm amplifier . . . always interested in scientific and technological developments . . . persistent in his desire for information—the rough with the smooth."

research be considered a national resource and a national responsibility whose support depends primarily upon the government of the United States. While some persons would maintain that this issue was settled when Congress established the National Science Foundation (NSF), the science advisers have claimed that the size of the Foundation's appropriations have, until recently, shown that the responsibility assumed by the government was unequal to that which is required by the national interest, especially in view of the spectacular rise in government spending for applied research and development. The President's science advisers have pointed out that the unremitting pressure to obtain new "hardware" has led to an overemphasis on development and technology even granting that government agencies other than the Foundation should, and do, support basic research. The PSAC has issued several public reports emphasizing the importance of basic research to the sustained growth of the nation's industrial power and the need for increased public support for basic research. Support by the taxpayer is indispensable, it is claimed, because universities, the traditional home of basic research, lack the resources to support basic research on the required scale, and because industry, which is concerned primarily with the development and sale of new products, lacks the immediate economic incentives to support basic research on a comprehensive basis. The PSAC has argued that economic progress and the defense of freedom depend upon basic research and that only the government can ensure an adequate investment in such research.

In advocating more support for basic research, the PSAC has listed several fields where progress has been handicapped by lack of funds and has thereby suggested that these fields deserve more attention, although it has not attempted to determine specific priorities among scientific disciplines. Recognizing how impossible it is to foresee which areas of science will yield the richest discoveries, the Committee has avoided judging the unpredictable. Nevertheless, the difficult question of priorities is being dealt with in broader ways. In urging more emphasis on basic research and rather less on costly developments, the Committee stated publicly that a relatively small increase in support of basic research "by reallocation of funds could have a tremendous impact on the national science program." [9] This was certainly a "priority" judgment between more research and more development, but not, to be sure, among basic research programs. The Committee has also suggested steps for improving the way in which government support is administered. It has emphasized that long-term, flexible patterns of support that offer basic research programs continuity and stability can be as important as increased funds. Still more pointed have been the Committee's advisory opinions in areas of applied research and development which have made it possible, in many cases, to establish priorities. It has reviewed large and costly programs in terms of their technical feasibility, the quality of manpower needed to carry them out, and their likely ultimate costs. In this way the Committee has served the President as a "definer of technical reality" [10] and helped him improve the determination of priorities.

Research facilities. The advance of science is confronting the President with a growing number of problems regarding government support for the great research instruments and facilities of modern science. The rapid growth of government operations in science, the advancement of science itself, and rapid improvements and inventions in scientific instrumentation have produced new demands for large, often costly, laboratories, facilities, and other capital needs of modern science. Great radio telescopes for astronomy, multi-million-dollar particle accelerators for high-energy physics, ships for oceanography, and instrumented satellites for meteorology illustrate but a few of the scientific fields where the technology of science is extending man's capacity to probe the physical universe at the same time that it is rapidly making obsolete his earlier means for doing so. New policy issues have arisen as the federal government has undertaken to provide for this elaborate instrumentation of modern science, and the President has naturally turned to his science advisers for help in resolving these issues.

[9] PSAC, *Strengthening American Science* (Washington, D.C., USGPO, 1958), p. 6.
[10] See, for example, PSAC report, *Introduction to Outer Space* (Washington, D.C., USGPO, 1958).

When these issues are highly technical the President's science advisers try to understand the "scientific need" for proposed new instruments and to evaluate alternative technical designs. One PSAC panel, for example, issued several advisory opinions endorsing government financing of the giant Stanford linear accelerator, while other panels have evaluated the capital requirements of research programs in oceanography and the atmospheric sciences.

One of the major issues that confronts the PSAC in considering scientific facilities is not primarily technical, however. This is the issue of how far the government should go in establishing or financing new research facilities either separate from universities or as part of universities proper. On the one hand, the growing need for new scientists suggests building research facilities at universities because separate research institutions might draw too many research scholars from training programs in universities. On the other hand, it is not always possible, or desirable, to build such research facilities as integral parts of universities when they are of a size and scale unsuitable for operation within the framework of regular academic departments or, furthermore, involve research which is heavily applied, highly programmatic, or classified and hence might be unsuitable for training independent investigators or would compromise university traditions of academic freedom. Even when research facilities could be used to advantage for both research and teaching it is not always practical to duplicate them at a number of institutions. The high cost of such instruments as the Stanford linear accelerator, for example, precludes duplication.

Thoughtfully conceived policies are clearly needed in order to plan for government support of expensive research facilities and to determine how and when they should be related to universities. In formulating such policies, experience would suggest a variety of approaches. In some cases a government-owned and operated facility, such as the proposed research institute on water resources in the Department of the Interior, appears desirable, especially if provision is made for use of the facilities by university scholars and graduate students. In other cases, there are genuine benefits to both research and teaching when several universities join together to staff and operate a large research facility which neither could do alone. The

Brookhaven National Laboratory and the National Radio Astronomy Observatory have been operated in this way with considerable success. In still other instances, as in the field of materials research, government-financed interdisciplinary laboratories on a number of university campuses are stimulating novel approaches and attracting more graduate students to fields of vital national importance.

These examples illustrate that no single, easy, administrative policy can take account of the diverse objectives of all federal agencies and the varied interests of all private institutions in financing research facilities. The President's science advisers must try to be both resourceful and wise in conceiving new policies for equipping science with the tools of scientific advance.

Education. The above examples also demonstrate that in their concern with government support of research and facilities the President's science advisers have had to be concerned with government policies for higher education. They have thus assumed the initiative in developing policies concerning the education and training of qualified new scientists and the enhancement of scientific literacy in the United States. This initiative is not surprising considering the natural instinct of all professionals to be concerned about the future of their professions; but the PSAC's keenly felt obligation to advise the President on ways to foster the future strength and leadership of American science leads to a direct and inevitable involvement in matters of educational policy.

The first PSAC report on education, "Education for the Age of Science," published in 1959, dealt broadly with national goals for strengthening science and engineering education. The report did not attempt to make policy. Instead it defined the objectives of policy. Its conclusions centered on the urgent need to increase the quality of science education by improving the content of courses in science both in high schools and colleges, raising the quality of teachers, and adapting school programs to meet the needs of talented and gifted students. Although the report included suggestions for moving ahead with these tasks it did not define the federal government's responsibility either for providing leadership or for underwriting part of the cost. These responsibilities could be strongly implied from the scope of the needs, but the Committee stopped short of articulating them.

Nevertheless, by entering this sensitive and controversial area of policy, the PSAC laid the groundwork for its own future actions.

The next effort at formulating educational policy resulted in a public report on "Scientific Progress, the Universities and the Federal Government," which covered the broad area of graduate education in science and especially its relationship to basic research. Here the PSAC's mandate was more obvious and the report stated at the outset that it considered the way in which the requirements for scientific progress "should affect the policies of both the Federal Government and the universities." [11] Unlike the earlier statement, this one was clear and unequivocal in giving the views of the Committee on the responsibilities of the federal government, for it said emphatically: *"From this responsibility the Federal Government has no escape. Either it [the federal government] will find the policies—and the resources—which permit our universities to flourish and their duties to be adequately discharged—or no one will."* [12]

The impact of the report has been difficult to assess, although it has undoubtedly led to modifications of federal policies and pointed the way toward further improvements in government-university relations in the future. The report makes clear that the government can no longer continue to support research at universities under the myth that it is merely buying or procuring research results from an individual scientist. The report also states how necessary it is for the government to consider the environment which produces both new research and new scientists and therefore adopt policies which will strengthen the educational enterprise by providing support for laboratories, teachers, and graduate students. But it has the weaknesses intrinsic in advisory opinions; it is not self-implementing and hence can only be adopted by those federal agencies which are persuaded. With the rapid expansion of the nation's requirements for more science and technology, hence more scientists and engineers, it was inevitable that this problem would warrant reconsideration.

Consequently, when President Kennedy asked the PSAC to examine the demands which the nation's expanding commitments in science and technology, especially those for space exploration, would make upon the nation's resources of scientific and technical personnel, the Committee initiated another major study of graduate education which resulted in the report published on December 12, 1962, entitled, "Meeting Manpower Needs in Science and Technology." This report recommended a greatly expanded program of graduate training in engineering, mathematics, and the physical sciences to meet future national commitments as the Committee then saw them. It further stated that the federal government, as the principal consumer of graduates trained in these fields, must assume the central responsibility for supporting the necessary efforts of expansion and acceleration. The recommendations in this report, unlike those of the earlier one, met with the prompt approval of the President and were incorporated into the legislative and budget proposals which he submitted to Congress in January, 1963.

In addition to these studies of graduate education, the PSAC has also reconsidered the problem of improving the teaching and learning of science in the schools. Shortly after President Kennedy took office, a new panel on educational research and development was established with the co-sponsorship of the Office of Education and the NSF. This panel seeks to encourage organized efforts for bringing together leading university scientists and scholars in certain subject matter fields with groups of high school and elementary teachers in order to improve and modernize the content of courses. If these efforts are successful, they could lead to major improvements in the quality of education through the preparation of new textbooks and learning aids of all kinds by the most qualified scholars. The federal government has already initiated similar projects in science and in foreign languages, but so far the need to extend these improvements to other areas of curriculum has far exceeded the resources available. As the panel stimulates more of the nation's top scholars to devote themselves to this work, more federal support for curriculum-improvement projects will be needed.

In taking the initiative to explore these few areas the President's science advisers have entered the otherwise empty arena of educational policy at the presidential level. They have had to concern themselves with policies for education in order to develop adequate policies for science. Their efforts have not always met with unqualified success. The lack of a clearly defined federal responsibility in education, the fragmented nature of federal support, and a patchwork of administrative practices have hampered the development of wise and coherent policies for education even more than they have for science. It is certain that the best efforts of the President's science advisers cannot fill the unmet needs of education for a higher place in our national scheme of values and for a higher place in the structure of the federal government. But until those needs are met, the science advisers can continue to play a constructive and helpful role as "educational advisers" to the President.

PLANNING FOR THE WELFARE OF SCIENCE

One might have expected that the pace of scientific discovery and its explosive effects on political institutions would make a comprehensive policy toward science an established fact. What exists instead is a collection of policies almost as diverse and novel as science itself. This body of policy, often called a "national science policy," is pervaded by the aspects of a fundamental dilemma that must be appreciated before it is possible to understand the role of the President's science advisers in planning for the welfare of science.

The first aspect of the dilemma is deeply rooted in the contradictory way in which the scientist and the public look at the nature of science. The scientist views science as a cultural activity, as man's attempt at an objective understanding of his universe. Although the scientist may have great interest in the application of his findings, he is not impelled simply by the utility or application of these findings. In most of science and in all of basic research, the scientist is also motivated by a search for new knowledge and in particular for meaningful understanding and generalization. The public, on the other hand, views science principally in terms of its practical utility. It supports the scientist because of the end results of his discoveries. Even basic research receives public support because of the impression that it is useful as the source of industrial innovations. Although the government's attitude as embodied in policy reflects the point of view of both the scientist and the public with all its interests, it primarily reflects the national interests of the public. Government's main concern is with technology, with the uses of science for national security and welfare, and not with the growth and development of science as a cultural activity.

Another aspect of the dilemma underlying science policy is the conflict between the cardinal desire of scientists for the self-government of science and the public responsibilities of government as the major patron of scientific activity. There is a contradiction between the growing dependence of science upon government support and the needs of science for an assured atmosphere of free inquiry. The rapid rise in public funds for science has been accompanied by a wise and conscious effort by government agencies to use scientists as advisers in administering federal support. There has also been a scrupulous attempt to avoid "directing" science in establishing policies for the support of basic research. In general, government administrators, individually, have accepted the view that scientists themselves know best what can be done and how to go about it.

The real hazards of political control, however, do not come from this quarter. They arise from the great decisions about defense and space programs, for example, and from the cumulative impact of many lesser decisions taken by a score of "autonomous" government agencies. The over-all effects of these vast programs and the cumulative effects of smaller decisions can profoundly alter the course of scientific activity. One of the major hazards in making decisions about defense and space programs arises from the fact that scientific manpower is a scarce resource and that such decisions will to an increasing degree determine how this scarce resource will be employed and hence how the economy as a whole may evolve. The hazard is aggravated by the fact that the influence of such decisions on scientific research is not generally recognized, since research expenditures constitute such a relatively small fraction of the gross national product.

It might appear to many persons that the NSF serves to guard against such hazards since the mission of the Foundation is to support basic research and education in science, and the policy of the Foundation is to let scientists decide what research is to be supported. Yet the other half-dozen agencies which administer the vast bulk of federal support are primarily concerned not with the welfare of American science, but with its products and its relevance to their operational missions. Each of these agencies calls upon scientists to participate in important decisions as does the NSF. In the last analysis, however, the larger questions affecting the health of science, such as how much of an agency's budget is to be allocated to research and development, how much is to be available for basic research, or how much, for instance, is to be expended on plasma physics or molecular biology, are likely to be decided by nonscientist policy-makers and administrators. More often than not these decisions will depend on operational or political factors rather than on technical ones. The decision of the Atomic Energy Commission to spend huge sums of money for elaborate hardware in connection with the fusion power program is an illustration of how nontechnical considerations can distort scientific programs and often lead to less effective, as well as more expensive, efforts to accomplish the goals which non-scientist policy-makers have set for themselves. Although scientists were to some extent a party to this decision, it was made primarily as a result of pressures from nonscientists, pressures related to national prestige and international scientific competition.

The advancement of science ultimately rests upon the creativity and freedom of the individual scientist. A scientist must have the freedom to carry out investigations as he thinks best and in response to the dictates of his research. Yet even in choosing his own research problem the scientist faces "the paradox of choice between doing what his interest impels him to do—and doing what some large part of society might seek to have done." [13] This aspect of the fundamental dilemma confronts all those engaged in creative work in literature, music, or the arts, but it is exaggerated in the sciences. With the growing volume of public support, there is mounting pressure on the scientist to produce the "things" and "hardware" that society wants to the exclusion of the "theories" and "ideas" that interest him.

The President's science advisers have sought a way out of the dilemma facing the individual scientist by supporting a high degree

[13] William O. Baker, "The Paradox of Choice," in Dael Wolfle, ed., *Symposium on Basic Research* (Washington, D.C., AAAS, 1959), p. 41

of autonomy for the scientific community in the allocation of scientific resources. They have thus advocated a deliberate government policy to promote more basic research in order to enhance the freedom of the individual scientist. In their view such support of basic research often results in achieving what society wants more quickly and effectively than support for projects which appear on the surface to be more germane to the interests of society. Nevertheless, as funds for basic research have increased there has been a growing demand on the part of both Congress and the Executive for more careful government planning, and this in turn has caused some scientists to believe that the attempt to provide more freedom may result in less freedom, that more government support will mean more government control.

The potential conflict between government responsibility and scientific autonomy occurs in its sharpest form as support of basic research increases. The need for autonomy is indisputable, for there is no agency of government, no committee, and no individual wise enough or prescient enough to know what scientists should do or how they should go about it. In basic research only the scientists themselves can pose their problems and plan their investigations. For this reason, many scientists have argued that government planning for science is not only unnecessary but inimical to healthy basic research. The sole task of government is allegedly to find out what scientists themselves consider important to do and to provide the resources with which to do it. Dr. Alan Waterman, the Director of the NSF, has said: "This means wholehearted approval of providing support for competent research wherever needed, and in particular for the capital facilities. . . ." [14] Apart from providing scientists with needed resources, the government should, according to this view, play a passive role, it should have no other decision-making authority in science.

Unfortunately, for those who hold this view, the government has not provided support for competent basic research wherever needed. On the contrary, in supporting science because of its importance for governmental missions, science has been distorted by too heavy an

[14] See *NSF Seventh Annual Report* (Washington, D.C., USGPO, 1957), p. x.

emphasis on development. Even in basic research the government has lavished support on some fields and neglected others, ample proof that priorities are being set largely in terms of the interest of the government. As a result, important areas of research remain unsupported if they fall between the interests of two departments. Many research opportunities thus lost may be of little interest to any one agency but may be of considerable importance to the nation as a whole.

The web of government policies and practices for supporting research at universities has meant, to some degree, that the government is interfering with the freedom of university research and lessening the ability of universities to keep their own programs in balance. With few exceptions, a serious shortage of capital facilities still persists in most universities. This is especially true of those facilities required for graduate research and training. There has, in fact, been little regard for the education of new scientists in the support programs of many federal agencies. For the most part, it has been an incidental by-product of federal support of research rather than a central and conscious purpose.

These problems have led many scientists to perceive that the most important decisions of all affecting scientific progress, decisions concerning the allocation of scientific resources, are in fact being made by the government. These scientists, unlike colleagues who fear more planning, feel, quite rightly in this writer's view, that such decisions should be planned for in ways that will take account of the interests of science and of scientific institutions, as well as the interests of the government, and that scientists should therefore have a larger voice in making them. Many scientists now participate in government decisions by reviewing specific research proposals, but they have little to say about the general division of funds between basic and applied research or the total allocation of support for science. These critical decisions are made by nonscientist administrators in many places, and, until recently, without any significant measure of scientific advice.

Fortunately, the President's science advisers have believed that a passive role for government will not suffice to ensure the balanced support of science consistent with the national interest. They have urged more government action, rather than less, in order to remove the restrictions hampering scientific progress and to create conditions conducive to scientific advance. Although they do not dispute the notion that no one is wise enough to prescribe in detail the content of basic research or to define in advance the research problems scientists should work on, they do maintain that it is possible to formulate general policies for the support of science and to institutionalize a long-range planning system. Long-range planning in this view does not imply master-minding science or deciding the substance of research, but rather the assurance of adequate support for individual research and careful appraisal of the special disciplines which require expensive research facilities. A review of the current situation reveals this need for a more aggressive policy toward the basic research needs of the nation.

TOWARD A PLANNING SYSTEM [15]

Since 1957 the debate over science planning has become increasingly academic. The President's science advisers have gradually evolved a planning system. The PSAC studies discussed earlier were initial attempts to develop government policies and plans for the support of basic research and science education and for financing research facilities. Recent developments suggest more systematic efforts at long-range planning for support of research at universities and for underwriting the costs of research in the special scientific disciplines which require expensive facilities.

Except for the special disciplines, research at universities is generally supported by means of a project grant or contract to an individual scientist. Under the "project system," government agencies rely on groups of independent scientists, acting as referees, to evaluate the scientific promise of research proposals and to rate them on the basis of merit. The agencies then consider these recommenda-

[15] The writer is indebted to Dr. George B. Kistiakowsky, former Special Assistant for Science and Technology to President Eisenhower, for many of the ideas expressed on this subject.

tions and the relevance of the proposed research to their missions, and award grants or contracts up to the limit of funds available.[16] The special advantage of the project system is that once the scientist himself decides where and how to explore, the importance and feasibility of what he wants to do is appraised and evaluated by his peers. Of course, this implies that the established scientists in a certain field are the best judges of new research ideas and of the scientists who would like to pursue work in that field. Unfortunately, there is growing evidence that this is not always true. Often great advances in one field come from scientists working in another field, as, for instance, the invasion of optics research by microwave physicists, or the intrusion into seismology of applied mathematics. This has led some scientists, as well as the writer, to the conclusion that the project system may place undue emphasis on the fashionable and conventional proposal and may discourage the support of really novel or high-risk research.[17]

The project system also has other disadvantages. The amount of funds available for research varies greatly among agencies, and consequently the ratio of the number of good proposals an agency receives to the number it can support may vary to the same extent. Thus there is no assurance that the best proposals received throughout the government will be supported. Moreover, each agency issues separate guidelines to its referees and follows its own rules in deciding overhead rates, the terms under which research equipment is furnished, and the fraction of a scientist's salary which can properly be charged against a contract; so it is perhaps inevitable that the project system does not take adequate account of the universities' own institutional objectives for education as well as research.

Obvious improvements would result from standardizing referee systems, from formulating uniform policies governing the terms of research contracts, and from other measures that would overcome the principal shortcomings of the project system. The PSAC has also

---

[16] In the case of the NSF, whose mission is to support basic research, the number of grants made, of course, is limited only by the availability of funds and the quality of research proposals.

[17] Dr. Harvey Brooks first made the writer aware of this disadvantage of the project system and provided the cited examples.

favored a system of institutional grants as a supplement to the project system that will help universities maintain a better balance between their teaching and research responsibilities.

Remedial measures alone, however, are not likely to assure a thriving university science. Improving administrative procedures will not assure adequate support for university research. It must be realized that this objective requires careful technical planning, closely integrated with the budget system, to supplement (if not supplant) the present system whereby resources often are allocated on the basis of *ad hoc* decisions made independently by many federal agencies. Although the amount of money spent by the government for basic and applied research at universities is only a small fraction of the government's total research and development expenditures,[18] this money is of major national importance because it is the primary source of support for basic research and for training new scientists.

In this kind of planning, the President's science advisers have a major role to play. Along with the Bureau of the Budget they can help the President determine the total amount of money to be allocated for support of scientific research at universities. Once this is decided, the choice of scientific projects can remain within the jurisdiction of individual agencies and their scientist-referees. The President's science advisers can also help plan the distribution of funds, not among scientific fields, but among categories of support—project research, institutional support, fellowships, and facilities—so as to permit universities to maintain and add to their strength as centers for both research and training.

There is also an urgent need for long-range planning for the sup-

---

[18] See NSF, *Federal Funds for Science* (Washington, D.C., USGPO, 1960), X, 9. For FY 1961 the percent distribution of $9.2 billion of federal funds for research and development was as follows: profit organizations, 63 percent; federal agencies, 22 percent; educational institutions, 11 percent; and all other, 4 percent. But even the 11 percent allocated of funds to educational institutions is somewhat misleading since the funds for university-managed, independent research centers are included. Research and development funds for universities "proper," namely, for teaching-related research, constituted only 7 percent of total federal funds for research and development in FY 1962, or about $688 million. This is the only part of government expenditures that can genuinely be regarded as connected with the training of new scientists.

port of special fields of research requiring costly facilities that far exceed any other research costs. Characteristically, research in these fields involves teams of scientists and sizable administrative staffs to manage the facilities and the numerous technicians required to operate them. In practically every case the costs are borne almost exclusively by the federal government, and the willingness of the government to support certain of these fields on a large scale depends on many factors; among the most important are national prestige, popular appeal, and the promise of practical applications.

Multi-million-dollar particle accelerators, rocket-boosters with satellite payloads, and oceanographic research vessels are more often supported because of Soviet competition, the glamour of the project, or the expected practical applications than because of the scientific promise of high-energy physics, space research, or oceanography. Almost any one of the kinds of special disciplines could, however, grow rapidly enough to require several hundred million dollars every year—space activities, of course, require billions—and it is conceivable that taken together they could overwhelm the scientific resources available to support the balanced growth of science as a whole.

This situation greatly worries many scientists: uncritical support could siphon funds away from the support of general university research and draw the nation's top scientific talent into a few narrow areas. Scientific resources to support research on other pressing national problems—mass urban transportation, international development, water and air pollution, and new energy sources—might not be available if support were lavished on a few special areas. And since no one can predict what segment of science will produce the next great advances, the nation's future scientific development could be seriously jeopardized by too great a concentration on a few fields of research.

To ignore long-range planning for the special disciplines, therefore, could be shortsighted and perhaps even perilous. These areas of science require a far different kind of planning than that which is appropriate to general university research. In planning for the support of relatively small research projects at universities, the President's science advisers need not judge the content of the research or weigh the relative merits of diverse proposals. These are the tasks of the scientist-referees. Planning for the special disciplines, on the other hand, requires hard choices among fields, or at least difficult judgments as to the desirable rate of growth of each one of them.

Although long confronted with the necessity for choice, the President's science advisers have been understandably reluctant to establish priorities and thereby confer either damnation or assent on the aspirations of fellow scientists. Using its panel system, the PSAC has reviewed reports written by specialists in a certain field and tried "to avoid the imbalance and over-enthusiasm that sometimes pops up in statements of a small group of enthusiasts in a given area. . . ." [19] However, it has looked at only a few of the costly disciplines, and at these one at a time as they came along, without basis for comparison. How they have wished for a system which would foretell the many possibilities for progress in science and, at the same time, reflect a broad consensus among scientists as to which were the most important.

To this end, both Dr. George Kistiakowsky and Dr. Jerome Wiesner, as presidential advisers, have turned to the National Academy of Sciences, an organization which is probably in a better position than any other organization of scientists to convey to the government the views of the scientific community as a whole, to lay the foundation for a planning system that would be based in the first instance on the initiative and judgment of scientists themselves. The Academy thus has been asked: (1) whether its sections, each of which is made up of leading scientists in a particular discipline such as physics, chemistry, or biology would separately evaluate the scientific promise of its fields and document the research goals and opportunities; (2) whether the Academy as a whole would advise the government on the relative promise of various special disciplines and make some judgments as to priorities among them. As has been editorialized in a scientific journal:

Only in terms of its own nature, needs and opportunities can we decide on the right amount of money for . . . research in a particular field. . . . The number of research workers available; the cost of salaries,

---

[19] See the remarks of Dr. George B. Kistiakowsky appearing in U.S. Congress H.R. Committee on Science and Astronautics, *Panel on Science and Technology, Fourth Meeting,* 87th Congress, 2nd Session (Washington, D.C., USGPO, 1962), p. 63.

equipment and services; the increases in knowledge and sometimes the useful applications that we can foresee—these are the guides that can best help in the planning of ideal budgets.[20]

Scientists themselves can best furnish the government with these guides, but they must also help resolve the difficult question of priorities because it is unlikely that "there will be sufficient money to provide optimal support for all desirable purposes." [21]

At the present time the Academy has not fully faced up to this essential role and there is a reluctance to do so; but someone must choose and it is in the interests of the scientists that they help make the hard choices. The alternative is to let the rapid growth of the special disciplines proceed at the expense of the broad support of science and to default to nonscientists on the most crucial decisions affecting scientific progress.

If these preliminary steps are taken, the President's science advisers will face a more manageable task in helping the President reach a balanced decision about the total government support of science. Knowing what scientists have to say collectively about the merit of certain scientific programs, the science advisers could consider the impact of the proposed support on other technical programs of the government and on other areas of science. Together with policy-makers from government agencies and the staff of the Bureau of the Budget, they could help assess nontechnical factors in terms of various national priorities and explore such questions as: Will an expanded research program in one area lead to predictable practical applications or to international gains? Is the proposed research directed toward an improved weapons system or toward more effective insecticides for crops? What gains in international prestige will result from a man on the moon as compared to desalination plants in underdeveloped countries? At the present time these questions are not being asked and there is little discussion of the relative importance of various factors in determining support for a special field. Not all the questions are equally germane. But it is still true that more consideration of both technical and nontechnical factors should lead to wiser judgments than are now possible concerning which special disciplines the government should support at a maxi-

[20] *Science,* CXXXVII, No. 3528 (August 10, 1962), 397.   [21] *Ibid.*

mum rate and in what areas federal support should be curtailed as self-defeating or injurious to the broad support of science.

CONCLUSION

Though still only dimly perceived, it is possible to trace the emerging outlines of a body of policy concerned with the strength and progress of science. In framing policies for the support of research and science education and for financing costly research facilities, the President's science advisers have in fact been making national science policies. More recent efforts at long-range planning for science within and outside of government are likely to extend the responsibilities and influence of the science advisers in this direction. Yet the great bulk of their energies is not committed to the development of science policies. As advisers to the President, they are more widely and intimately concerned with the role of science in policy, with the relationships between science and national defense, science and foreign policy, and science and domestic welfare.

Growing responsibilities in these other areas absorb most of the time of the President's science advisers. They would be sufficient to preclude these advisers from serving as spokesmen for American science, but there are more fundamental reasons against their doing so. In helping the President understand the technical issues that underlie decisions on military technology, foreign aid, or a nuclear test ban, and in advising on ways by which science can be used to attain other national objectives, the President's science advisers cannot confine their advice to what is solely in the interests of science. They must help the President employ science in the national interest even if at times this is at the expense of things scientists would prefer to do.

Because the President's science advisers are themselves scientists they have a natural concern for a strong, healthy science and feel an obligation to help the President assure its future. But they cannot "represent" the scientific community on matters of science policy. They are not selected to represent the extraordinary range and diversity of disciplines that together comprise modern science. A useful group of comparable size could not be selected on this basis. Furthermore, these advisers are agents of the Presidency and a part of the government, and they must accommodate the interests of science to the realities of government and to the public interest. One of their main obligations is to help the President allocate scarce resources among all the diverse claims of science and among all the competing claimants for federal dollars, of which science is only one. The President's science advisers are thus the mediators between science and government [22] and not the advocates of science.

Scientists who hailed the appointment of the President's science advisers as establishing representatives for science in the White House should not be disappointed to find out that their representation is not unqualified. In a very real sense science sits in the highest councils of government; yet the burdens of responsibility and of vastly increased influence require a new order of statesmanship and restraint on the part of the President's science advisers. While it is their duty to see that the claims of science are fully heard, they must also be willing to participate actively in the process of adjusting the claims of science to the claims of other interests.

Whether or not science gets all the support it deserves, or even needs, scientists can take comfort from the fact that both a Republican and a Democratic President have seen fit to appoint their own science advisers. Never before has science had a more sympathetic ear or more sophisticated understanding at such a strategic place in government. Never before have scientists had more to say about the decisions that most affect science.

In fact, government and science are now joined in a common and indispensable partnership. Government is dependent upon science as an essential resource for national security and welfare, while science cannot flourish without government support. The great task of the President's science advisers is to foster and advance the partnership between science and government. They have not fashioned, nor are they likely to fashion, a comprehensive, national science policy. Such a policy, if it exists at all, will largely remain the sum of individual policies of agencies which support science and will reflect the influence of many political forces. But the President's science ad-

[22] See essay by Brooks in this volume.

visers have formulated and advanced many national policies aimed
at achieving a greater measure of harmony and coherence in government's relations with science. If they continue to build a bridge of
understanding between science and government, they can help assure the nation's future scientific progress and the government's effective use of science for many national goals.

Scientists, Foreign Policy, and Politics

WARNER R. SCHILLING

*Associate Professor of Public Law and Government
at Columbia University*

This essay is a revised version of an article published in *The American Political Science Review*, LVI, No. 2 (June, 1962), and appears here with the permission of the American Political Science Association.

[W]e must take, so far as we can, a picture of the world into our minds. Is it not a startling circumstance for one thing that the great discoveries of science, that the quiet study of men in laboratories, that the thoughtful developments which have taken place in quiet lecture rooms, have now been turned to the destruction of civilization? . . . The enemy whom we have just overcome had at its seats of learning some of the principal centres of scientific study and discovery, and used them in order to make destruction sudden and complete; and only the watchful, continuous co-operation of men can see to it that science, as well as armed men, is kept within the harness of civilization.[1]

These words were spoken in Paris, in January, 1919, by Woodrow Wilson, addressing the second Plenary Session of the Peace Conference. Wilson believed he had found a watchdog for civilization in the League of Nations. In this he was mistaken. Science and armed men have indeed been harnessed, but in order to promote and maintain the goals of conflicting polities. Whether in the pursuit

---

[1] State Department, *Papers Relating to the Foreign Relations of the United States, The Peace Conference* (13 vols., Washington, D.C., USGPO, 1942–47), III, 179.

An earlier version of this essay was prepared for discussion at the Fifth Congress of the International Political Science Association in Paris, September, 1961. The points made in the essay owe much to the comment and counsel of William T. R. Fox.

of these ends the cause of civilization will yet be served remains, it is to be hoped, an open question.

The cooperation of scientists and armed men was not a new relationship, even in Wilson's day. In the United States, for example, the president of the American Association for the Advancement of Science had declared in 1861:

> [I]t is easy to see that there are few applications of science which do not bear on the interests of commerce and navigation, naval or military concerns, the customs, the lighthouses, the public lands, post offices or post roads, either directly or remotely. If all examination is refused . . . the Government may lose a most important advantage.[2]

As a result of the interest of a number of American scientists and government officials, the National Academy of Sciences was established in 1863 for the purpose of providing scientific advice to the United States government. The use made of this Academy by the War Department between 1863 and 1913 bespeaks a bygone era. During those years the Department requested that the Academy constitute scientific committees on exactly five matters: "On the Question of Tests for the Purity of Whiskey; On the Preservation of Paint on Army Knapsacks; On Galvanic Action from Association of Zinc and Iron; On the Exploration of the Yellowstone; On Questions of Meteorological Science and its Applications."[3]

It would be incorrect to presume from this list that the War Department was uninterested in new weapons systems. Until about the turn of the century, military technology, like industrial technology, generally developed independently of advances in basic scientific knowledge. Thus, in 1915, when Wilson's Secretary of the Navy decided to establish a "Department of Invention and Development" in the hope of securing effective weapons with which to combat that "new and terrible engine of warfare . . . the submarine," it was the inventor, Thomas Edison, who was asked to head the new organization.[4] Although the contributions of university and industrial

---

[2] Quoted in U.S. Congress, Staff Study of the Senate Committee on Government Operations, *Science and Technology Act of 1958*, 85th Congress, 2d Session (Washington, D.C., USGPO, 1958), p. 110.

[3] *Ibid.*, p. 115.

[4] See Daniels's letter to Edison, in Josephus Daniels, *The Wilson Era: Years*

scientists to the fighting of World War I were marked enough to have caught Wilson's imagination, it was not until a generation later, with the advent of World War II, that the mobilization of scientists brought military results which were of great and in some instances decisive importance to the course of combat.

What has transformed the relationship between science and war has been the fact that in the twentieth century the development of technology has become increasingly dependent upon advances in basic knowledge about the physical world. Moreover, in the technically advanced nations, both the rate of technological innovation and the growth of new scientific knowledge have been increasing exponentially. As crudely measured by the volume of scientific publication, scientific knowledge has been doubling every ten to fifteen years.[5] In a non-Wilsonian world, the consequences of these conditions for national security policy have been as necessary as they are obvious. As the United States and the Soviet Union throw one weapons system after another into the effort to maintain at least a balance of terror, neither dares fall behind in either the discovery of new physical relationships or in the application of scientific knowledge to military hardware and political-military strategy. Thus, by the end of the first decade of the Cold War, about 50 percent of the engineers in the United States and 25 percent of the scientists were employed by the federal government, either directly or on contract, and about 65 percent of the scientific research in universities and 57 percent of that in private industry was government-financed.[6]

Indicative of the new relationship between science and war, figures and graphs comparing the Great Powers with regard to numbers of scientists and engineers have become as familiar as those in the 1930s which compared the Powers with regard to their output of steel, coal, and oil. Nor is it only in the military field that science and

---

of Peace, 1910–1917 (Chapel Hill, N.C., The University of North Carolina Press, 1944), p. 491.

[5] Ellis A. Johnson, "The Crisis in Science and Technology and its Effect on Military Development," *Operations Research*, VI, No. 1 (January–February, 1958), 14–15.

[6] See Lee A. DuBridge, "The American Scientist: 1955," *Yale Review* (September, 1955), p. 13, and the *Bulletin of the Atomic Scientists*, XIII, No. 3 (March, 1957), 82, and XVII, Nos. 5–6 (May–June, 1961), 254. The figure for private industry is for the year 1959; the others are for the year 1955.

technology have become vital to the course of foreign policy. Science has been harnessed to the advancement of foreign policy goals in such diverse fields as the exploration of space, birth and disease control, weather modification, economic development, and global communications.[7]

Present and future developments in science and technology are certain to bring a host of problems and opportunities to those responsible for the conduct of foreign policy. In recognition of this fact, the governments of the major Powers have endeavored to find ways to make themselves more alert to such developments and more active in determining the course of science and technology. The United States and the Soviet Union are the most extensively engaged in this effort, but it should not be forgotten that the nations of western and central Europe were among the pioneers in cultivating the relationship between science and government. The three elements that have revolutionized current military technology and strategy (electronics, missiles, and nuclear weapons) had their harbingers in the World War II development of British radar, the German V-2, and the American A-bomb, and it is noteworthy that the two European developments were conceived, initiated, and directed by officials and employees of established government organizations. In contrast, the American A-bomb was the result of conceptions and initiatives that came from outside the government—and primarily from exiled Europeans at that.

As an integral part of the efforts of governments to become both more responsive to and responsible for the development of science and technology, scientists have been invited into the highest councils of government, and it is with some of the problems occasioned by the presence of these "new" participants in the making of national policy that the remainder of this essay will be concerned. Although some illustrative material will be drawn from the experience of other governments, this essay focuses on problems associated with the participation of scientists in the American policy process.

---

[7] For a more detailed treatment of some of the points in the preceding paragraphs and a general discussion of the effect of science on international relations, see Warner R. Schilling, "Science, Technology, and Foreign Policy," *Journal of International Affairs*, XIII, No. 1 (Winter, 1959), 7–18.

Needless to say, the problems in policy-making that may arise will vary greatly with the kind of scientist participating (oceanographer, theoretical physicist, specialist in space medicine, industrial chemist), with the nature of the policy issue at stake (weapons development, science education, public health, the exploration of space, the allocation of funds for basic research), and with the manner in which the scientist is involved in the policy process (member of the attentive public, adviser to the President, worker in a government laboratory, official in an executive department or agency). This essay will make no attempt to deal systematically with the combinations possible among these three variables (profession, issue, and involvement). The discussion will be confined to a few of the central problems that the layman and the scientist are likely to encounter in working together on national security issues, and the treatment, as will become evident, will be of a very general and suggestive order.

The central problems occasioned by the participation of scientists in the determination of high policy are not nearly so novel as is generally supposed. The scientist has been brought into the councils of government because he possesses specialized skills and information believed relevant to the identification and resolution of particular policy problems. His relationship to the policy process is therefore a familiar one, that of an expert. Just as Sputnik I precipitated the establishment of a Special Assistant to the President for Science and Technology, so the earlier problems of fighting World War II and insuring postwar employment had brought the Joint Chiefs of Staff and the Council of Economic Advisers into the Offices of the President.

The central problems in policy-making posed by the entry of scientists into the policy process are thus formally no different from those associated with any other expert involved in the determination of national security policy. In particular, four such problems can be noted. (1) Like all experts, scientists will at times disagree, and the nonscientist (be he politician, administrator, or an expert in some other field) will confront the problem of choosing a course of action in the face of conflicting scientific advice. (2) Like all experts, scientists will at times manifest certain predispositions toward the resolution of the policy problems on which their advice is sought, and the nonscientist will confront the problem of identifying the policy pre- dilections peculiar to scientists and being on his guard against them. (3) The nonscientist and scientist will confront one problem in com- mon, and that is how to organize themselves to maximize the contri- bution that science can make to the government's programs, oppor- tunities, and choices. (4) The scientist will confront a problem com- mon to all experts who participate in the American policy process, and that is how to engage in politics without debasing the coinage of his own expertise.

THE PROBLEM OF CONFLICTING ADVICE

The difficulties the nonscientist confronts in choosing a course of action in the face of conflicting scientific advice seem inherently no more formidable than those a nonexpert would face in deciding what to do in the event of conflicting advice from economists, soldiers, or specialists on Soviet foreign policy. There are at least seven proce- dures that the nonexpert can follow in such circumstances, singly or in combination, and they appear to have about the same promise, for better or for worse, regardless of the kind of experts involved.[8]

The first step the nonscientist can take is to make certain that it is really conflicting *scientific* advice he is receiving. In the fall of 1949 President Truman asked Secretary Acheson to look into the disputes then current within the Atomic Energy Commission and elsewhere about the consequences of undertaking an intensive effort to make an H-bomb. Upon investigation the Secretary of State concluded that the scientists involved were not really very far apart except on the foreign policy issues that were his and Truman's responsibility to decide.[9]

Procedures two and three are simple: the nonscientist may be

---

[8] *Cf.* the implication in the following remarks of Glenn T. Seaborg, the Chairman of the Atomic Energy Commission: "Scientists don't necessarily have to make the final political decisions, but it might be easier to let a capable scientist learn political reality than to teach a politician science." Quoted in the *Bulletin of the Atomic Scientists*, XVII, No. 2 (February, 1961), 79.

[9] In this and subsequent undocumented references this writer has drawn upon personal interviews during 1956–58 with participants in the H-bomb decision.

guided by quantitative or qualitative features of the division (he can side with the majority, or with that side whose past record is the more confidence-inspiring). Failing these, there is, four, the "principle of least harm," and, five, the "principle of minimal choice." In the former, one chooses that course of action which appears to involve the least cost if the technical premise on which it is based proves to be wrong. Thus in World War II, given the American belief that the Germans were hard at work on an A-bomb, it seemed more sensible to spend $2 billion on the assumption that the bomb could be made than to do little or nothing on the assumption that it could not. In the case of the "principle of minimal choice," one chooses that course of action which seems to close off the least number of future alternatives. This was the character of President Truman's first decision on the H-bomb. He decided to go ahead in the effort to explore the feasibility of an H-bomb, but nothing was decided about technical steps of a greater political or military consequence (for example, testing a device if one were fabricated, or preparing to produce the materials that would be required for weapons production in the event of a successful test).[10]

In the case of procedure six the nonscientist can make his choice among conflicting scientists on the basis of whichever technical estimate is most in accord with policy on which he was already intent. (In contrast to the first procedure, where the nonscientist endeavors to factor out of the conflict the policy preferences of the scientists, here he is factoring into the conflict his own policy preferences.) In the spring of 1942, the British scientists Henry Tizard and F. A. Lindemann (Lord Cherwell) diverged by a factor of five in their estimates of the destruction that could be accomplished by an all-out campaign to bomb the homes of German civilians and also in their judgments about the consequences that even the lesser amount of destruction would have for the military course of the war. (Lindemann thought that it would be "catastrophic," Tizard that it would

---

[10] For the "principle of least harm," see Bernard Brodie, "Strategy as a Science," *World Politics,* I, No. 4 (July, 1949), 479n. On the H-bomb choice, see Warner R. Schilling, "The H-Bomb Decision: How to Decide Without Actually Choosing," *Political Science Quarterly,* LXXVI, No. 1 (March, 1961), 37–38.

be "most damaging" but not "decisive.") The importance of the issue lay in the fact that the Naval Staff was pressing Churchill to allocate some of the bombers that the Air Staff planned to use in the campaign to the Naval Staff's own antisubmarine effort. The Air Staff, which had long been persuaded of the efficacy of strategic bombing, found Lindemann's calculations "simple, clear and convincing." The Naval Staff was similarly impressed by Tizard's. The final decisions were Churchill's, and he was greatly influenced by Lindemann's estimate—an influence presumably not unrelated to his own interest in presenting the Russians with a dramatically visible contribution to the war against Germany.[11]

In procedure seven the nonscientist is guided by his own sense for the scientific and technical problems involved. In the 1949 H-bomb debate, some of the politicians involved were little deterred by the fact that the scientists were by no means confident that they could make such a weapon and by the possibility that an all-out but failing effort might entail very high costs for the A-bomb program. These politicians were willing to press ahead in part because of their belief that the scientists were not really aware of their own potential. Similarly, when the German soldiers, scientists, and engineers engaged in the development of the V-2 divided on the question of whether it should be launched from mobile or fixed batteries, Hitler's own technical enthusiasm for large, hardened bunkers led him, unwisely as it turned out, to decide on behalf of the latter.[12]

In concluding this survey of the problem of conflicting advice, it should be noted that one of the more likely outcomes is that the ac-

---

[11] See Sir Charles Webster and Noble Franklin, *The Strategic Air Offensive Against Germany, 1939–1945* (London, H.M. Stationery Office, 1961), Vol. 1, chap. 6, especially 331–36, 340–43, 371, and Winston S. Churchill, *The Second World War: The Hinge of Fate* (Boston, Houghton Mifflin, 1950), pp. 121, 328, 333–34. For more spirited accounts, see C. P. Snow, *Science and Government* (Cambridge, Mass., Harvard University Press, 1961), pp. 47–51, the review of this book by P. M. S. Blackett in *Scientific American*, CCIV, No. 4 (April, 1961), 192–94; the Earl of Birkenhead, *The Professor and the Prime Minister* (Boston, Houghton Mifflin, 1962), pp. 257–67, and C. P. Snow, *Appendix to Science and Government* (Cambridge, Mass., Harvard University Press, 1962), pp. 23–30.

[12] Maj. Gen. Walter Dornberger, *V-2* (New York, Ballantine Books, 1954), pp. 97, 158–60, and Lt. Gen. James M. Gavin, *War and Peace in the Space Age* (New York, Harper and Bros., 1958), pp. 76–77.

tions of the contending scientists may prove much more influential than the procedures followed by the nonscientist. Divided experts will not always be equal in their physical or personal access to the decision-maker, in the persistence with which they state their case, or in the force and clarity of their arguments. Thus, in the H-bomb debate, there were instances where equally qualified scientists differed greatly in the time and energy they spent circulating their views of the technical (and political) prospects, and such differences were by no means without consequence for the judgments of others.[13]

THE PROBLEM OF BIAS

Discussion of the policy predispositions displayed by scientists must be entered with considerable caution. The major theoretical premise involved is that all experts will evidence certain predilections with regard to policy and policy-making which are the result of the character of their expertise: their skills, knowledge, and experience. Since experts differ in the skills, knowledge, and experience they command (or in the responsibilities with which they are charged), they will differ in the biases they characteristically exhibit. Thus scientists, soldiers, and diplomats jointly concerned with a policy problem are likely to approach the question of how and in what manner it should be resolved with rather dissimilar predispositions.

[13] Note should also be taken of the problem the policy-maker faces when all his experts *agree*. This writer is unable to suggest a useful procedure here (other than variations on procedures five, six, and seven above); but that the problem is a real one can be seen in the conclusion of the German physicists that it would be infeasible for any Power to develop an atomic bomb during World War II. Some of the German scientists later stated that political considerations were partly responsible for their advice and for the fact that they made so little progress themselves on an A-bomb (*cf.* procedure one).

The German work on the A-bomb during World War II is described in Samuel A. Goudsmit, *Alsos* (New York, Henry Schuman, 1947). For various appraisals of the influence exercised by political considerations, see Robert Jungk, *Brighter Than a Thousand Suns* (New York, Harcourt, Brace and Co., 1958), pp. 88–104, Hans A. Bethe, "Review of *Brighter Than a Thousand Suns*," *Bulletin of the Atomic Scientists*, XIV, No. 10 (December, 1958), 427, and William L. Laurence, *Men and Atoms* (New York, Simon and Schuster, 1959), pp. 90–93.

These points, however, are easier stated than demonstrated. To begin with, it should be clear that insofar as policy is concerned "the scientific mind" is as much a chimera as "the military mind." Scientists, like soldiers and the rest of us, differ greatly in the ideas they have about the political world and the things that will (or ought to) happen in it, and their views on foreign policy matters are far more likely to be reflective of these differences than conditioned by their common professional skills and interests. Moreover, even if differences in expertise or responsibility were the only factors determining the views of policy-makers (and they certainly are not), one would still have to take account of the fact that scientists are as varied in their professional skills and pursuits as soldiers. The perspectives of a theoretical physicist engaged in basic research are no more to be equated with those of an organic chemist engaged in applying extant knowledge to the improvement of an industrial product than is the outlook of a staff officer in Washington drafting a war plan to be considered identical with that of a general in charge of a theater of operations.

In addition to these difficulties, analysis must also contend with the fact that it is directed toward a moving target. The policy perspectives that a physicist may have developed as a result of two decades in a university laboratory are unlikely to endure without change after a few years on a Washington advisory committee. Many American scientists are well along the same route that transformed the policy perspectives of large numbers of the American military profession during the war and immediate postwar years. As a result of new problems and new responsibilities, these soldiers acquired new skills, knowledge, and experience. In consequence, with regard to their approach to foreign policy, some are, for all practical purposes, interchangeable between the Pentagon and the State Department, and one could wish that there were more diplomats equally well equipped to work on both sides of the Potomac.

With these reservations in mind, six policy perspectives will be presented here which seem moderately characteristic of many scientists, most of them physicists, who have participated in national security policy in recent times. Most of these predispositions were first evidenced during their work with the military during World War II, and the extent and manner in which they have been later operative in reference to larger foreign policy issues is not always easy to document, since most of the sources are still classified. Needless to say, in outlining these predispositions, one is presenting a cross between a caricature and a Weberian ideal type, not describing real people. In discussing these predispositions, this writer does not mean to convey the impression that they are either "good" or "bad" from the point of view of policy or policy-making, or that one or another of these predispositions may not also be evidenced by groups other than scientists. The point to this discussion is that if certain orders of scientists are indeed prone to these or other policy predispositions, the nonscientist will be wise to be alert to them, even if on occasion he should conclude that they are all for the good.

Naïve utopianism or naïve belligerency. C. P. Snow has described the scientist as an impatient optimist in his approach to social wrongs; he is quick to search for something to do and inclined to expect favorable results.[14] Certainly, the scientist's profession inclines him to look at problems in terms of searching for a solution to them. When this perspective is turned to problems of international politics, however, the scientist's approach often appears open to the characterization of "naïve utopianism or naïve belligerency." [15] His approach to international relations appears simplistic and mechanistic. It is almost as if he conceives of policy being made primarily by forward-looking, solution-oriented, rational-thinking types like himself.

In these perspectives the scientist is likely to find little in common with the diplomat (who is inclined to believe that most of his problems have no solution, and who is in any event too busy with the crises of the day to plan for tomorrow), or with the politician (whose approach to problems is so spasmodic as to seem neither analytical nor rational, and whose policy positions are anyway soon blurred by his efforts to accommodate to the positions of others), or with the professional student of international politics (who, when the opportunity permits, lectures the scientist on the elegant complexity of the

---

[14] C. P. Snow, *The Two Cultures and the Scientific Revolution* (New York, Cambridge University Press, 1959), pp. 9–11.

[15] The author is indebted to Hans Speier for the phrasing of this point.

political process, but who never seems, to the scientist at least, to have any really good ideas about what to do). It is perhaps these differences in perspective that lead the scientist on occasion to seem "intellectually arrogant"; it is as if he concludes that those who have no promising solutions or are not seeking them cannot be very bright. In his predisposition toward action and solutions, the scientist comes closest to sharing the predilection of the soldier for decision, which may be one reason why their partnership has been so spectacularly successful.

The "whole-problem approach." The first grant made by the United States government for experimental research was in 1832 to the Franklin Institute. The scientists were asked to investigate the reasons for explosions in steamboat boilers. They reported back not only with a technical explanation but with a draft bill to provide for federal regulation of steamboats.[16] In this they evidenced the scientist's predilection for the "whole-problem approach." The reluctance of scientists to apply their expertise to mere fragments of the total problem, especially under conditions where those who prescribe the fragments do not reveal the whole of which they are a part, was evident in the work of both British and American scientists during World War II. Military officials initially approached the scientists with requests for the development of particular weapons and devices without revealing the military problems or reasoning responsible for their requests. The scientists objected to this procedure, and they were eventually able to persuade the soldiers to inform them of the general military problems involved in order that the scientists might reach their own conclusions about the kinds of weapons and devices the military would need to meet those problems.[17]

[16] Don K. Price, *Government and Science* (New York, New York University Press, 1954), pp. 10–11.

[17] This persuasion was largely accomplished through demonstrations of the military utility of the scientists' taking such an approach, although in the early history of the M.I.T. Radiation Laboratory a certain amount of polite bargaining was apparently practiced. One scientist involved, whenever told that the reason for a request was a problem for Washington, not him, to worry about, adopted the practice of working on something else until he was given a description of the problem involved. For a brief summary of the British experience, see Alexander Haddow, "The Scientist as Citizen," *Bulletin of the Atomic Scientists*, XII, No. 7 (September, 1956), 247.

In 1952, in connection with an Air Force project on air defense, a group of American scientists were asked to review the prospects for improving the nation's continental air defense. The scientists concluded that some new and promising systems were possible, and they submitted an estimate of what the developments might cost. They also recommended that the money be spent. The Air Force did not approve the recommendation, and as is customary in Washington the disputants on both sides began to search for allies and to leak their cases to the press. Certain Air Force officials, who feared that additional funds for air defense would come at the expense of dollars otherwise available for the Strategic Air Command and who were convinced that this would be militarily undesirable, charged that the scientists by entering into matters of military strategy and budget policy had exceeded both their assignment and their expertise. Commenting on this charge, one of the scientists involved later explained that he would have little interest in working on a study project that did not have the potential for leading into the question of whether the conclusions should be acted upon.[18]

The predisposition to want to be told and to deal with the whole problem no doubt has its base in the professional experience of scientists (and one of the central credos of science) that good ideas on a problem may come from the most unexpected quarters and that the widest possible dissemination of information about a problem will significantly enhance its chances for an early solution.[19] Still, there are

[18] *Cf.* the following exchange between Gordon Gray and Jerrold Zacharias during the Oppenheimer hearing. Gray: "If you were directing a study which had to do with electronics, a pretty clearly defined field, and it started to come up with recommendations with respect to foreign policy, would you feel that an official of the Defense Department who urged that you stick to electronics was acting with impropriety?" Zacharias: "I think I would not direct a project that was as restrictive as that, sir, as to be restricted only to electronics." Atomic Energy Commission, *In the Matter of J. Robert Oppenheimer, Transcript of Hearing Before Personnel Security Board* (Washington, D.C., USGPO, 1954), p. 930.

For some of the issues involved in the 1952 air defense study, see *ibid.*, pp. 598–99, 749–50, 763–65, 923–24, 930–31, 935, and 938, and also the account in Price, *Government and Science*, pp. 136–38.

[19] General Leslie Groves, who directed the Manhattan Project, was especially sensitive to the scientists' tendency to take on the whole problem. (Some even advised him on how the garbage should be collected at Los Alamos, an act which may possibly have reflected self- rather than scientific interest.) One

problems and problems; some are open to determinate solutions, and others can be resolved only through the exercise of political power. The point about the "whole-problem approach," as the air-defense example illustrates, is that it not only helps propel the scientists from an advisory to a political role but it serves to make the scientist somewhat blind to the fact that he is so moving. In its most extreme form, the "whole-problem approach" coupled with the "intellectual arrogance" perspective can lead to instances like the following: on one high-level advisory committee concerned with several areas of national security policy, a scientist whose formal claim to participation was a knowledge of infrared-ray phenomena was reportedly quite free with his proposals for what political policies should be adopted with regard to the United Nations.

Quantum jumps versus improvements. A number of scientists have advanced the proposition that the military tend to be more interested in improving existing weapons than in developing radically new ones, and they have urged that a separate civilian agency be established to undertake such development. Both scientists and soldiers have explained this difference in their approach to military research and development, "quantum jumps versus improvements," with the hypothesis that the soldier's interest in developing entirely new weapons must always be inhibited by his concern for the possibility that war may come in the near future, since in this event his interests are best served by improving existing weapons. It has also been suggested that military leaders, who must be prepared at any time to ask others to take up the weapons at hand and fight with them, cannot afford to let themselves or others become too impressed with the deficiencies of those weapons as compared with others that might have been developed.[20]

An explanation for this difference, less flattering to the military, is the occasional assertion by scientists that theirs is a profession which stimulates original and creative thought, while that of the military

---

reason for his effort to compartmentalize the work scientists were doing was his fear that "if I brought them into the whole project, they would never do their own job. There was just too much of scientific interest, and they would just be frittering from one thing to another." *Oppenheimer Transcript,* p. 164.

[20] See, for example, Lloyd V. Berkner, "Science and National Strength," *Bulletin of the Atomic Scientists,* IX, No. 5 (June, 1953), 155, 180.

tends to develop minds which accept the existing situation without too much question. As indicated in the discussion of the first predilection, this is a judgment which the scientist may extend to the diplomat and the politician as well.

The difficulty with quantum jumps in foreign policy, however, is that the structure of both the domestic and the international political process is normally such as to make them infeasible. Thus, diplomats and politicians are accustomed to seeing the same old policy problems come around year after year, and they are generally intent on policies which promise only slow and modest change. Scientists, on the other hand, have been demanding and searching for quantum jumps in foreign policy ever since the end of World War II. It is symptomatic that the first proposal developed by the Advisory Committee on Science and Technology to the Democratic National Advisory Council, established in 1959, was for the creation of a new scientific agency, independent of the State and Defense Departments, whose function would be "to face all the problems of disarmament." [21]

Technology for its own sweet sake. In the summer of 1945, after the A-bomb had been tested but before the first drop on Japan, the Director of the Los Alamos Laboratory, J. Robert Oppenheimer, suggested to his superior, General Leslie Groves, that if some improvements were made in the design of the bomb it would be more effective. Groves decided against the improvements because he did not want to incur any delay in the use of the bomb, which he expected would end the war with Japan. In the summer of 1943, after the Director of the German V-2 project, General Dornberger, had finally secured a first-class priority for the use of the weapon, those responsible for producing it in quantity were increasingly handicapped by the scientists and engineers who kept improving but changing its design. Dornberger was finally obliged to issue a flat order against any further improvements.[22]

There was nothing irresponsible in these scientists' actions. Charged with the technical development of weapons, they would

[21] See the *Bulletin of the Atomic Scientists*, XV, No. 10 (December, 1959), 412.

[22] *Oppenheimer Transcript*, p. 33, and Dornberger, *V-2*, pp. 134–37.

have been remiss in their responsibilities if they had failed to call attention to the prospects for improvement. The point to the examples is that scientists and engineers, in the pursuit of their own responsibilities and interests, may easily lose sight of those of the policy-maker.

The scientists on the General Advisory Committee to the Atomic Energy Commission who recommended against the development of an H-bomb in 1949 did so in part because of their concern for the foreign-policy consequences of introducing a weapon of such destructive power into the world. Oppenheimer, the Chairman of the Committee, later stated that the thermonuclear design developed by Edward Teller in 1951 was "technically so sweet" that if it had been available in 1949 the Committee would probably not have made the recommendation that it did. Since with a technically more promising design at hand one might suppose that the Committee's foreign-policy concerns would have been all the greater, some observers have concluded that in the pursuit of his technical interests the scientist can also easily lose sight of his own policy concerns.[23]

Such a judgment ignores the complexity of the Committee's position. For example, one of the reasons why the Committee thought the United States should take the initiative in renouncing the H-bomb was precisely because the device then in view seemed likely to be both difficult to make and of dubious military value. It was thought that for this reason the Russians might be willing to follow the American example and that if they did not the United States would not have risked much by the delay. These were considerations which obviously would have been changed if a technically more promising design had been available in 1949.[24] Still, the comments of several scientists close to these events are not without relevance. It is their feeling that there are times when the technician does take over, that when the scientist is faced with an interesting and challenging problem his inclination is to get to work on it, and that under

---

[23] *Oppenheimer Transcript*, p. 251. For an extreme judgment, see Jungk, *Brighter Than a Thousand Suns*, p. 296.

[24] See Oppenheimer's statements in *Oppenheimer Transcript*, pp. 81, 251, 897, and Schilling, "The H-Bomb Decision: How to Decide Without Actually Choosing," pp. 30–36.

these circumstances he should not be the first person to be expected to keep larger policy considerations in balance.

This predisposition, "technology for its own sweet sake," appears to have its roots in two more of science's central credos: the belief in the value of pursuing knowledge for its own sake and the belief that the best motivation for the direction of research is the strength and character of individual curiosities. But the direction and strength of scientific interests and curiosities is not necessarily coincident with the requirements of military or foreign policy. One of the most recent examples of the scientist's capacity to get caught up in a challenging problem (assigned, to be sure, by policy-makers) is afforded by the ingenious ideas scientists have conceived for evading nuclear-test detection systems and for the design of new systems to detect those evasions. In the light of the later course of negotiations, an American statesman who believed there was considerable foreign-policy gain in a test-ban treaty and who believed that the Russians were at one time seriously interested in such a treaty might well conclude that the formula developed by the British scientist Watson-Watt for meeting wartime military requirements—"Give them the third best to go with; the second comes too late, the best never comes"—was not without its implications for meeting peacetime foreign policy requirements.[25] This observation is not intended as an argument that the interests of the United States would have been better served by a test-ban treaty with a "third best" detection system than by no treaty at all. The point is rather that the policy-maker must be sensitive to the prospect that because of the constant advance of technology his only real choices may be of this order.

The sense for paradise lost. This predisposition is likely to be more characteristic of the scientists who had their graduate training and early professional experience in the years before World War II than of those who have known only war or Cold War conditions.[26] The prewar scientists took it as an article of faith that certain conditions

[25] Sir Robert Watson-Watt, *Three Steps to Victory* (London, Odhams, 1957), p. 74.

[26] In 1955 slightly more than half of the active research physicists in the United States were under forty years of age and had received their doctorates after December 7, 1941. DuBridge, "The American Scientist: 1955," p. 1.

were essential for the progress of science, in particular that scientists be free to select their research problems and that both scientists and scientific information be free to move among as well as within nations.[27] All of these conditions were violated during World War II, and as a result of the Cold War they were never fully reestablished. The nuclear physicists had had perhaps the most highly developed sense of international community. They were relatively few in number, had close personal relationships at home and abroad, and had been experiencing an exciting exchange of discoveries since Rutherford identified the nucleus in 1911. They also lost the most, for theirs was militarily the most sensitive knowledge, and the pages of the *Bulletin of the Atomic Scientists* offer eloquent testimony to their ideological disturbance.

The result is that the senior scientists tend to be especially sensitive to possibilities which hold some promise for restoring the former order. They may usually be found on the side (or in front) of those urging freer exchange of scientific and military information with allied governments, less secrecy in the circulation of scientific (and sometimes military) information, and more extensive cultural, and especially scientific, exchanges with the Soviet Union. Similarly, the major activities of the Foreign Policy Panel of the President's Science Advisory Committee (PSAC) and of the Office of the Science Adviser to the Secretary of State have been in connection with the Science Attaché program, the facilitation of international scientific programs and conferences, and the exchange of scientists with the Soviet Union.[28]

Science serves mankind. For at least 300 years the Western scientific tradition has assumed that the unrestricted generation of new knowledge about the world was a social good. Over these years

---

[27] These assumptions are excellently set forth in Margaret Smith Stahl, "Splits and Schisms: Nuclear and Social," unpublished doctoral dissertation, University of Wisconsin, 1946, chap. 4.

[28] For the activities of the Panel and the Office, see James R. Killian, Jr., "Science and Public Policy," address to the American Association for the Advancement of Science, December 29, 1958, as printed in U.S. Congress, Report of the Senate Committee on Government Operations, *Science Program—86th Congress,* 86th Congress, 1st Session (Washington, D.C., USGPO, 1959), pp. 12–13, and *The Science Adviser of the Department of State* (Washington, D.C., USGPO, 1960), State Department Publ. No. 7056.

science in its purest form (the discovery of the facts of nature for knowledge's sake alone) became increasingly an autonomous social institution; research scientists were largely disassociated from the practical applications of their discoveries, but they took it for granted that these discoveries would ultimately benefit mankind.[29] The advent of nuclear and bacteriological weapons systems which have the potential of destroying so much of mankind and his works has called this faith sharply into question. It does not take much imagination to wonder if man, in view of his apparent inability to escape from the order of conflicts which have historically resulted in war, would not be better off in a world where the knowledge that has made the new weapons possible did not exist. For some of the senior nuclear physicists this is more than a philosophical question. They are unable to avoid a sense of personal responsibility; they reason from the premise that they were few, and if they had acted differently weapons development might not have taken the turn it did.

In the immediate postwar years, the apparent contradiction between the good of science and the evil of war was resolved by the expectation that the very destructiveness of the new weapons would lead man to renounce at last the folly of war. The course of foreign policy in later years has weakened these expectations but not destroyed them, as the recent flurry of arms-control proposals premised on the rational self-interest of both sides in avoiding mutual destruction testifies.

The need to preserve their sense of service to mankind led some American scientists to refuse to work on weapons. Similarly, there are reports that several Russian scientists were imprisoned, exiled, or placed under surveillance for refusing to participate in weapons work between 1945 and 1953, and a number of Germany's elite physicists announced in 1957 that they would have no part in nuclear weapons work.[30] Such cases are dramatic, but nowhere have they

---

[29] See Stahl, "Splits and Schisms," chap. 4.

[30] See Arnold Kramish, *Atomic Energy in the Soviet Union* (Stanford, Calif., Stanford University Press, 1959), p. 105. Kramish states that it is not certain whether the objections of the Russian scientists were technical or political. For the declaration of the German physicists, see the *Bulletin of the Atomic Scientists*, XIII, No. 6 (June, 1957), 228.

prevented the development of weapons on which governments were determined. The more consequential resolutions have been those in which scientists have simply identified the good of mankind with the strength of their nation or have endeavored to develop new weapons systems which would be as effective as the old in promoting national policy but which would result in less slaughter if used. This was part of the rationale behind the recommendation made by a group of American scientists in 1951 that the government undertake the development and production of a large number of A-bombs for tactical use in the ground defense of Western Europe. Their hope was that such an innovation would relieve the United States of the burden of having to rely solely on the threat of strategic bombing to contain the Red Army.[31]

The failure of the United States to orbit a satellite before the Soviet Union did was the result of the State Department's insensitivity to the political implications of the event and the decision of the President and the Secretary of Defense not to let a satellite program interfere with military missile programs. A small part of the story, however, is to be found in the reluctance of some of the American scientists involved in the programming of the International Geophysical Year to see an American IGY satellite propelled by an operational military weapon. Their preference for the less-developed but nonmilitary Vanguard over the Army's Redstone appears to have reflected a combination of the "sense for paradise lost" and the "science serves mankind" predispositions, in this case an interest in showing the world the peaceful side of science and in demonstrating that the scientists of the world could cooperate in the interests of knowledge as well as compete in the interests of nations.[32]

THE PROBLEMS OF ORGANIZATION AND POLITICS

With regard to the two remaining problems to be discussed—how to organize relations between science and government and how the scientist can participate in policy-making and still keep his expert

---

[31] *Oppenheimer Transcript*, pp. 584, 594–95, 891–94.
[32] See Walter Sullivan, *Assault on the Unknown* (New York, McGraw-Hill, 1961), pp. 79–81.

standing—four points seem deserving of special emphasis: (1) the problem of organization, especially in the area of foreign policy, is still very much in the research and development stage, and so it may long remain, considering the precedent set by the problem of how to relate military experts and foreign policy; (2) in many areas of policy it will never be possible to specify what constitutes "the best" organization; the way in which policy-makers are organized is not without influence on the kind of policies they will produce, and so long as there are differences over policy there will be no agreement about organization; (3) in the American political system, at least, the science expert at the high-policy level has no real hope of keeping out of politics; his only choice is in the character of his political style; and, finally, (4) it should not be forgotten that organization and policy-making are not the same as policy; successful instances of foreign policy capitalizing on or guiding developments in science and technology will not automatically follow just because scientists have been liberally injected into the policy-making process.

Organization. Current American organization in the area of science and foreign policy still reflects the emergency responses to the Russian ICBM and Sputnik I. One effect of these events was that scientists were rushed to the most important single center of power, the Office of the President, by means of the creation of the Special Assistant to the President for Science and Technology and the President's Science Advisory Committee.

The President certainly needs men around him who are sensitive to the areas of interaction between science and foreign policy. But a case can be made for the proposition that the center of gravity for the input of scientific advice into the policy-making process should be at a lower level than the White House. The President's political interests lie in keeping the staff about him small and generalized. Well-developed plans and programs will have a better chance of maturing in the larger and more diversified facilities that departments and agencies can provide. Secondly, as C. P. Snow concludes in his account of the differences between Tizard and Lindemann, there are risks in having a single science adviser sitting next to the center of political power. Although it should be noted that Churchill fared better with a single science adviser than Hitler did with none

("The Führer has dreamed," Dornberger was told, "that no [V-2] will ever reach England"), Snow's point has merit and it holds for institutions as well as for individuals.[33] The President will generally find his choices facilitated by the existence of multiple and independent sources of scientific advice.

This is a condition that already prevails in the case of many of the departments and agencies whose actions have significant foreign policy consequences, especially in the use of scientists by the Department of Defense, the Atomic Energy Commission, and the National Aeronautics and Space Administration. It is, however, a condition notably absent in the case of the Department of State. As it now stands, the President has more scientists to advise him on the scientific and technical aspects of various foreign policy issues, particularly in the national security field, than has the Secretary of State.[34]

Established in February, 1951, the Office of the Science Adviser in the Department of State has yet to become a point of vantage in the determination of high departmental policy. Deprived in its original charter of any jurisdiction in the atomic energy field, the Office was moribund within four years of its birth. The number of overseas science attachés administered by the Office went from a peak of eleven in 1952 to zero at the end of 1955, and the Office itself languished without a scientist from February, 1954, to January, 1958. Resurrected in the aftermath of Sputnik I, the Office—as of February, 1962—consisted of some fourteen science attachés overseas and a Washington staff of six, of whom only three, including the Director, were professional scientists. Nor were these three scientists supplemented by technical personnel elsewhere in the Department. There were no scientists, full or part-time, in the Department's offices for

[33] Snow, *Science and Government*, pp. 66–68, and Dornberger, *V-2*, p. 87.
[34] There are eighteen scientists on the PSAC; its working panels also contain participants from outside the Committee. In December, 1958, the Committee and the Office of the Special Assistant for Science and Technology had together some 75 scientists and engineers serving part-time. See Killian, "Science and Public Policy," p. 8. The work of the Committee and the Office are additionally described and appraised in U.S. Congress, Staff Study of the Subcommittee on National Policy Machinery, Senate Committee on Government Operations, *Science Organization and the President's Office*, 87th Congress, 1st Session (Washington, D.C., USGPO, 1961).

space and atomic energy, political-military affairs, or policy planning. Of the Department's line offices, only the Bureau of Intelligence and Research maintained a technical staff.

As might be inferred from these arrangements, most of the policymakers concerned believed that their needs for scientific advice were adequately met through formal and informal communication with scientists employed in the operating agencies and departments and with the President's own Science Advisory Committee. The Department's Science Adviser, as a participant in the activities of both the President's Committee and the Federal Council on Science and Technology, stood available to facilitate such communication. Otherwise, both the demands placed upon the Office and its own interests served to limit its activity, as previously noted, to a relatively narrow range of foreign policy problems.

In the summer of 1962, spurred by a recommendation from the President's Science Advisory Committee, the Department reorganized the Office into the Office of International Scientific Affairs with a provision for expanded personnel (perhaps a total of eighteen, including nine scientists) and a charter designed to lead it into more active participation in the policy or line offices. Moreover, as a result of the Department's decision in the spring to disband the office for space and atomic energy and to divide its responsibilities among a variety of bureaus and offices, the new Office now shares with several other bureaus a mandate over the "peaceful" uses of space and atomic energy. Although this writing is too close to these events to assay the results of the reorganization, the Office would appear to have little prospect of becoming for the Secretary of State the functional equivalent of the President's scientific advisory apparatus, at least in the areas where science and technology impinge on national security policy. Responsibility for the military applications of space and atomic energy were distributed to the European Bureau and the Office for Political-Military Affairs, and here the use of scientists and the Department's science adviser remains as before.[35]

---

[35] The projected size of the new Office is not out of line with that of others in the State Department. The Office for Political-Military Affairs, for example, numbers some fourteen people, of whom one has the formal responsibility for monitoring the military applications of space and atomic energy.

Whether the Department of State would be better served by an "in-house" scientific competence in these fields is a question that an outside observer cannot easily answer. Much depends on the validity of the expectations that the Department can rely on the scientists of the operating agencies and the President's Committee to alert it to developments and information relevant to foreign policy. Even more depends on how determined the Department is to play an active and influential part in shaping the scientific and technical activities of the government to conform to *its* conception of national needs and priorities. (The two conditions are, of course, not unrelated. The more influence the Department exercises in determining the goals and programs of other agencies, the more confident it can be that scientists in those agencies will call the Department's attention to goals and programs which they believe to be receiving too much or too little attention.) In the final analysis, the question of the Department's organizational needs can only be answered in terms of the strength and content of its policy interests. In the field of national security policy, the Department has yet to define its responsibilities and identify its interests in such a manner as to point to the need to expand its modest political staff, much less to create a science advisory body to help this staff monitor and direct the course of science and technology as they affect such policy.

Organization and purpose. Since administrative organizations exist for the purpose of serving policy goals and implementing policy programs, it is to be expected that those who differ on the goals and programs of policy will differ about the proper design of administrative organizations. The desire of many scientists in 1945 to see atomic energy used for peaceful rather than military purposes was one of the reasons for their political campaign to place the postwar atomic energy program in the hands of a civilian commission instead of the War Department. Similarly, more recent differences

For information on the Office of the Science Adviser, see State Department, *The Science Adviser of the Department of State,* The New York *Times,* July 2, 1962, and September 15, 1962, and Graham DuShane, "Full Circle," *Science,* 129, No. 3291 (January 24, 1958), 175. Additional information was secured from interviews with Department officials in February of 1962 and 1963. The description and interpretation made above are, of course, entirely this writer's responsibility.

about how to organize the government's space effort reflect, in part, policy differences about whether space will or should be an area for major military operations.

The same point can be seen in the proposal to create a Department of Science and Technology which would include the variety of "little" science programs now scattered throughout the Executive structure (for example, those of the Weather Bureau, National Bureau of Standards, and the Antarctic Office), but would exclude those of the Department of Defense, the Atomic Energy Commission, and the Space Administration. The hope behind this proposal is that, combined together, the "little" programs would be able to compete more effectively in the struggle for government dollars with the "big" science programs of the military, atomic energy, and space organizations.[36]

The question of the "best" science organization is thus inescapably tied to the question of what is the "best" science policy. But who can demonstrate whether science and foreign policy would be better served by allocating dollars to a program to control weather or to a program to explore Mars? There are no determinate solutions to problems of this order. Neither, for that matter, is there any one "right" amount of the nation's scientific resources that should be allocated to basic as compared to applied research. Differences on policy questions such as these are unavoidable among scientists and nonscientists alike, and they can be resolved in but one manner: through the interplay of power and interest in a political arena.

This condition, plus the increasing dependence of scientific programs and research on government funds, plus the increasing consequences of the choices the government makes in allocating those funds, all promise to put the politicians and the scientists under increasing pressure. As the opportunities for further development in each of a thousand different scientific fields mushroom with the acceleration of scientific knowledge, whatever the government decides to support, it will be deciding *not* to support more. Indeed, it is not too difficult to see the scientists becoming practiced advocates and

---

[36] See Lloyd V. Berkner, "National Science Policy and the Future," address at Johns Hopkins University, December 16, 1958, as printed in *Science Program— 86th Congress*, pp. 116–18.

lobbyists for the government's support of their cherished fields and projects, or to imagine the day when the politicians start to complain about "interscience rivalry" and begin to fancy that, if only there were a single Chief of Science, competition and duplication could be ended and the nation could have an integrated science policy.

Scientists in politics. The American political system is not one that insulates its experts from the politics of choice.[37] The scientist involved in high-policy matters is likely to find himself propelled into the political arena, either by a push from behind or by his own interest in seeing that the "right" choices are made. Some of the incentives the scientist may have to follow up his advice with an effort to see that it is accepted (and to take a hand in a few other matters while he is at it) were outlined and illustrated in the preceding section. It is equally important to recognize that the scientist may find himself on the political firing line, placed there by a politician interested in using the scientist's prestige as an "expert" to disarm the critics of his (the politician's) choices.

Thus, prior to the moratorium on nuclear tests, the Eisenhower administration appeared to be using scientists and their scientific facts on fall-out as a means of justifying and defending a policy that was obviously compounded of a variety of considerations besides that of the radiological hazard. The comparison with Truman's use of the prestige of the Joint Chiefs of Staff to defend his choices in the Korean War comes easily to mind. So, too, do the statements of various Republican leaders that they had lost confidence in the Joint Chiefs and their determination, when they came to power, to get rid of the "Democratic" Chiefs and to appoint Chiefs in sympathy with Republican policies.

The scientist, in short, is not likely to orbit the centers of political power emitting upon request "beeps" of purely technical information. He will inevitably be pulled into the political arena. If his participation there is to be either productive or personally satisfying, both the scientist and the nonscientist need to be highly conscious of

[37] This point, especially as it relates to science experts, is discussed in Price, *Government and Science*, pp. 61–62, and in Herman Finer, "Government and the Expert," *Bulletin of the Atomic Scientists*, XII, No. 9 (November, 1956), 331–32.

the character of their activity and the problems involved. The scientist (and many a nonscientist) must learn that the making of foreign policy is not a quest for the "right" answers to the problems of our time. There are only hard choices, the consequences of which will be uncertain and the making of which will often seem interminable in time and irrational in procedure.

The debate and disagreement over these choices will be heated and confused under the best of circumstances, but emotion and misunderstanding can be eased if scientists and nonscientists are both alert to the limits as well as the potential of the scientist's contribution. On the scientist's part, there is the obvious need to exercise the utmost care in making clear to himself and to others the areas where he speaks as a concerned citizen and those where he speaks as a professional expert. More difficult will be the task of learning how and to whom to address himself in each of these capacities when he is dissatisfied with the outcome of a policy decision in which he has participated. There is, as Don K. Price has pointed out, no clear code in Washington to govern the conduct of dissenting experts, only a "flexible" set of possible relationships with one's immediate superiors and those whose authority competes with or exceeds that of one's superiors. In contrast to the soldier, who can find some although not complete guidance in the doctrine of "civilian control," the very nature of the scientist's intellectual habits and many of his policy predispositions may make especially difficult his task in determining the limits to which he can stretch his dissent.[38]

On their part, the nonscientists need to recognize that scientists can hardly be expected to remain politically indifferent or inactive about the policy issues with which they are involved (especially when no one else in Washington practices such restraint). It was the naïveté of this expectation that was so appalling in the conclusion of the Gray Board that Oppenheimer was a security risk because (among other reasons) "he may have departed his role as scientific adviser to exercise highly persuasive influence in matters in which his convictions were not necessarily a reflection of technical judg-

[38] See the discussion in Price, *Government and Science*, pp. 131, 133, 138–42. The point about the scientists' lacking a tradition of civilian control was suggested by William T. R. Fox.

ment, and also not necessarily related to the protection of the strongest offensive military interests of the country." [39]

It is unlikely that civil-scientist relations will ever get any worse than this. With time and experience one can expect many of these problems to be eased, but it would be unrealistic to expect them to disappear. Military experts have participated in the making of foreign policy far longer than scientists, and the question of how they can best do so is still the subject of more than a little disagreement.

Policy processes and policy. In closing this discussion of scientists and the problems of their organizational and political relationships to others engaged in the determination of foreign policy, it is important to remember that the policy process can bring minds together but it cannot make them think. It is worth noting that in the political and administrative structure of the Soviet Union no scientist is as institutionally close to the Premier as is the Special Assistant for Science and Technology to the President of the United States and that there is no equivalent of the Science Advisory Office in the Russian Ministry of Foreign Affairs. [40] Yet one would not say that the foreign

---

[39] AEC, *In the Matter of J. Robert Oppenheimer, Texts of Principal Documents and Letters* (Washington, D.C., USGPO, 1954), pp. 19–20. Note the policy predisposition in the phrase "strongest offensive military interests."

It should not be comfortable for an American to reflect on the career of Peter Kapitsa, a Soviet physicist who was a student of Rutherford and who worked in England from 1922 to 1934 and then returned to the Soviet Union. Kapitsa was placed under house arrest in 1947 and remained there until after Stalin's death. Kapitsa has told Western scientists and newsmen that his arrest was the result of his refusal to work on nuclear energy for military purposes. Kramish believes that his arrest was due to the government's dissatisfaction with his advice on certain technical approaches to weapons development. In either event, it is noteworthy that Kapitsa is believed to have since become, on an informal basis, one of Khrushchev's main science advisers. On the matter of his arrest, see the report by Harrison Salisbury in the New York *Times*, July 11, 1956, the *Bulletin of the Atomic Scientists*, XIII, No. 1 (January, 1957), 38, and Kramish, *Atomic Energy in the Soviet Union*, pp. 109–110. The information on his recent activity was supplied by the staff of the Subcommittee on National Policy Machinery, Senate Committee on Government Operations.

[40] On Soviet government and science organization, see U.S. Congress, Report of the Subcommittee on National Policy Machinery, Senate Committee on Government Operations, *National Policy Machinery in the Soviet Union*, 86th Congress, 2d Session (Washington, D.C., USGPO, 1949), pp. 24–35, 59–62, and Nicholas DeWitt, "Reorganization of Science and Research in the U.S.S.R.," *Science*, CXXXIII, No. 3469 (June 23, 1961), 1981–91. The points made above were additionally confirmed by the staff of the Subcommittee on National Policy Machinery.

policy of the Soviet Union has appeared either ineffectual or insensitive in its response to developments in science and technology.

The circumstances attendant on the development of radar by the British from 1935 to 1940 provide a useful insight into both the potential and the limits of effective organization. Essential, obviously, were the scientific and technical ideas that Watson-Watt and his colleagues had in mind in 1935, ideas which in turn were the result of the earlier years of research they had been free to conduct in the facilities of a government laboratory. Certainly, it was important that there were administrative scientists in the Air Ministry who were so alert to the military problems of the Air Force that they could see on their own initiative the need to establish a special scientific committee for the study of air defense (the Tizard Committee) and who were so alert to the work of the scientific community that they made their first request for information to Watson-Watt.[41] Of consequence, too, was the fact that the personal and political relations of the members of the Tizard Committee with the members of the military, administrative, and political hierarchies whose interest and cooperation were vital for the subsequent progress of the research and development program were relations characterized by mutual ease, respect, and understanding.

But these conditions would not have led from the formation of the Tizard Committee in 1935 to a chain of operational radar stations by 1940 and a Fighter Command practiced in their use if it had not been for the military ideas of members of the Royal Air Force. It was they who first thought of the formation of a committee to look specifically into the problem of detection, they who recommended more funds than those first proposed by the Tizard Committee for the development of an electromagnetic detection system, and they who were responsible for the decision to start constructing the stations

[41] The circumstances provide an interesting variation of the "whole-problem approach." The Tizard Committee was initially interested in techniques for destroying aircraft or their crews, and Watson-Watt was asked in 1935 to investigate the possibility of using electromagnetic radiation for this purpose. He reported that such a use was apparently infeasible. In any event, he went on to note, the aircraft would first have to be located, and, if anyone was interested, electromagnetic radiation might be useful for this. Watson-Watt, *Three Steps to Victory*, pp. 81–83.

and training the personnel while the equipment was still under development.[42] The explanation for this interest and support is to be found in their theories about the next World War. They believed the Germans were planning to engage in the strategic bombing of Great Britain, and they wished to be prepared for it.[43]

The point is obvious but important. British scientists and science organization were in the final measure only ready tools. They were good tools, but the use to which they were put was the result of the kind of ideas the military men had about war. The same will hold in the other areas in which science may affect foreign policy. The contributions that science and technology will bring to international politics will largely turn, not so much on the particular arrangements of scientists in the policy-making process, but on the purposes of statesmen and the theories they have about the political world in which they live.

[42] For the development of radar, see *ibid.*, pp. 108–9, Snow, *Science and Government*, pp. 24–38, 60–61, 74–75, P. M. S. Blackett, "Tizard and the Science of War," *Nature*, CXXCV, No. 4714 (March 5, 1960), 648–49, and Basil Collier, *The Defense of the United Kingdom* (London, H.M. Stationery Office, 1957), pp. 33, 36–39.

[43] Ironically, the British were mistaken in their theory. The German Air Force had no such strategy in mind, and in 1940, when it tried to improvise a strategic bombing campaign, it had neither the equipment nor the doctrine with which to conduct the campaign effectively. See Herbert Dinerstein, "The Impact of Air Power on the International Scene: 1933–1940," *Military Affairs,* XIX, No. 2 (Summer, 1955), 65–71, Telford Taylor, *The March of Conquest* (New York, Simon and Schuster, 1958), pp. 24–30, and Adolf Galland, *The First and the Last* (New York, Ballantine Books, 1954), chaps. 2–5.

Strategy and the Natural Scientists

ALBERT WOHLSTETTER

Ford Research Professor
at University of California, Berkeley

ROLES OF SCIENTISTS IN ARMS
AND ARMS CONTROL

It will come as no news that, in one sense or another of the word
"science," scientists today crucially affect decisions on national and
international security; and therefore the fate of us all. After radar
and jets and the A-bomb and the H-bomb and intercontinental rockets this statement surely is obvious enough. But what does it mean?
Like much else that is obvious, it is not very clear. Just how do the
results of scientific research and the methods of science and the scientists themselves actually figure in decisions on arms and arms control? And how is the role of the scientist in such matters related to
the more familiar functions of the politician, the military man, and
the ordinary citizen? Above all, what does "scientist" mean in such
statements?

Even partial answers to these hard questions might help us deal
with some others that are harder and trouble us more. If by "science"
is meant a difficult and specialized discipline currently accessible
only to the few, a trained minority, what does this do to the democratic process? At the end of his term in office, President Eisenhower
spoke of the danger that "public policy could itself become the captive of a scientific-technological elite." On the other hand, scientists,
it seems, might become the captives. When scientists are drawn into
the pulling and hauling of "politics," what happens to the freedom
and objectivity of science or scientists? Again, defense decisions
must sometimes be made in secret for national ends in a partially
hostile world. Where scientists are involved in such decisions, what

does this mean for the vital features of science as a fallible but open, verifiable and self-correcting enterprise?

Especially in the two years or so since Sir Charles Snow's Godkin Lectures, discussion of these and related issues has been intense, sometimes bitter, and I think on the whole useful. But the issues have provided matter for both of Sir Charles's renowned "Two Cultures"—exciting literary material and a supply of blunt weapons for the factional quarrels and feuds among scientists. As a result, while there has been some light shed, there has also been much mystification. The Godkin Lectures begin with the dark words:

> One of the most bizarre features of any advanced industrial society in our time is that the cardinal choices have to be made by a handful of men: in secret: and, at least in legal form, by men who cannot have a first-hand knowledge of what those choices depend upon or what their results may be.
>
> When I say "advanced industrial society" I am thinking in the first place of the three in which I am most interested—the United States, the Soviet Union, and my own country. And when I say the "cardinal choices," I mean those which determine in the crudest sense whether we live or die.[1]

This opening sets C. P. Snow's major theme. In developing it he indicated that his cardinal choices are "scientific choices": [2] "government science," [3] a specific "domain of science." [4] And, as is now famous, he illustrated his theme with a dramatic story of the two English scientists, Sir Henry Tizard and F. A. Lindemann (Lord Cherwell) and their role in relation to the vital decisions on air defense and strategic bombing in England just before and during World War II.

If Sir Charles is right, the cardinal choices of the United States, the United Kingdom, and the Soviet Union can be directly understood only by scientists, and yet are and must be, "at least in legal form," made by nonscientists who are exposed to the advice of only a few. Sir Charles, who is at home in both the Scientific Culture and the Literary one, moves so easily from one to the other that we are

---

[1] C. P. Snow, *Science and Government* (Cambridge, Mass., Harvard University Press, 1961), p. 1.
[2] See, for example, *ibid.*, pp. 55 and 56.
[3] *Ibid.*, pp. 54–56.   [4] *Ibid.*, p. 55.

never quite sure how to take lessons from what he calls his "cautionary" tales. Are they literally true? Or are they literature? The critical response to the Godkin Lectures by less partisan participants in the events they describe suggests that these stories may be fables.[5] Nonetheless, even a fable may contain a useful moral: the troubling questions remain.

Distinguishing some of the many functions performed by scientists in national defense not only may clarify these hard questions, but it might conceivably improve performance of the functions. Some of these roles are easily confused. Administrators and Congressmen sometimes take scientists as experts in fields in which they are not; however, scientists themselves have not always been clear about the distinctions. It is not surprising therefore that the public

[5] Snow has published an *Appendix to Science and Government* (Cambridge, Mass., Harvard University Press, 1962). It is presented as an answer to his critics, but hardly fits the bill: It simply ignores most of the specific criticisms. Except for partisans in the quarrel, like Blackett who supplied the model for Snow's account, neither the principal participants in these events nor the records support Snow.

Perhaps the most important critiques of Snow's story of the role of Tizard and Lindemann are: Sir Robert Watson-Watt, "The Truth about Churchill's Aide," *The Saturday Review of Literature*, XLIV, No. 9 (March 4, 1961), 49–53; R. V. Jones, "Scientists at War—Lindemann v. Tizard," *The London Times*, April 6, 7, and 8, 1961. See also Jones's portion of the Biographical Memoir on Sir Henry Tizard, *Biographical Memoirs of Fellows of the Royal Society* (London, The Royal Society of London, 1961), Vol. VII, "A Partial View," a review of Snow's book appearing in *The London Times Literary Supplement*, April 14, 1961.

Watson-Watt and R. V. Jones are probably the most important witnesses on the radar, infrared and air defense issues. Jones's account has been checked against the records of the Air Ministry and of the Cabinet Offices involved. The official four-volume history, *The Strategic Air Offensive Against Germany, 1939–1945*, by Sir Charles Webster and Noble Frankland (London, H.M. Stationery Office, 1961), is the major source on the bombing controversy.

On bombing, Snow cites and quotes extensively from the official history, but fails to mention the summary evaluation of Snow's account by the senior author of that history, Sir Charles Webster, in his review of *Science and Government* in the London Sunday *Times*, April 9, 1961: "Sir Charles's method, to my mind, gives a very distorted view." The author of the review in *The Times Literary Supplement* said, in summary: "C. P. Snow follows these disputes through to the great bombing debates of 1942 when Cherwell and Tizard had their argument about the statistics of the damage which would be caused by Bomber Command. His analysis, however, is of little value because in this matter C. P. Snow loses sight of, or does not know, the facts. The bombing policy being attacked and defended was not Lord Cherwell's. It was not attacked by Sir Henry Tizard and it was not the policy described by C. P. Snow."

is somewhat confused. A little more precision, then, may be generally useful.

We might begin by looking more closely at C. P. Snow's account of the scientists and the "cardinal choices" in an industrial society:

> [W]hen I say the "cardinal choices," I mean those which determine in the crudest sense whether we live or die. For instance, the choice in England and the United States in 1940 and 1941, to go ahead with work on the fission bomb: the choice in 1945 to use that bomb when it was made: the choice in the United States and the Soviet Union, in the late forties, to make the fusion bomb: the choice, which led to a different result in the United States and the Soviet Union, about intercontinental missiles.
>
> It is in the making of weapons of absolute destruction that you can see my central theme at its sharpest and most dramatic, or most melodramatic if you like.[6]

These are the sorts of choices, then, which Snow refers to as "secret scientific choices," or a "domain of science and decision," and he makes quite clear what he includes under "science" and "scientists": "By 'scientists' here I mean people trained in the natural sciences, not only engineers, though I want them too."[7] Such a usage of the word "scientist" has become quite commonplace in the field of nuclear policy. It is a popular usage, and, since "science" is an honorific word, especially popular with the scientists so defined. Nonetheless it is worth pausing over. It contains some of the root confusions in discussions of the relation of science to the major decisions of governments.

Offhand, the definition would seem to be a case of semantic preemption. Or at least odd. Strictly, it would exclude mathematics, once known as the Queen of the Sciences; but the usage is not that strict. Rather more important, and odd, it would include a heating and air-conditioning engineer, say, and exclude an excellent political scientist or sociologist such as Edward Shils, or a distinguished and well-equipped economist like Paul Samuelson. These are matters of definition, one might say, perhaps only a poor or inappropriate choice of words. However, they are connected in Snow's account with matters of fact. Most important, in the limited sense of his

[6] Snow, *Science and Government*, p. 1.   [7] *Ibid.*, p. 80.

definition, the cardinal choices referred to by Snow are not simply, as he suggests, a domain of "science."

The decision at the start of World War II to develop a fission bomb, or the decision to use it against Japan, or the decision to develop an H-bomb, or to bomb German cities during World War II, called for much more than natural science and engineering. Such decisions have narrowly technological components, but they involve just as essentially a great many other elements: military operations and counter operations by an enemy, the economics of industrial production, the social and political effects of bombing on populations, and many others. Some of these other factors are qualitative. Many are quantitative, and in this very broad sense "technical." (They involve numbers and may be related in a numerical model.) However, even these latter do not fit into any of the narrowly technical traditional disciplines of natural science or engineering. They do not, for example, come under the heading of electrical engineering or physical chemistry. And natural scientists and engineers do not normally, in the course of acquiring their graduate degrees, acquire a professional acquaintance with subjects such as the cost of buying and operating a fighter bomber or the disaster behavior of urban populations. Nor do they ordinarily find these subjects essential in the course of engineering work in developing a bomb.

In fact, in addressing the complex cardinal choices, one of the inadequacies sometimes displayed by physical scientists in dealing with these larger questions is that they may ignore, or assume implicitly or simply receive, or themselves casually estimate without enough study the values of those variables that fall outside the traditional natural science disciplines. The cardinal choices, in Snow's sense, cannot be well made solely on estimates of the feasibility or infeasibility of some piece of hardware. They are political and military strategic decisions. Technology is an important part, but very far from the whole of strategy.

Snow is not the only one who makes the confusion. It is a very widespread practice among scientists concerned with public policy, and especially those who direct urgent popular appeals. The letter Bertrand Russell sent in 1955 to heads of state, enclosing a call for what later became the Pugwash Conferences, began: "I enclose a statement, signed by some of the most eminent scientific authorities on nuclear warfare." [8] The signers were indeed without exception eminent scientists, but among the ten physicists, chemists, and a mathematical logician who were included not one, to my knowledge, had done any empirical study of military operations likely in a nuclear war.

Similarly, at the head of petitions advocating some specific nuclear policy it is usual to find sentences that run: "As scientists we have knowledge of the dangers involved," [9] followed by the signatures of tens or even thousands of scientists, only a few of whom have examined the empirical evidence on more than one or two of the many alternative dangers involved in the policy choice. Simply as a scientist no one has a knowledge of these complex choices. For Snow this should be obvious, since Lindemann was an able physicist, admired, for example, by Albert Einstein.

Snow exhibits his rather innocent view of the matter by saying: "If he [Tizard, that is] had been able to submit the bombing controversy to the Fellows of the Royal Society, or the general population of professional scientists, Lindemann would not have lasted a week. But of course Tizard could do no such thing: and that is true of most conflicts in government science and of all secret choices." [10] The bombing controversy in 1942, as is not unusual in such policy disputes, was somewhat ill-defined.[11] It had to do, among other matters, with the relative emphasis in air strategy on offense or defense,

[8] Bertrand Russell, *Has Man a Future?* (New York, Simon and Schuster, 1962), p. 59.

[9] So the petition circulated by Linus Pauling in 1958 for a test ban, quoted in Russell, *ibid.*, p. 50. I might say that this is not a comment on the test ban. While I have disagreements with both of the principal scientific factions on the subject, I believe that a test ban with adequate controls has a positive though modest utility, and have consistently favored it for many years.

[10] Snow, *Science and Government*, p. 56.

[11] "We must be most careful," Air Vice-Marshal Bottomley wrote in 1940, "that our memos and correspondence are clear and not subject to misunderstanding, especially in war. . . . If we can't put out a useful clear helpful directive . . . it is better not to put anything out." Sir Charles Webster and Noble Frankland, the authors of the British history *The Strategic Air Offensive Against Germany*, remarked in connection with the bombing policy: "These admirable sentiments did not flourish in the confusion and controversy of war [Vol. I, 325n 1]." They hardly flourish even in peace, though there is more time then to cultivate them.

with how, for example, to allocate resources between the strategic bombing of German towns and the air defense of coastal shipping. Besides the choice of allocation between Bomber Command and Coastal Command, there were also the requirements for long-range reconnaissance in the Indian Ocean and the demands of the Army in the Middle East.[12] This is hardly the kind of thing one would normally submit to a decision of the Fellows of the Royal Society or the general population of natural scientists and engineers—and not simply, or in principle, because of the difficulties of secrecy.

A good answer to the allocation question depended on a great many things, including, on the one hand, how rapidly bombers would be manufactured, how soon after manufacture they could be made an operational part of the military forces, losses that might be expected from enemy defenses, the expected number of sorties in the operational life of these bombers, the shape and population density of German cities and the types of building in them, the efficiency of the German fire-fighting services, and the reaction of populations to the stress of air raids. On the other hand, it included the effectiveness of these same bombers against enemy ships of war,[13] the Allied shipping and supplies likely to be saved, the military worth of these supplies, etc., etc. These are not matters found in physics textbooks. Nor could the Fellows of the Royal Society be expected to qualify for independent judgment on them in the course of a week.[14]

Over a longer period, such questions are open to study, but, and

---

[12] *Ibid.*, pp. 325, 330.

[13] The use of Bomber Command's planes on the three German battle cruisers at Brest had been expensive and not very effective: "Between 10th December 1941, when Bomber Command had been directed to focus its principal attack on the three German battle cruisers at Brest, and 20th January 1942, no less than thirty-seven percent of the total Bomber Command effort had been harnessed to this unrewarding task. Such a state of affairs, though acceptable to the Air Staff before the *Gee* apparatus was ready for operations, became most irksome when they had enough sets to equip a reasonable proportion of the bomber force [*ibid.*, p. 320]."

[14] In fact, in a telltale footnote in *Science and Government*, Snow admits that "the controversy would have had to be submitted with a large amount of factual background," and adds, "It was precisely in the misuse of this factual background that Lindemann's statistics went wrong [Notes, p. 87n35]." But of course it is never clear just precisely what is relevant; and if all the facts and their relevance could be stipulated for the general population of scientists, the problem of solution might be trivial.

this is a critical point, they are open to study and answer by a much wider group than engineers and natural scientists. And at such study there is little evidence to suggest that the technologists are signally best. Not only are some of the principal variables subject matter for the behavioral sciences rather than physics, but the appropriate methods of study also may be closer to the methods of some behavioral sciences. P. M. S. Blackett, writing in 1943, not long after the bombing controversy, pointed out in an excellent essay on operational research that the mathematical methods he employed are in general use:

[I]n those branches of science whose subject matter has similar characteristics. These characteristics are that a limited amount of numerical data is ascertainable about phenomena of great complexity. The problems of analysing war operations are almost all of this type and are therefore rather nearer, in general, to many problems, say, of biology or of economics, than to most problems of physics, where usually a great deal of numerical data is ascertainable about relatively simple phenomena.[15]

Perhaps even more important, while the job of gathering and examining relevant empirical data might be very laborious, the gist of the methods for using the data is quite generally accessible. The methods are continuous with common sense, within the grasp of an intelligent administrator, and, given time, open to his skeptical questioning.

I would stress the phrase "given time." Without time on these complex questions, a government official is not likely to have a full understanding and may make some poor choices. This is also true, however, of the technologist or the analyst of tactics or strategies. One of the principal differences I want to bring out between our present situation in a long period of peace and the circumstances in which decision had to be made in World War II is that today we frequently have time. It is a salient difference bearing on the question of how technologists, strategists, and military and political men may figure in cardinal choices. The major peacetime decisions are seldom final. In short, given time, the decision-maker without a de-

---

[15] P. M. S. Blackett, "Operational Research," *The Advancement of Science* (Quarterly Journal of the British Association), V (April, 1948), 29. The original was circulated during the War.

gree in physics, mathematics, or for that matter, mathematical economics, is quite capable of having a "first-hand knowledge of what those choices depend upon or what their result might be." [16] And he often will have time.

In the view of some scientists it would appear that judgment on these matters does not really require time or a great deal of grubby work. It is, according to Snow, more a matter of intuition, an attribute of a few gifted men, a kind of "prescience." This quality evidently is present especially in scientists, that is, natural scientists and engineers, who have the "future in their bones." [17] They have, Snow tells us, "something to give which our kind of existential society is desperately short of: so short of, that it fails to recognise of what it is starved. That is foresight." [18] Foresight is "not quite knowledge," but "much more an expectation of knowledge to come . . . something that a scientist, if he has this kind of sensitivity latent in him, picks up during his scientific experience." [19] Some men other than natural scientists have this gift, but much more rarely and in a lesser degree. Snow, for example, compares unfavorably a memorandum of Stimson's which had a bit of prescience with the famous Franck report to the Secretary of War in June, 1945, written by a group of Chicago natural scientists.

It is the lack of this gift among administrators which kept a phrase from one of the old Icelandic sagas nagging at Snow's mind:

> "Snorri was the wisest man in Iceland who had not the gift of foresight."
> Foresight in this quotation meant something supernatural, but nevertheless the phrase stayed with me.[20]

"Nevertheless?" I would say the supernatural meaning fits rather well. This "prescience" has in it a good deal that is prescientific. It is related to the popular view of the scientist as wizard. Snow goes on:

> Foresight in this quotation meant something supernatural, but nevertheless the phrase stayed with me. The wisest man who had not the gift

---

[16] Snow, *Science and Government*, p. 1.
[17] C. P. Snow, *The Two Cultures and the Scientific Revolution* (New York, Cambridge University Press, 1959), p. 11.
[18] Snow, *Science and Government*, p. 81.   [19] *Ibid.*, p. 82.
[20] *Ibid.*, pp. 83–84. "Foresight," according to Snow, "in modern translation sometimes appears as 'prescience' [88n49]."

of foresight. The more I have seen of Western Societies, the more it nags at me. It nags at me in the United States, just as in Western Europe. We are immensely competent; we know our own pattern of operations like the palm of our hands. It is not enough. That is why I want some scientists mixed up in our affairs. It would be bitter if, when this storm of history is over, the best epitaph that anyone could write of us was only that: "The wisest men who had not the gift of foresight." [21]

Popular fantasies relating the pursuits of science to sorcery and to an almost superhuman thaumaturgy make such a view of prescience rather widely credible. Statesmen as well as laymen talk in these terms of the mysteries of science. Churchill entitled a chapter of his memorable history of World War II "The Wizard War," and began it with this explanation:

During the human struggle between the British and German Air Forces, between pilot and pilot, between anti-aircraft batteries and aircraft, between ruthless bombing and the fortitude of the British people, another conflict was going on step by step, month by month. This was a secret war, whose battles were lost or won unknown to the public, and only with difficulty comprehended, even now, to those outside the small high scientific circles concerned. No such warfare had ever been waged by mortal men. The terms in which it could be recorded or talked about were unintelligible to ordinary folk.[22]

"Human struggle," "mortal men," "ordinary folk"—a "secret war" of "small high scientific circles"—"unintelligible"—in this aura of unintelligibility it is not hard to accept superhuman endowments in the scientist. Snow's notion of a nearly preternatural insight that gives physical scientists a power of prophecy denied to lesser men, such as politicians, soldiers, and behavioral scientists, seems plausible. Comparable notions are rather commonplace in scientists' discussions of nuclear affairs. Russell again provides illustration: "Neither in America, nor in Russia, nor yet in Britain or France, did statesmen or public opinion show any of that long range wisdom which had inspired the best of the scientists," [23] he says, in talking of the postwar development of policy. And, in the same vein, on the appeals of the scientists at the end of World War II, he comments:

[21] *Ibid.*, p. 84.
[22] Sir Winston Churchill, *Their Finest Hour* (Boston, Houghton Mifflin, 1949), p. 381.
[23] Russell, *Has Man a Future?*, p. 27.

"The scientists were hampered by the fact that they were supposed to be unworldly men, out of touch with reality, and incapable of realistic judgments as to policy. Subsequent experience, however, has confirmed all that they said and has shown that it was they, and not the generals and politicians, who had insight into what was needed." [24]

We may not, as Mr. Eisenhower fears, become captive of a scientific elite, but it would seem from these quotations that scientists, or at least the best scientists, may indeed be The Elect. Many of them have felt charged with a prodigious mission and a great moral urgency. Spurred by an apocalyptic vision of world annihilation, they urge a drastic transformation in the conduct of world affairs in the immediate future. They have been passionately sure that the choices are stark and clear—annihilation on the one hand or a paradise on earth. "Remember your humanity, and forget the rest. If you can do so, the way lies open to a new Paradise; if you cannot, there lies before you the risk of universal death." [25]

For many of the scientists there is very little time. C. P. Snow predicted at the end of 1960 that if events proceed on their present course, nuclear war is "a certainty . . . within at the most ten years" [26]—which does not leave much time. The clock on the cover of the *Bulletin of the Atomic Scientists* started so near twelve that it had to be set back a while ago.

The scientists feel that they have a special responsibility in bringing about a new sort of world. They are free of the insincerities and dubious motives of the traditional actors on the political scene; they are interested only in clarification and truth.[27] Their very unpolitical character can help.[28] Furthermore, the cooperative and potentially universal nature of the scientific enterprise is at hand as a model for

[24] *Ibid.*, pp. 18–19.
[25] Call for the first of the series of conferences later named "Pugwash."
[26] C. P. Snow, "The Moral Un-Neutrality of Science," address to the 1960 AAAS meeting, reprinted in *Science,* CXXXIII, No. 3448 (January 27, 1961), 255–59. I have briefly discussed this and related predictions by scientists in "Nuclear Sharing: NATO and the N + 1 Country," *Foreign Affairs,* XXXIX, No. 3 (April, 1961), 360.
[27] See, for example, Leo Szilard, *The Voice of the Dolphins* (New York, Simon and Schuster, 1961), p. 26.
[28] See Russell, *Has Man a Future?*, p. 23.

a future world order, and the scientists can be vital agents in bringing that order about. "Scientists of the World Unite!," the title of an article by a Princeton physicist appearing immediately after World War II, sounds the right note.

This vision of the responsibility of the scientists, "a greater responsibility than is pressing on any other body of men," [29] puts him in a very different role from the scientist as technologist or the scientist dealing by tentative and empirical methods with broader questions or cardinal choices. It is fortified, however, by the confusion between technologist and strategist and by the related notion of the scientist as specially endowed, a seer or prophet.

The notion bears a strange resemblance to the image of the prophet in the chiliastic and apocalyptic movements which swept Europe centuries ago in times of great disorientation, anxiety, and instability. It has some inspirational uses, but a great many disabilities. Like past eschatology, it encourages schismatics, and the feuds among scientists have been intolerant and implicitly rather bloody. Snow's tale of Lindemann and Tizard unconsciously illustrates the point: Lindemann is the dark angel, sadistic and violent, without the gift of foresight. And Blackett, a tireless, passionate battler against the forces of darkness, uses the story in his innumerable present feuds.

But, most important, this urgent, tense feeling of mission can sometimes bias the technological studies, and even more tends to discourage the use of the patient and tentative method of science, as distinct from the *authority* of science, in assisting the cardinal choices of which Snow speaks. It has led in some cases to a rather surprising antirationalism.

As technologists, strategists, or seers, scientists affect decisions on national and international security—but in different ways. They play these roles well or poorly in many places. Some work inside the government, some as members of universities, institutes, or corporations under grants from or contracts with the government. Others who have no organizational connection with the government affect policy by the work they produce, sometimes unintentionally.

[29] Snow, "The Moral Un-Neutrality of Science," p. 259.

Some do it by such deliberate, overtly political activity as lobbying or leading mass marches. Let us look a little more closely at each of these roles.

TECHNOLOGISTS

Instead of always talking of "physical science and engineering," which is a mouthful, I will find it easier in what follows frequently to use the single word "technology." This short cut has some disadvantages, but on the whole smaller ones than the alternative of using the single word "scientist." My physicist friends never liked grouping electrical engineers with physicists as "scientists"; they are not altogether happy at putting physicists together with electrical engineers as "technologists." But for one thing the alternative usage, as I have suggested, implicitly consigns behavioral science to some nether world of non-science. And, in any case, stressing the engineering half of "physical science and engineering" is less misleading for my purpose, since I am concerned with the scientists only as they figure in cardinal choice, in decisions on what to make or do, and specifically with physical science as it affects the state of the physical arts. As shorthand therefore I will sometimes talk simply of "technology" and "technologists."

But under this head I include, first of all, a great deal of scientific work which is not explicitly directed at "hardware," even though it does frequently turn out to have such a use—and sometimes in unexpected ways. The Office of Naval Research, for example, has been outstanding in sponsoring such work, but a rather sizeable amount of all the work of scientists in government, in the employ of government contractors, or at universities is of this character. Half the basic research in the country has for some time now been financed by the federal government, and most of that by the military services and Atomic Energy Commission.[30] Needless to say, scientific work not sponsored by the government is done at universities and private corporations, and sometimes has enormous technical effects revolution-

[30] See Don K. Price, J. Stefan Dupré, and W. Eric Gustafson, "Current Trends in Science Policy in the United States," *Impact of Science on Society*, X. No. 3 (1960), 187–213.

izing problems of strategy. Nuclear technology and computer technology are only the most dramatic examples of this. There is of course no sharp line between science and technology, and so undirected science frequently has unintended effects on hardware.

Secondly, a large part of the research and development effort is overtly directed toward the design of hardware important in the functioning of national defense. Some of this or some analogous hardware would play a role in international security arrangements, either as the arms of an international force or as detection and identification devices for international control setups. The Bell Telephone Laboratories, which I will use as an example to make several of the distinctions I intend to elaborate, is perhaps the world's largest private industrial research laboratory. It devotes something like half its effort to the design of hardware for national defense.

The third sort of technological work done in connection with national security involves the operation of government technical facilities. For example, the California Institute of Technology operates the Jet Propulsion Laboratory; the International Telephone and Telegraph operates the Distant Early Warning (DEW) Line; Pan American Airlines runs Cape Canaveral for the government. This kind of activity does not require much explanation for our purpose.

A fourth category of science and engineering work for national security is more recent and therefore less familiar—the technical support of military operating commands. This may require a little explanation. It is in fulfilling this sort of function that the System Development Corporation of Santa Monica has used a couple of thousand people. It involves such tasks as taking the complex systems of hardware designed under the aegis of Lincoln Laboratory or Space Technology Laboratories and working with the operational commands, such as the Air Defense Command or the Strategic Air Command, for which these systems were designed, on their detailed adaptation to needs. So the System Development Corporation has worked out the detailed computer programs for the individual SAGE centers designed by Lincoln Laboratory for the Air Defense Command. It is similarly concerned with the adaptation of command and control equipment developed by MITRE and Lincoln Laboratory for the use of the Strategic Air Command.

A fifth category of technology, already mentioned, goes by the name, in current government jargon, "systems engineering and technical direction" or, more briefly and still more mysteriously, "SE/TD." Such systems engineering involves more than the design of a piece of hardware. It involves the coordination of the design of a great many hardware components and the design of a system which involves nonhardware components, namely, men. So Space Technology Laboratories and Aerospace have had the responsibility for engineering complex missile systems including not only the vehicles but the ground support of these vehicles. The design of the SAGE system by Lincoln Laboratory similarly involved among other things the complex meshing of ground radars, ground data handling, air defense control of fighter aircraft, the communication between radar sites, air defense control centers, and fighter pilots. The development of the so-called Geneva system for detection and identification of underground nuclear explosions involves such systems engineering. Systems engineering for arms and arms control bears a close relation to the design of conflict-solving systems or what I shall refer to briefly later as conflict systems. For the most part, however, it is a traditional or intermediate form between peacetime systems engineering and the explicit design of conflict systems.

In practice, systems engineering for such weapons systems or for international control systems bears more direct analogy with systems engineering as it has come to be understood in the peacetime communications and power industries. The Bell Telephone System, for example, (1) is technologically extremely complex, (2) involves a great multiplicity of interdependent components, men as well as machines, (3) uses the disciplines of psychology and economics as well as physics and the natural sciences, though to a much smaller extent, in determining such matters as the breaking point of human memory reached in lengthening telephone numbers,[31] as well as the breaking point for human patience in the length of a waiting line for completing a phone call. And the Bell planners try to look ahead for ten or twenty years. The complexity may be suggested by the fact that

---

[31] Judging superficially, from the emotions roused by the new all-digit telephone numbers the planners may have made a mistake in estimate here.

there are some 75 million stations in the country, each of which has to be connected up with every other by a variety of links involving microwave relays, coaxial cables, etc. It involves, in other words, some 75 million times 75 million connections—a very large number. The actual path of connections is determined by the state of the system at the time of the call, the links that are busy as well as the lines that are down or out of order because of weather or other causes.

The fearsome complexity of the Minuteman missile system then has some precedent in power supply and telephone systems, though there are different and sometimes wholly new technologies that are involved. Much of the work, moreover, in systems engineering in national defense has rather the same character as systems engineering in these peacetime fields. However, there is a basic difference between systems engineered for "normal" peacetime uses and systems that are designed for use in wartime or for keeping the peace in peacetime. Bell Telephone Laboratories made one of the first studies of a continental air defense system (CADS) in this country. The authors of several of the CADS reports stressed the enormously greater complexity of the continental air defense problem. However, the heart of the difference lies in something other than its great complexity. It is that systems designed for keeping the peace or fighting a war are "conflict systems," which I have yet to describe. This leads to the second major role of scientists that I have listed and that I have called loosely up to now "strategist." To be more exact, it is a role in the systematic study and design of the major alternatives for conflict systems.

I have constructed a variety of nonexhaustive categories and subcategories of technologists; before turning to the strategists I would like to break all these categories at the edges. Near the start of my list of five kinds of technological work in national security, I said that the line between category one, scientific research undirected at hardware, and category two, the explicit work of hardware design, was vague, uneven, and quite arbitrary. In fact all of these categories defy neatness, and it's a good thing they do. Just as within the sciences themselves connections among apparently unrelated fields frequently suggest new solutions, so there is a very fluid interchange among all of these sorts of work, and frequent shifts in function by the same person.

Far-fetched but fruitful connections are often seen by the men doing the research themselves, sometimes by men who spend much of their time viewing several fields and guiding research or giving scientific advice. But by its very nature much of the most useful scientific advice must be highly uncertain. It is heuristic; it points to some paths as fruitful, others as likely to lead to a dead end. Sometimes it is based on little more than experience and feeling. "It is in the nature of research," as Robert Oppenheimer has said, "that you pay your 'two bits' first, that you go in and you don't know what you are going to see." [32] Nonetheless, vague but fruitful hunches characterize all creative work from basic science to complex political military strategy. How they figure in the creation of even such highly precise and certain constructions as pure mathematics has been described by quite a few mathematicians of the first rank.[33] The human being, unlike most electronic automata up to now, performs search by much more subtle and complex methods than an exhaustive serial examination of all alternatives.

On the other hand, hunches as to what is feasible and likely to be useful are by no means the same as proof or experimental confirmation. And the implications of a technological change get hazier as these implications get further from the terms of natural science only. They can be much embroiled by the complexities of human conflict. This raises some critical problems. It is hard not to guess that something is feasible if you would like it to happen, and infeasible if you would like it to go away. Precisely where scientific advice may be most useful in finding new paths or avoiding detours, it can also set us off on a wild-goose chase; or worst of all, block inquiry. The distinguished men who have done creative work in some specialized field of science are precisely those whose hunches have paid off. Of course it has taken hard work to confirm these hunches. Even then

---

[32] J. Robert Oppenheimer, *The Open Mind* (New York, Simon and Schuster, 1955), p. 7.

[33] For example, see Jacques Hadamard, *The Psychology of Invention in the Mathematical Field* (Princeton, N.J., Princeton University Press, 1945). See also the writings of Felix Klein, Henri Poincaré, and George Polya.

past accomplishment confers only a limited ability to guide others in the same line of work. Gregor Mendel, after achieving his own greatest work in obscurity, took the advice of von Naegeli, a better known and distinguished botanist of the time, "to change from experiments on peas to work on hawkweed, a plant not at all suitable at that time for the study of inheritance of separate characteristics. The result was that Mendel labored in a blind alley for the rest of his scientific life." [34] Nonetheless, even where detailed confirmation has not been attempted, and even outside their specialized fields, the bare hunches of distinguished men are likely to carry much weight —in particular where the specialized success has been of spectacular general import.

The achievements of the Manhattan Project, then, endowed the casual judgments of even its humble participants with unexpected authority: "The scientists quickly discovered, to their embarrassment, that 'atom' was a magic word in Washington and that they, the only ones who fully understood its meaning, were looked upon as glamour boys. Some people, dimly conscious of the fact that they were up against a new kind of problem, regarded them as the men who knew all the answers." [35] As the physicist S. K. Allison described it:

Suddenly physicists were exhibited as lions at Washington tea-parties, were invited to conventions of social scientists, where their opinions on society were respectfully listened to by life-long experts in the field, attended conventions of religious orders and discoursed on theology, were asked to endorse plans for world government, and to give simplified lectures on the nucleus to Congressional committees.[36]

Or to quote another scientist, just after public disclosure of the Manhattan Project's success: "Before the war we were supposed to be completely ignorant of the world and inexperienced in its ways. But now we are regarded as the ultimate authorities on all possible sub-

[34] Bernard Barber, "Resistance by Scientists to Scientific Discovery," *Science*, XXXIV, No. 3479 (September 1, 1961), 600.

[35] Daniel Lang, "That's Four Times 10⁻⁴ Ergs, Old Man," *The New Yorker*, XXII, No. 4 (November 16, 1946), 91.

[36] S. K. Allison, "The State of Physics; or the Perils of Being Important," *Bulletin of the Atomic Scientists*, VI, No. 1 (January, 1950), 3.

jects, from nylon stockings to the best form of international organization." [37]

Though world government and high strategy continue to be subjects for the *obiter dicta* of physicists, their informal authority has somewhat narrowed in range since those first heady days of 1945. Nonetheless, neither the boundaries between the different kinds of technology nor those between technology and the other components of cardinal choice are water-tight, and informal advice easily spills over. It is hard sometimes to tell whether a physicist is talking about seismometers or Russian intentions. Informal advice is less likely to be constrained by professional canons of definition, relevance, and proof, and the hazards of confusion grow as the advice of technologists is applied in the arena of conflicting human purpose.

STRATEGISTS

Conflict systems and cooperative systems. To bring out the role of scientists in the analysis and design of conflict systems, let me start by saying something about the differences between such systems and others. For the ordinary purposes of peacetime communication, in telephony, for example, conflict plays only a rather minor part. Somebody in the Bell Telephone System has to worry about slugs or plugged nickels in their coin boxes, but in general Bell does not have to worry about anybody jamming their microwave relay as an interruption of their normal peacetime business.[38] This is precisely what distinguishes the "normal" everyday peacetime business of communication from a system for *keeping* the peace—or fighting a war. In designing a system for continental air defense or for retaliating after an attack, the role of an opposing will or intelligence is fundamental. Basic strategic or tactical choices are or should be

---

[37] Quoted by Robert Jungk, *Brighter Than a Thousand Suns* (New York, Harcourt, Brace and Co., 1958), p. 236.

[38] Because of this freedom from serious concern about an enemy, peacetime business is liable to interruption, for example, by cranks. Some eccentrics recently sabotaged a microwave relay in Utah and Nevada, stopping service for hours. While this was inconvenient, it was not critical for peacetime affairs. The saboteurs in fact intended the incident to be symbolic of what might happen in abnormal times, such as war.

made with an actual enemy or any of several potential enemies in mind. Such choices are designed to protect or to further your own interest in the face of actions which might counter it, that is, benefit your opponent at your expense. They are labeled with some accuracy "countermeasures." In the basic strategic choices, then, the interaction of another side's men and machines with our side's men and machines is the central problem. The interactions of the men and machines within our side are subsidiary—it is that part of the job that resembles the normal pursuit of peacetime design in power supply or telephone systems.

On the other hand, what I have described as systems engineering in the national defense field is by and large work in which the conflict elements are not in the center of the analysis. They are treated by assumption or suppressed. Most of the design work proceeds in terms of intermediate design objectives stated in physical terms. For example, one may design a missile system to achieve certain combinations of reliability, accuracy, or payload requirements. These requirements are in general given in the analysis, they are not the results of the systems engineering itself. They may, for example, be stated as requirements by the military users of the system. Thus in practice such weapons systems engineering very much resembles the traditional systems engineering of peacetime telephony.

It is usual in books on systems engineering in referring to a military system such as the Continental Air Defense System to stress that it is enormously more complex than, say, the Canadian post office with its automatic methods for sorting and routing mail, or the General Electric "Louisville System" which controls several factories using high-speed electronic data processing, or even the highly complicated Bell Telephone System itself. A well known text, for example, says: "Clearly, the air defense system is so enormous and so complex that we would scarcely begin to examine its problems even if there were no military secrecy involved." [39] The difference, however, I would stress again, is not simply or mainly one of size or complexity. More crucially it is that in military systems (but also in arms control

---

[39] Harry H. Goode, and Robert E. Machol, *Systems Engineering* (New York, McGraw-Hill, 1957), p. 34.

or disarmament schemes!) conflicting as well as cooperative interests are central.

Of course this does not mean that interest conflicts are not involved at all in what I have referred to as "normal systems engineering." I have begun by saying that they are. The distinction is not hard and fast, it is a matter of degree. However, in the normal systems engineering for familiar peacetime applications the conflict is rather minor. Perhaps it is significant that systems engineering has flourished in the utilities, such as power and communications, and in government, that is, places where competition has not been prominent. Engineering as straightforward applied physical science has been able to cope with such problems with only a modest call on other disciplines.

It is clear also that in the design of a weapon system to meet certain physical performance specifications the problem of the possibility of countermeasures is always at least latent. However, the very large volume of day-to-day work that goes under the head of systems engineering in national defense has only to a very modest extent concerned itself with the systematic investigation of the conflicting interaction of opposing strategies. It has largely been concerned with the application of natural science and sometimes the development of new physical technologies, and with the meshing of men and machines on our side. Even in the crash studies in which technologists have avowed an interest and, as Warner Schilling describes, the right to consider "the whole problem," they have concentrated on the technologies and the rest has been mainly presupposition and *obiter dicta*. The broad strategic issues have rarely been woven into the analysis.

The major choices in the field of national defense or arms control involve the selection of design requirements, objectives, or criteria for hardware, or they involve analogous selection of objectives for operation. They involve, in short, a critique of goals normally accepted as given in the systems engineering work described earlier. They are the kind of thing Snow has in mind in his "cardinal choices": the decision to develop the H-bomb, use the A-bomb, or devote a considerable proportion of the strategic-force budget to protecting the strategic force rather than simply to expanding it, and so on. In all such choices interactions with possible enemy strategies are essential and at least latent. Too frequently such choices have been made with only a very rudimentary consideration of such matters. What I mean by conflict systems design and analysis, however, is the *explicit* outline and study of alternative systems of interdependent parts where the comparative performance of a system is affected not only by the machines and the men who are elements in the system but also by the opposing behavior of men and machines outside the system. In particular, I mean the design of systems on the basis of an explicit analysis of the effects of opposing strategies.

Several observations are in order here. First, while conflicting interests are a major element in the systems that I am talking about, whether they are systems of arms or of arms control, nothing I have said implies that such conflicts are total in the sense that all the interests of the contending parties are in opposition, so that whatever one party loses, another party gains. It's conceivable that in some rather elementary conflicts among, say, the Congolese or Naga of not long ago, the victor might not simply gain what the vanquished loses —he might gain the vanquished. He could eat him. However, even conflicts among cannibals can turn out badly for both sides. They are not "total" in the sense defined. Both sides can be worse off at the end than when they started. Today, it is familiar to just about everybody that wars, and nuclear wars especially, may be a lot more complicated in the probable ending distribution of awards and penalties. It's likely that not even Bertrand Russell thinks that the mad generals in the Pentagon expect to eat their victims. Furthermore, it is clear to almost everyone that the outcome of a nuclear war could leave both sides worse off than they were at the outset. In short, while conflict is central in the problems that I am talking about under the head of conflict systems analysis, such conflicts are almost always partial —some interests are in common.

Secondly, in talking of the design of conflict systems it should not be but probably is necessary to stress that I do not speak of creating conflict, of constructing interests that are in conflict, of war-mongering. A casual, candid look at the world will convince us that conflicting interests exist in plenty. Conflict systems studies concern the design of systems to survive opposition, weather conflict, and operate and achieve aims in the face of conflicting aims. Such systems are conflict-worthy in the sense that a ship is seaworthy. One way of avoiding the misleading impression that conflicts are being created might be to say that the systems studied are "conflict-solving systems." But such a phrase is not only too long to use all the time—it has difficulties of its own. In achieving one's aims one might or might not want to reduce or eliminate conflict. It is true and important to say that conflicts may be resolved without fighting; also that some sorts of military preparation may intensify hostile fears and make a mutually destructive conflict more probable. Both of these points are relevant in the analysis and design of conflict systems. On the other hand, the stereotype that preparedness invariably makes war more probable vastly oversimplifies matters. By anticipating conflicts we sometimes make them less likely, and a failure to prepare against an attack has sometimes invited it. Moreover, fighting has been one way, if not the best, for resolving conflict.

Thirdly, the distinction between a national or alliance defense arrangement and a formal arms control or disarmament agreement with one's enemy rests largely on the degree of formality of the cooperation between adversaries. Many informal acts taken unilaterally in national defense might be in the common interest by stabilizing the situation, making accidental war less likely, for example, or by making less likely a war of any kind in which both sides suffered greatly. On the other hand, the formality of agreements does not abolish conflicting interests, and sometimes agreements can be perverted to further the interests of one side rather than another. This point, while obvious, tends to get lost by the natural scientists and engineers whose normal activities do not place the fact of conflict in the forefront of their work.

Importance of countermeasures. The description given of conflict systems makes plain the importance of an explicit consideration of countermeasures and counters to these countermeasures in an adequate design of strategies. This is always easier to recognize in the abstract than it is to observe in concrete practice. One designs a strategy, a system of operation, or some new equipment imbedded in a new system of operation, and almost inevitably conceives something of an affection for it. Especially if a great deal of work and intelligence have been expended on its elaboration, the possibility that an ingenious adversary might evade or spoil its performance is unpleasant to contemplate.

Politicians and military men have all at one time or another allowed their fondness for some pet scheme or device to lead them into wishful negligence of some obvious counter. And while some scientists have been both realistic and ingenious in this respect, there are a great many cases where they too have been wishful. When a man concentrates for years on a technically brilliant design of a warning system against a specified, rather straightforward sort of attack, he might very well be aggrieved at the specter of an enemy who simply flies around or over or under it, or worse, flies into it so frequently in time of peace as to destroy much of its utility in warning of the outbreak of war. It is easier to contemplate an enemy who flies into one's warning and defenses properly and at the right time. Such wishfulness has in the past led to concentration on what I have called "Western-preferred Soviet strategies," [40] which assume "artificial constraints on the Soviet use of the capabilities attributed to them" and which "suggest that the Soviet leaders will be rather bumbling, or better, cooperative."

Of course the Soviet leaders might be either or both. If so, one should be prepared to benefit by it. However, faced with an intelligent adversary who has some strong interests in conflict with our own, it would be imprudent to rely on either his total cooperation or his total stupidity and inertia. Any conscientious designer of a system which is intended to weather opposition must spend a large part of his time wearing the hat of his opponent. Since in the real world he is likely to have more than one potential opponent, and several allies with partially conflicting interests, this can get to be quite a hat trick. But wearing even two hats is something of a personal strain.

On my own observation, I would say that it is a rare scientist (or for that matter a rare anybody) who can with equanimity wear both

---

[40] Albert Wohlstetter, "The Delicate Balance of Terror," *Foreign Affairs*, XXXVII, No. 1 (January, 1959), 213. The phrase, "Western preferred Soviet strategies," is used in the longer version published as P-1472, the Rand Corporation, December, 1958.

of two hats: design a system well and then wholeheartedly knock it down; even as a preface to building it up again in a way that will sustain the shocks. More frequently you can find a scientist extremely ingenious in thinking up counters to a policy on his own side *rivalling* the one he is recommending. Then he can work up a little enthusiasm. (Then, in fact, he may be carried away, and devise for his rival a hypothetical enemy who is not merely ingenious, but hardly subject to any realistic limitation.)

Taking a possible enemy's countermeasures against one's own devices into systematic account is easier, of course, in time of war when he is there to remind you; when he is actual and not just possible. In peacetime, to analyze painstakingly the weakness in a policy one is proposing is painful, and may even seem masochistic. Wishfulness then is not subject to immediate test. Sometimes there is a practical dilemma. Ferreting out, for a hypothetical enemy, the weaknesses in a policy one is pressing and believes essential is almost sure to increase the normal resistance to it and may appear to be a diversion of energy. All of this is much worse in time of peace, but there are plenty of wartime instances too.

I can illustrate some of the foregoing with several examples drawn from World War II and its immediate prelude. (1) The first concerns the English invention of "Window," or as we in the United States call it, "chaff." Window consisted of small, appropriately cut pieces of metal which reflected radar waves. It was a cheap and effective way of confusing radar. The brilliant physicist, R. V. Jones, who made many vital contributions to the Allied war effort, proposed it in 1937. He has described the circumstances of his proposal in an unpublished lecture. The merits of radar and infrared were being argued. Despite Snow's indications to the contrary, it is clear that both Lindemann and Tizard supported both radar and infrared, though not with equal emphasis.[41] Jones was working on infrared as

---

[41] Lindemann's minority report, which caused the breakup of the Tizard Committee, pressed for still higher priority to radar, called for placing not only radar but the new communications needed to make it effective under the brilliant Watson-Watt. (R. V. Jones, "Scientists at War—Lindemann v. Tizard.") Tizard's interest in infrared was great enough for him to ask Jones to leave Lindemann's Clarendon Laboratories and work on it in Tizard's own shop at the Imperial College. (R. V. Jones, unpublished lecture, July 19, 1962.)

a complement to the current radar to make up for its probable deficiencies at close range. There was some talk of shutting down research on infrared because of its vulnerability to countermeasures. It was then that Jones, according to his own amusing account, came up with the idea of Window which showed to those stressing radar that "they weren't so invulnerable themselves." Lindemann, who had been backing infrared very strongly, loved it.

(2) Whatever the circumstances of its proposal, Window was clearly an important thing to push, both as a possible weapon against German radars and as a preliminary to studying the possibility of counter-countermeasures to preserve the functioning of English radar. The Battle of Britain hinged on radar's effective operation. Yet it would be understandable if the authorities responsible for British radar, including Watson-Watt, its prime inventor, found it hard, as Jones suggests, to back tests of something aimed at spoiling the performance of what Watson-Watt has correctly called his "beautiful invention." (His phrase, to render it more exactly, is "my beautiful and invulnerable invention," which is less accurate and more poignant.) Tizard, who was bending all of his fruitful efforts at integrating radar into the British Air Defense System, also never quite had the time and the heart to order trials for this device, which the Germans had conceived of but fortunately had not developed for operational use by 1940. (There may have been some parallel emotions on the German side.[42]) Delaying tests of Window was not obviously wrong. To demonstrate the vulnerability of radar might have built resistance to its installation. In any case, it meant taking some effort away from the vital task of getting radar in place. Nonetheless, if the Germans had developed Window and used it in the Battle of Britain in 1940, this crucial decision in World War II and, indeed, in history, might have gone the other way. It wasn't until early 1942 that at the instigation of Lindemann trials of Window were carried out. They were a great success in jamming both ground and air-borne British radar.

(3) In spite of its proven potency, the British delayed in using

---

[42] See Sir Winston Churchill, *The Hinge of Fate* (Vol. IV of *The Second World War*, Boston, Houghton Mifflin, 1950), pp. 256 ff.

Window against the Germans. A contemporary suggests that those concerned with defense radar found it hard to see even German defense radar spoiled. Be that as it may, those responsible for air defense in England, had in any case, to fear that the English use of Window might lead to its use by the Germans against English defenses. And Lindemann, it appears, was persuaded by this argument.[43] But even if both sides used this countermeasure, it seems the English would have gained decisively more at any time after the middle of 1942. So, at any rate, if R. V. Jones is right.[44] Such issues are seldom open and shut, and I have not myself gone through the calculations of net advantage. Nonetheless English Intelligence by the end of 1942 had established that (1) the German bomber force was decimated and deeply engaged in Russia and not in a good position to exploit the use of such a countermeasure against the English defenses, and (2) the Germans already knew the principle of Window. This last point meant at least that the British would not be telling the Germans much in displaying the device. It was also argued by Jones at the time that the German failure to develop their own device meant that they knew well where the net advantage lay. This argument is less convincing, since we might imagine a German Jones making the same argument about the British. Nonetheless when finally used in mid-1943, Window reduced English bomber losses to fighters over Hamburg by nine-tenths and there was no comparable gain by the Germans. Jones believes that "the fundamental opposition to our own use of 'Window' was not based on disinterested rational grounds. It arose because—like the Colonel on the River Kwai—some of our own authorities most closely associated with radar could hardly bring themselves to face a countermeasure that might greatly reduce the effectiveness of the system they had built up, and they were at least subconsciously trying to postpone an evil day." [45]

[43] See Earl of Birkenhead, *The Professor and the Prime Minister* (Boston, Houghton Mifflin, 1962), p. 256.
[44] R. V. Jones, *The Radio War*, quoted in the Earl of Birkenhead, *The Professor and the Prime Minister*, p. 256; see also R. V. Jones, "Emotion, Science and the Bomber Offensive," *The Listener*, LXVI (November 30, 1961), 207–9.
[45] R. V. Jones, "Emotion, Science and the Bomber Offensive."

Each of the three aspects of this one case illustrates the difficulty technologists feel in destroying their own as distinct from a rival device, and therefore in wearing two hats.

Anyone who has searched diligently for a device which in hostile hands might demolish what he had been building the previous year is not likely to forget the sickening sensation of finding it. Yet that is the occupational hazard of a working strategist, a conscientious and systematic designer of conflict systems. An honest strategist doesn't need an enemy—or even a Hungarian friend.

That is, he doesn't need a reminder. Yet most of us do. In time of peace we easily forget that keeping the peace obliges us to envisage concretely the possibility of war, always, that is, to wear at least two hats.

Wearing two hats is not only something of a personal strain; it can actually lead to quarrels among friends, or at least organizations, on the same side. I could more than match these English illustrations with some American examples in the postwar period. The inventor of an ingenious measure may come to regard the inventor of an even more ingenious countermeasure with some distaste or even detestation. Whose side does the fellow think he is on?

All of which is true enough for the design of some national or alliance weapon system for possible use in a war. The personal strain and the strain on friendship is likely to be even worse where the system to be designed is an international control system. For while in a national defense measure the element of opposition by an enemy in time of war is, and even in time of peace should be, as plain as can be, it is not so plain in the case of an international system. Here one has an agreement with an adversary, and it is even more tempting to believe that he will cooperate. A cooperative or Western-preferred strategy is even more frequent and a scientist who works on evasion schemes is almost certain to be regarded as a leper. Isn't he opposing the agreement and ruining the possibility of international control? This is a nearly universal attitude. It was frequently voiced in protest against studies of possible ways to evade the test ban. Now it may be that for the psychological reasons I have already described some of the men who find it easiest to work on evasion schemes are those who oppose the agreement. Nonetheless anyone who is soberly in favor of an agreement with adequate safeguards should systematically and seriously wear both hats all the time.

I will give just two illustrations of how in the case of the test ban the two principal opposing factions have each found it hard to deal with countermeasures, except where they support a point of view propounded anyway.

First Edward Teller: Dr. Teller in my view has performed an important service for anyone looking for a test ban with adequate controls by thinking ingeniously about the possibilities of evading the various control systems that have been proposed. On the other hand, when it has come to supporting his views on the importance of testing, he has suggested that we would lose more than the Russians would if we both stopped testing. As the victim of aggression, in contrast to the aggressor, we have a harder job. Therefore, he reasons, testing will enable us to develop the more sophisticated weapons we need for use in defense. However, in this argument he ignores the fact that the Russians will also be developing their weapons of aggression as counters to our defense, and there is no *a priori* reason for believing that they won't make more rapid increases in their "easier" job than we in our difficult one. In the past the development of nuclear weapons has favored the offense. In short, when it comes to the exploitation of tests in the development of weapons, Dr. Teller ignores countermeasures—they do not suit his argument. He has been extremely ingenious in considering enemy countermeasures in control systems—these countermeasures do suit his argument.

Next Hans Bethe: Dr. Bethe has been the symmetrical opposite of Dr. Teller on this matter as on others. As far as evasion schemes are concerned he has said that he was embarrassed at presenting to the Russians the possibility conjured up by another American because it "implied that we considered the Russians capable of cheating on a massive scale. I think that they would have been quite justified if they had considered this an insult." [46] This suggests that it is all right to set up a police system, but not against potential crooks. His own energies in any case were devoted to the measures rather than the

---

[46] Hans Bethe, "The Case for Ending Nuclear Tests," *The Atlantic Monthly,* CCVI, No. 8 (August, 1960), 46.

countermeasures. On the other hand, when it came to evaluating the military worth of weapons that might be developed with the aid of testing, for instance, antimissile missiles, Dr. Bethe could frequently think of nothing except enemy countermeasures which would reduce their military worth to nearly zero. Dr. Bethe, like Blackett, is, without any extensive strategic study, quite certain that enemy countermeasures such as decoys would make a defense against ballistic missiles useless, or even harmful, in any reasonably likely contingency.

Two points are suggested by this discussion of countermeasures. First, physical scientists and engineers may find it hard to deal with an enemy countermeasure, except where it spoils a system they themselves dislike on other grounds. This, I believe, is sometimes associated with an aversion to focusing their attention on the fact of hostility. In a profound comment on the scientific investigation of nature, Einstein once remarked: "Der Herr Gott ist raffiniert, aber boshaft ist Er nicht." What is true of nature, however, is unfortunately not necessarily the case for countries with conflicting interests. They are sometimes not merely subtle, but "plain mean." Many of the articulate scientists, especially when considering arms control agreements, prefer to think of harmony rather than conflict. The difficulty they have in contemplating countermeasures stems from hostility to the fact of hostility itself. In this way they slip more easily into the role of prophet and agent of a perfectly peaceful world.

The second point is that the valuation of countermeasures in military conflict systems is likely to be very complicated and to require painstaking analysis, seldom undertaken by the technologists themselves. It involves for one thing an extensive canvass of potential military operations on both sides and their possible interactions. I believe neither Dr. Teller nor Dr. Bethe has done this sort of systematic analysis of the military worth of the weapons they talk about. Both are experts in the basic technology of bomb design— but that is quite another matter.

Conflict system design in the major countries. Questions of military worth are broader than physics and in some ways harder. They are of course not purely military questions any more than they are purely technological. They may involve a forbidding nest of problems including political and economic as well as military and technological questions. However, in the questions that have called for systematic analysis, characteristically there has been no experience precisely in point: They refer to a near or distant future affected by novel techniques and political uncertainties. Experts are seldom "expert beyond experience," and analysis is needed, not to replace intuition, but to sharpen, supplement, and make it more public and verifiable.

In England especially, during World War II, systematic empirical analysis of tactical alternatives had its first notable successes. And in England as distinct from the United States some of the best known scientists were engaged in this activity. P. M. S. Blackett was one of the founding fathers. The kind of decision assisted by such analysis was, for example, the choice of effective search patterns for a given destroyer force to use in locating submarines along specified routes.

The English called this study of tactical choice "operational research," and in the United States it was called "operations analysis." Of course it continues today in both countries. Some contemporary examples might be the analysis of methods for releasing a nuclear bomb at low altitude, or efficient methods of sampling in some specified inspection systems for an arms control arrangement.

Such choices are important, but they are clearly smaller choices than those Snow refers to as "cardinal." In the cardinal choices the decision is on strategy rather than tactics. For example, in shaping a deterrent force that will not be operational for several years, we may ask: How can we allocate new resources for this force between expanding it in number or protecting it? This has been a strategic issue of fateful importance, but one that was studied, hotly contested in a classified forum, and to a considerable extent acted on years before it became public knowledge. Almost all of Snow's own examples involve similarly broad issues that, with the exception of the decision to develop the A-bomb, were debated in public. One that Snow cites might be rephrased explicitly as an allocation question: Should resources in the research and development of nuclear weaponry be devoted to developing a fusion bomb or should an increase in resources be concentrated on fission weapons for theater warfare and air defense?

The systematic study of such broader and more complex issues was called "systems analysis" in contrast with "operations analysis" by Edwin Paxson, a pioneer in the development of some of its techniques after World War II. For our purpose Paxson's term is too close to the well-entrenched phrase "systems engineering," which designates something rather different. As is clear from my description in the preceding section, conflict is not as essential a consideration in systems engineering and it makes much less call upon the behavioral disciplines. Since defining the role of the various scientific disciplines in cardinal choice is part of my purpose, to reduce confusion I use the word "strategy" or "strategic studies" mostly to describe research on the major and longer-run alternatives in the design of conflict systems. And I reserve the words "operations analysis" or "operational research" for the same sort of study of the small and short-run alternatives.

My choice of language deliberately suggests that there is no sharp dividing line between operational research and systematic strategic studies. "Strategic" contrasts with "tactical" as "big" contrasts with "small," "tall" with "short," or "near" with "far." But I draw the faint line somewhat farther on the "far" side than was customary during World War II. Operational research, as the name suggests, concerned how best to operate with given forces and specified equipment. During World War II one talked of its application to strategy. What was then referred to as a strategic problem, for example, the brilliant plan for submarine search in the Bay of Biscay, had to do with the management of large, but specified forces. Such a use of the vague word "strategy" was clear enough for the purpose. For peacetime research, however, the time scale for possible conflicts and the lag between decision and effect is much more extended. It is useful now to reserve the word "strategy" for longer-run as well as large problems. In that case the choice lies not merely among alternative operations, as in operational research, but also among forces of different size and composition, and with alternative equipments, most of which may as yet be nonexistent.

The quantitative methods of science, as might be expected, were less helpful on the broader issues of World War II than on the smaller ones. In the typical operational research problem on tactical alternatives there was a relatively small number of interdependent variables, and some proximate objective rather obviously desirable, suggesting an appropriate criterion. For the larger issues operational research techniques were likely to be used, if at all, on only a fragment of the problem. Some of these points may be illustrated once again by the disagreement of Tizard and Blackett in 1942.

The famous calculations of Tizard, Lindemann, and Blackett were rough and ready and related only to a small part of the wider problem of allocating resources among Bomber Command for use in a strategic offensive, Coastal Command for use against U-boats and the protection of Allied shipping, and, wider still, the Middle East and Far East Commands. The issues between the men were not very precisely defined and the clash was not head on.

Lindemann meant his calculations to be merely illustrative. He had no definite time in mind by which the bombing was to be completed and summed up the results vaguely as "catastrophic." Tizard was not opposed to the bombing policy, and did not deny that it would be "catastrophic." He just said it would not be "decisive"— which Lindemann did not deny. Neither would the use of aircraft against U-boats be decisive. The criterion of decisiveness was really relevant only for an all-or-none allocation decision: all for Bomber Command, say, or all for Coastal Command. But Lindemann did not disagree with Tizard on this point either. He wrote to Tizard: "You say that 689 Wellingtons are earmarked for Coastal Command, and should therefore be subtracted. This is a matter of policy, which may, and probably should, be decided in that sense." [47] There is, so far as I know, no public record or claim that either attempted calculations for the allocation problem as such. To do this would have meant, at the least, measuring the contribution of additional resources made to Coastal Command as well as to Bomber Command (in fact the Wellingtons' performance in attacks on shipping was uncertain too), and would have meant comparing the contribution in each case in terms of some over-all common objective. This in turn would have required time for thought about criteria and, in order to be sound and realistic, would have presented formidable analytical problems, though it would not have taken very fancy mathematics.

[47] Earl of Birkenhead, *The Professor and the Prime Minister*, p. 264.

(The arithmetic involved in the calculations performed was roughly of the order of that required to fill out a tax return, and would not tax most Cabinet members with the time to go through them—even Cabinet members drawn from the Other Culture.)

The famous men in England who were involved in operational research for the most part ceased to be concerned with that sort of work after the War, and the principal choices affecting the West shifted to the United States. In the United States, however, the best known and most outstanding of the scientists who made their reputations before or during the last war, were in general concerned neither with operational research nor the quantitative study of strategic alternatives. For the most part they were concerned with technology —with the development of the bomb, or radar, or the like. This continues to be the case in spite of the fact that very many of these technologists have strong views on the strategic alternatives. For the most part these views have been arrived at informally.

Of course most decisions on the cardinal choices are made informally, with a less than systematic weighing of pro and con. Such problems are in general so complicated that to a large extent this will very likely always be so. Moreover, in the nature of the case, the systematic studies are fallible themselves and will frequently be in error. However, we need as much systematic illumination of these issues as we can get. The murk is very dark indeed, and we can benefit by lighting even a corner briefly. Moreover, some quantitative empirical studies of strategic alternatives have turned up new strategic concepts and new recommendations in both hardware and operations, and some have stood up very well. It would have been hard to arrive at the recommendations of these studies by unaided intuition, or to convince anyone if you had.

Some of these studies have in recent times been declassified and offer useful examples of empirical analysis of a complex policy choice. Certain major differences between this kind of study and operational research on tactical alternatives in World War II are implicit in the description already given of the latter: (1) they refer usually to a more distant future in which both we and our adversaries have greater flexibility for choice, including the choice of new equipment; (2) as a result there are many more interdependent variables to be considered; (3) the uncertainties are much larger; (4) objectives and rules of choice are much less obvious. The problems plaguing the analyst near the outset are likely to be even more confused than the issues confronting Lindemann and Tizard on strategic bombing.

Another difference, sometimes stated, for example, by former practitioners of operational research in World War II, is that World War II operational research had a great deal of data available, whereas strategic studies in the postwar period do not. This belief has encouraged casual judgments on such issues as the problems of deterrence and the vulnerability of strategic forces, on the grounds that no empirical evidence exists in any case. The belief is quite mistaken. Of course we have no wartime operational data drawn from World War III, and hope we never will. On the other hand, there are plenty of relevant data, some of it in better form now than then. Voluminous data has been derived from peacetime operations and logistics, tests of existing equipment and components in future equipment, theoretical analyses of equipment design, state of the arts studies, and intelligence on enemy operations.

Both wartime tactical analysis and the present peacetime strategic analysis need and use data. Moreover, for an analysis of phenomena such as surprise attack, the peacetime operational data have direct relevance: the victim would be found at outbreak in the middle of his peacetime operations. No sensible and warranted conclusion about matters like the threat of surprise attack is possible without empirical knowledge of such questions as the actual location and performance of radars with respect to the bases they might alert, methods of raid recognition, the time needed to make the vehicles on the bases ready, their pattern of peacetime movement, the number of target points they present, the arrangements for sending and receiving go-orders, and many other matters.

Blackett pointed out in an article written during the War and published afterwards that operational research had to be done in or near operations rooms, since the operational data "are not, and on secrecy grounds, cannot, in general, be made available to the technical establishments." [48] The situation has not changed for quantitative

---

[48] Blackett, "Operational Research," p. 27. While Blackett himself once understood this very well, his writings since the War forget it. See his "Critique of

empirical research on tactical and strategic issues today in time of peace. Yet it is not widely understood. A famous physicist who writes a blurb on the realism of a thrilling novel about fail-safe procedures and accidental war is likely to endow such thrillers with an authority they do not merit and which on this subject he scarcely has to transmit. The popular assumption is that within the classified community information flow approaches perfection, that data accessible to one man with clearance is accessible to all. Nothing could be further from the truth. To a very large extent, as Blackett says, the men who advise on technology or work in the technical establishments designing weapons are well enough informed for their own day-to-day technological tasks, but are seldom in possession of either the data or the time essential for evaluating strategic and tactical issues. Confusion on this subject in the minds of both the scientists and the public is one of the things that makes it hard to discriminate between the quite distinct roles of technologist and strategist.

The opportunity for serious evaluation of strategic choice by the public is even more limited. This without a doubt raises grave questions for the democracies. One is the basic problem of how, in keeping some information from the enemy, we can avoid so limiting its use by our own experts that we wipe out any relative gain. Another is the familiar and critical problem of controlling the experts in government, those in executive or advisory roles. Another, less frequently discussed, is the demagogic opportunities for exploiting the fact of secrecy by the government's critics. The political storm over Intelligence during the recent Cuban missile crisis provides an example that should make us thoughtful. Russell Baker's satiric recipe for becoming a one-man senatorial investigating committee includes the following sequence of basic press releases: " '(1) Senator Survine announced today that he is undertaking a one-man investigation into charges . . .'; 'Senator Survine called upon the CIA today to

---

Some Contemporary Defence Thinking," *Encounter*, XVI, No. 4 (April, 1961), 9–17, and especially his *Atomic Weapons and East-West Relations* (Cambridge, England, Cambridge University Press, 1956) where he insisted that the public is hardly any worse off than governments in evaluating defense issues, and then based much of his analysis on the assumption, known to be wrong in the classified community at the time, that hydrogen warheads could not be put in rockets and on a considerable number of erroneous operational assumptions as well.

issue all the facts about Americans engaged in espionage inside Cuba . . .'; 'Senator Survine revealed today that the CIA had refused to meet his demand for all the facts. . . .' " [49]

Such implausible appeals for candor about aerial reconnaissance or other intelligence on potential adversaries and ourselves have issued from both political parties, depending on which one was out of power. And scientists have sometimes been identified with these appeals or made some of their own. So Professor Blackett called on Klaus Knorr to produce convincing evidence on how it would be possible at the time for Russia to achieve an effective first-strike against American strategic forces.[50] Scientists sometimes, it seems to me, have oversimplified the issues of secrecy. Snow alludes to the problem and I shall return to it. Here I will only say that I believe there is no total solution, but part of any improvement in the matter is to recognize that there are limits. This might to some extent restrain both casual expertise and other forms of demagogy. The problem is not new. During the debates on the British bombing policy in 1942, the historians of the bombing offensive against Germany tell us that among those Sir Archibald Sinclair had to face was a group of "irresponsible and ill-informed members of Parliament" who used some "most peculiar operational arguments," and yet Sir Archibald could "make no mention of the most important consideration of all, the introduction of radar navigation. . . . This fact serves to illustrate the limitations of the public discussion of war policies." [51]

These are not just wartime limitations. They affect the limitations of public discussion of defense today. In this respect there is no essential difference between operational research in time of war and conflict systems analysis in time of peace.

One difference between wartime and peacetime research is central and obvious enough in its immediate meaning, but rather more subtle in its extended consequences. It affects the crucial problem of how to treat conflict in peacetime. In peacetime because combat

[49] Russell Baker, the New York *Times*, western edition, March 5, 1963, in his column entitled "Observer."

[50] Blackett, "Critique of Some Contemporary Defence Thinking."

[51] Webster and Frankland, *The Strategic Air Offensive Against Germany*, Vol. I, pp. 330–31.

with the enemy is only potential, even the degree of hostility of his interests is less certain, more questionable and fluid—possibly, one can always hope, not really there at all, overridden by the interests he shares with us in avoiding combat. When we are locked in combat, we know the enemy has at least some interests opposed to ours, because he is shooting at us. Then hostility is likely to seem unremitting, unconditional, total. It is not even then. We have something in common even with an enemy in actual combat. In peace we tend to the opposite extreme.[52] It is quite true that short of such implausible extremes there are factual difficulties in measuring what a potential adversary will get out of opposing us. And this is one of the persistent problems of conflict systems analysis in peacetime.

Most of the differences I have listed make the postwar systems studies of strategic alternatives more difficult than World War II operational research on tactics. However, these differences also suggest why the postwar studies are even more essential. The differences are traceable to the fact that the problems are harder and still further beyond the reach of the unaided intuition of experts, whether they are technologists, military men, or statesmen. There are fortunately a few respects in which we are better off today. One is that we have much better computing facilities and technical aids. Another, much more important, which I have already hinted at, is that there is in general more time, more time for the study and more time for its criticism and review at many levels of the government.

The studies that have worked out best have focused less on the mathematical manipulations of the analysis (these are indispensable, but quite subordinate) and much more on a careful framing of the questions, a critique of the accepted goals, a cautious interpretation of the limits of the analysis itself, and a patient treatment of the areas of uncertainty. A conflict-system study will not eliminate uncertainty. Indeed, the handling of the uncertainties is one of the

---

[52] Many writers have suggested that the wartime extreme follows the peacetime one naturally. The enemy in war is absolutely evil, partly because by making war he betrays our picture of him as sharing with us all essential interests in peace. American tendencies in time of war toward unpolitical military extremes, Dean Acheson suggests, are a kind of outraged pacifism. Mr. Kennan and others have made similar observations.

most important measures of its sophistication and adequacy. A principal aim of such a study should be to design a system which can live through a variety of uncertain contingencies. This removes the need for prophesying intuitively and without error the technological and political cataclysms actually in store. You can get along then fairly well even without "the future in your bones."

One detailed conflict-systems study,[53] done between the spring of 1951 and the spring of 1953, constructed and analyzed broadly different alternative ways of basing and operating strategic forces for the decade of the 1950s. The best of the systems evolved was shown to be able to withstand a large number of political disasters (losses of base rights, etc.) as well as a considerable range of hard luck in the relative technical and operational developments of Russian forces compared to our own. It performed well in achieving each of our shifting major objectives—in particular, the vital one of deterring a well-designed first-strike. On the other hand, the system of basing and operation that had been officially programmed would not have been able to weather attack by an enemy with one-tenth the nuclear capability then attributed to the Russians for the relevant time period—and that in an era, we know now, when the intelligence estimates were optimistic from our point of view.

The system evolved in the course of the study was not intended to consider every possibility, no matter how fantastic. However, it did soberly canvass not only the "most probable" case, but any one that appeared likely enough to be worth considering at all. In this way it came to consider, along with many circumstances that turned out in the event not to be relevant, the essential contingencies for the period. The authors were far from prescient, and fortunately did not have to be. Rather such a study illustrates the improvements possible without prescience. In reliability of performance as well as cost the system dominated the one programmed earlier by a great margin. The analysis clarified some of our key strategic objectives, and, in particular, the crucial importance of a distinction between a first-strike and second-strike capability.

---

[53] Described in Chapter 3 of *An Appreciation of Analysis for Military Decisions*, E. S. Quade, ed., to be published.

The distinction itself and the problematic nature of a second-strike capability were hardly understood among the physical scientists, mathematical logicians, and engineers writing on nuclear policy. A typical comment might be cited from Hans Bethe:

> Our cities may be devastated. . . . But it would not seriously affect our power for immediate retaliation. Our atomic bombs . . . and our planes will presumably be so distributed that they cannot all be wiped out at the same time, and would hence still be ready to take off and reduce the country of the aggressor to at least the same state as our own.[54]

The adverb "presumably" contains a world of wish and hardly suggests an awareness either of programs then current or of the enormous complexity of the problem of "distributing" and protecting all of the many elements of a system required for retaliation. In Lord Russell's thinking, as recently as 1959, the adverb "presumably" plays the same casual role:

> [O]n the Western side, and presumably also on that of Russia, great pains have been taken to insure that a surprise attack shall not be decisive and shall not make retaliation impossible. I think we must, therefore, assume that the full potentialities of nuclear devastation will be developed against East and West equally.[55]

Among other things, such a statement seems to assume rather untypically that anything the chaps on either the Eastern or the Western side take pains to assure will definitely come about. Russell's discussion of the accident problem is similarly plagued with vague presumptions: "Since it is assumed, probably rightly, that a Great Power, if embarked upon nuclear war, would begin by destroying the seat of government of the enemy, it is inferred that subordinate commanders must not wait for orders from headquarters but must carry out plans previously arranged to meet the emergency."[56]

The imprecision of the language, "it is assumed, probably rightly," "it is inferred" (by whom?), displays a rather standard innocence of

---

[54] "The Hydrogen Bomb," in George Fielding Eliot (ed.), *The H-Bomb* (New York, Didier, 1950), p. 70.

[55] Bertrand Russell, *Common Sense and Nuclear Warfare* (London, George Allen and Unwin, 1959), pp. 22–23.

[56] *Ibid.*, p. 47.

the complex interconnection of the problem of deterring deliberate attack and also keeping low the probability of "accidental" war. In fact, it is not at all clear that a war would start with the destruction of the seat of government, and Mr. Kennedy and Mr. McNamara have made very clear that subordinate commanders do not have the power Lord Russell so easily attributes to them. There are of course very large uncertainties in these matters that remain even when one is in full possession of classified data, and it is these uncertainties that should be at the center of a study of conflict systems.

The role of uncertainty in decision-making as well as in system studies to aid decision is so prominent that it is worth dwelling on, especially as it is related in several ways to some recent obscurantism. Erich Fromm doesn't hesitate to call "paranoid" attempts to prepare for anything other than the probable events. By this definition all of us who live in normally fire-safe neighborhoods and houses and nonetheless take out fire insurance are paranoid. On the contrary, it would be simply irrational to stake everything on a "most likely" event where the uncertainties are so large and intrinsic. This would be true even if we were quite sure we knew which were the most likely events and could agree on what are useful objectives in these contingencies.

However, the gift of prescience is not only hard to come by oneself, it is difficult to identify in others. Snow, who should be a great connoisseur of prescience, has run into difficulties. He derides Lindemann for backing infrared detection: "This seemed wildly impracticable then. . . . It seems even more wildly impracticable now." [57] Chinese Communist pilots downed by Sidewinder missiles with infrared seekers would disagree. This appears to be a case, in short, where Lindemann's prescience exceeds Snow's present knowledge of what has long since happened. Snow—and Blackett—take much too literally one of the lessons Snow draws from his cautionary tale: "The prime importance, in any crisis of action, of being positive what you want to do. . . . It is not so relevant whether you are right or wrong." [58]

In fact, serious study of the large uncertainties in the major stra-

[57] Snow, *Science and Government*, p. 34.   [58] *Ibid.*, p. 73.

tegic choices we have had to make suggests the opposite. Bertrand Russell in a better day once said, perhaps overstating the matter a bit: "The opinions that are held with passion are always those for which no good ground exists; indeed the passion is the measure of the holder's lack of rational conviction." [59] Passionate assurance on these intrinsically uncertain matters is not justifiable on logical grounds. Some technologists who are most articulate on matters of public policy in the defense and arms control field should worry us most in their moments of boundless conviction, when they assume the role of seers. The tentative and admittedly fallible methods they have used in their narrower professional field seem even more appropriate in the complex and uncertain areas of cardinal choice.

I have tried to stress the fallibility and limitations of empirical work in strategy. These limitations are forgotten sometimes by the strategists themselves, and for them too there are temptations in the combination of authority that may have been well earned by sober study in some particular area of strategy and the secrecy that might hide the fact that such authority does not automatically extend to strategic issues they have not studied. There is something grand about the notion of grand strategy, and it can encourage a rather magisterial air of omniscience. However, though the transfer of training from one strategic problem to another is rather larger than that from basic physics to strategy, it is still limited. And the transfer of information is particularly limited. A man who has done good work on the protection of strategic forces is not inevitably an authority on civil defense, conventional war in Europe, and guerrilla warfare in South Vietnam. Protecting strategic forces is closer than bomb technology, but not enough. There are some hazards then of strategists shading into seers.

The useful public writings on strategy candidly recognize the data limitations imposed by secrecy. They are likely then to deal more with fundamental conceptual problems and less with concrete empirical issues of policy. For example, they may consider the difference between a first-strike and a second-strike capability and the

[59] Quoted in Charles Hussey, "Earl, Philosopher, Logician, Rebel," the New York *Times Magazine*, May 13, 1962, p. 10.

meaning of nuclear deterrence, or the long-run conditions for stability or instability of mutual deterrence, or the implications of "general and comprehensive disarmament," and so on. Such conceptual analyses can be extremely illuminating. For their purpose hypothetical illustrations, history, and fragmentary public data on the present may do very well. But they differ substantially from a detailed empirical comparison of alternative and planned methods for operating strategic forces in the face of feasible enemy opposition in the late 1950s, or the effects of bombardment rockets placed in Cuba on the strategic balance today, or an estimate of the military worth of a specific active defense against rockets in a wide variety of reasonably likely contingencies in the 1960s. There can be no certainty on such matters, but to write seriously about them at all requires thought and much information.[60]

Don Price in his brilliant essay, "The Scientific Establishment," has developed with admirable lucidity the difference between the role of the scientist in the United States and the picture that Snow attributes to the United States, the United Kingdom, and the Soviet Union.[61] In the United States the scientists have had unmatched opportunities for getting a direct political hearing for their ideas on policy. On every one of the cardinal choices cited by Snow scientists have been heard, and by top decision-makers. (On the other hand, I know of no clear evidence that in the Soviet Union scientists have affected the cardinal choices either on the basis of their prescience or on the basis of systematic study of major alternatives.) By and large, in the United States the problem of scientists and strategists, I think, is not so much in being heard as in *saying* something, that is, saying something that is the result of thought and empirical study.

---

[60] A great deal of nonsense has been written in the last few years suggesting that strategists feel that with some mysterious combination of games, game theory, and electronic computers, and apparently without much need for data, they can spin out nearly infallible answers to concrete questions of policy. I have no space here to deal with this stereotype but do so at some length in my forthcoming article, "Sin and Games in America." Long before the recent flood of criticism of the supposed widespread use of "two-person games" to solve policy problems, many strategists and many game theorists as well had written cautionary comments about the stringently limited applicability of game theory today and the modest use of computers, etc.

[61] See the essay by Price in this volume.

Without these, of course, there still is prescience, and the role of the seer.

SEERS

Scientists right, generals and politicians wrong? That the physical scientists and engineers have been right on the cardinal choices since the last war and that ordinary mortals have been wrong is believed very widely—and not only in the community of physical scientists and engineers. Snow in his discussion of their prescience on these vital strategic issues is simply expressing some current folklore in which the scientist appears as a gigantic figure, mysterious, but endowed with powers not unlike those of the *prophetae* of the late medieval world. The passages from Lord Russell which I have cited earlier as examples of the belief that the scientists have been right and the generals and politicians wrong can easily be multiplied.

There is no doubt that many scientists have had extremely penetrating and useful perceptions from time to time on the major problems that beset us. The insight of Szilard and others on the military importance of the early fission experiments is a durable witness to this. On the other hand the belief that they have been right and ordinary humans wrong will hardly sustain a look at the record of policies on cardinal choices recommended by physical scientists and engineers since the last war. It would not be hard to gather an anthology of mistaken technological and seeming-technological predictions by distinguished scientists. (Like Simon Newcomb's demonstration, shortly after the Wright brothers flew at Kitty Hawk, that heavier than air craft would be incapable of sustained flight; [62] or Rutherford's judgment, less than a decade before the first sustained nuclear chain reaction, that we were never likely to be

---

[62] "The demonstration that no possible combination of known substances, known forms of machinery, and known forms of force can be united in a practicable machine by which men shall fly long distances through the air, seems to the writer as complete as it is possible for the demonstration of any physical fact to be." Simon Newcomb, "The Outlook for the Flying Machine," in *Side-Lights on Astronomy* (New York and London, Harper and Bros., 1906), Chap. 21, p. 345.

able to control atomic energy to a useful extent; [63] or Vannevar Bush's statement, in press when President Truman announced the first Russian bomb test, that "it is a far cry indeed from the time when the enemy has a bomb;" [64] or Bush's belief expressed in 1949 that intercontinental rockets would be extremely inaccurate and astronomically expensive; [65] or Blackett's casual rejection in 1956 of the technical feasibility of putting H-bombs in intercontinental missiles—at a time when it had been known for more than two years to be feasible in the classified literature and had in fact played an important part in the decision vastly to accelerate the ICBM program in the United States.)

Such an anthology itself would be sobering and therefore not without utility. However, an even more relevant survey should cover the views of the scientists on the major strategic choices, that is, on the political-military implications of technological change. I will do a little of each. First, I will take one example of a seeming-technological prediction, namely, the prophecy by scientists of the Russian acquisition of nuclear bombs. This is perhaps the most frequently cited example of superior scientific prescience. Then with respect to the explicit strategic views of scientists I will outline briefly the succession of their opinions since the War on the important subject of defense in its broad meaning of limiting damage.

Prophesying the Russian bomb. In the issue of the *Bulletin of the Atomic Scientists* put out immediately after Mr. Truman's announcement of Joe I, the editor printed a series of articles entitled, "Did the Soviet Bomb Come Sooner than Expected?" [66] Its purpose was to answer the question: How accurate were the scientists in estimating the length of time needed by Russia to produce an atom bomb? The answer, substantiated by extensive quotation, was that they were very accurate indeed, and in particular compared most favorably in this respect with the "wartime administrators," such as General

[63] Rutherford, Address to the British Association for the Advancement of Science, *London Times*, September 12, 1933, p. 7.

[64] Vannevar Bush, in *Time*, LIX (November 21, 1949), 76. See also his *Modern Arms and Free Man* (New York, Simon and Schuster, 1949), p. 124.

[65] Vannevar Bush, "Scientific Weapons and a Future War," *Life*, XXVII (November 14, 1949).

[66] *Bulletin of the Atomic Scientists* (October, 1949), pp. 262, ff.

Groves, Vannevar Bush, and James Conant. The scientists who had hit it on the nose included Langmuir, Urey, Seitz, and the Franck Committee, among whose members was the editor of the *Bulletin*.

Do these quotations show that the natural scientists in general, or at least the scientists listed, are more reliable prophets in such matters than the administrators or anybody else? The belief that they are is a fundamental part of the contemporary folklore.

High marks for prophecy should be distributed on the basis of a more complete score card for the prophets. Nostradamus made predictions that turned out awfully well. For example, he foretold the death, four years later, of Henry II in a tournament. On the other hand he made predictions that didn't pan out at all. He made many predictions. Was anticipation of the Russian bomb based on some method of analysis which, given the same sort of information, might reliably yield sound predictions in the future? Or was it the result of some mysterious gift of the scientists, some gift of foresight which is "not yet knowledge so much as an expectation of knowledge to come," something they have in their bones that would serve to distinguish them, as Snow suggests, from ordinary mortals? Or was it a lucky hit? There are a number of peculiarities about the evidence offered that might make us uneasy.

The first odd thing is the treatment of Bush and Conant. On Snow's definition, to say nothing of more rigorous ones, they rate, and rather high, as scientists. Snow wants some scientists on top rather than on tap precisely because they have the future in their bones. It would be most unfortunate then if, as soon as they got on top, they lost their power of prophecy, as is implied for Bush and Conant.

Secondly, the successful prophesies cited cluster in 1945–46. In these years the scientists were urging the Baruch-Acheson-Lilienthal plan as the only alternative to the imminent spread of nuclear weapons. After December, 1946, when the Russians turned the plan down, many scientists, including some quoted for their successful prophecy, reversed their views and, in 1948 and 1949, predicted that it would be many years before the Russians got the bomb! Meanwhile the explosion was getting closer.

For example, the editor of the *Bulletin* in 1948, the year before the first Russian nuclear test, had changed the forecast he underwrote in the Franck Report. He surmised in 1948 that Russia "probably expects to acquire ['atomic bombs'] in five or ten years" [67]—not very different from the poor Vannevar Bush predictions. There were other such lengthenings of forecasts of Russian atomic capability among American scientists [68] and science reporters,[69] and also in England.[70]

Thirdly, Bush and Conant, degraded to the role of administrator, were "good" as well as "bad" prophets as to the date of the Russian bomb. In fact it seems they guessed right sooner than the others quoted. A little search of the literature shows them on record on September 30, 1944, stating: "The present advantage of the United States and Britain was temporary. Any nation with good technical and scientific resources could overtake them in three or four years." [71] In September, 1945, a forecast by Dr. Bush, according to some, was the closest hit of all.[72]

Fourthly, even the "good" 1945–46 predictions, examined more

---

[67] "The Narrow Way Out," *Bulletin of the Atomic Scientists,* IV, No. 6 (June, 1948), p. 186.

[68] See Karl T. Compton, the New York *Times,* December 8, 1948, who was reported as saying "he did not believe Russia had the atomic bomb or would have it in the near future."

Dr. Ralph Lapp who had recently been Executive Secretary of the Atomic Energy Committee of the Defense Department's Research and Development Board, and before that Assistant Director of the Metallurgical Laboratories of Chicago, wrote in *Must We Hide?* (Cambridge, Mass., Addison-Wesley, 1949), p. 10: "It seems reasonable to assume that other nations will not develop bombs until 1952, seven years after our first atomic test. . . . We feel that we are being rather conservative in choosing 1952, for there are a number of competent authorities who say that it will take much longer for others to develop the bomb." And "it will be about 1960 before others can conceivably have a sizeable supply of A-bombs. But this is only one part of the story. *To have the bombs is not enough.* They must be delivered to their targets." Dr. Lapp suggested that this left us time for the difficult task of dispersing our cities.

[69] William Laurence of the New York *Times* on March 10, 1948, reported that the first Soviet bomb could not be produced before mid-1952 and it would be twenty-five years before they could overtake us.

[70] For example, the English physicist, M. L. Oliphant, according to the New York *Times,* March 29, 1948, p. 9, said: "Those of us taking part in the atomic energy project do not believe that within the Russian sphere there can be sufficient knowledge or specialized skill to build a successful plant for many years to come."

[71] Richard G. Hewlett and Oscar E. Anderson, Jr., *The New World, 1939–1946* (Vol. I of *A History of the Atomic Energy Commission,* University Park, Pa., Pennsylvania State University Press, 1962), p. 329.

[72] In conversation with Forrestal. Cited in Lewis L. Strauss, *Men and Decisions* (New York, Doubleday, 1962), p. 439.

closely, appear less uncannily prophetic. These predictions covered countries other than Russia, and here they did not make out very well. Dr. Langmuir expected Russia to be the fourth country to explode a bomb, to be preceded by Canada as well as England.[73] Dr. Urey appears to have contemplated a half-dozen countries entering the nuclear club in as few as five years.[74] Happily these forecasts were wrong.[75]

Scientists have often treated the process of nuclear diffusion as mechanically as the diffusion of a gas. This method has been endemic since World War II. Three years ago Snow assured the American Association for the Advancement of Science that "all physical scientists . . . *know* that for a dozen or more states, it will only take perhaps six years, perhaps less" to acquire fission and fusion bombs.[76] How many would wager, from the vantage-point of 1963, that by 1966 or sooner there will be a dozen more new entrants to the nuclear club? Not very many who have looked at the relevant evidence.

More important for our immediate purpose, however, is the nature of the evidence that is relevant. Only a small part of it is physics. Forecasts of the progress of a military atomic energy program are not simply matters of technology. They try to foresee a complex sequence of national decisions. Each sequence is affected by the decisions of other countries, by domestic costs, and by national estimates of military and political worth.

Predicting the date of the Russian acquisition of nuclear weapons

[73] *Hearings before the Special Committee on Atomic Energy,* 1946, pp. 136–7.
[74] *Ibid.,* p. 97.
[75] I have written at somewhat greater length on the subject of nuclear diffusion in "Nuclear Sharing: NATO and the N + 1 Country." *The Nth Country Problem and Arms Control,* a pamphlet published by the National Planning Association, Washington, D.C., 1960, is perhaps the best known presentation in recent years arguing for the probability of very widespread and early diffusion of military programs of atomic energy. It is fair to say that Cristoph Hohenemser, one of its authors, has recently attempted to redress some of the pamphlet's lacks. In his paper, "The Nth Country Problem Today," he takes into account some of the problems of delivering weapons and some of the interactions between the capabilities of small and large nations. The first book-length study, *The Spread of Nuclear Weapons,* by Leonard Beaton and John Maddox is a very useful contribution which recognizes the difference between bomb production and military nuclear capability, and it surveys the actual plans of a large number of countries.
[76] Snow, "The Moral Un-Neutrality of Science," p. 259.

seemed to be a matter of technology, since the political and military assumptions involved were generally inexplicit. The views of scientists on the possibilities and worth of defense, however, are not only matters of strategy, but they are much more explicitly so.

Scientists as seers on strategy. A retrospect of the views of scientists on such matters as air defense, civil defense, long-range bombing (and specifically the bombing of cities versus the bombing of military targets), battlefield nuclear weapons, the function of secrecy in nuclear technology, the advisability of nuclear sharing, and the sincerity of Russian intentions would suggest that their vision has not been unclouded.

This is not to say that "the politicians and the generals" were right. They too, I would stress, have frequently been in error. That is another long story. It would be hard to show, however, that the physical scientists and engineers have been wiser or more realistic—or more moral. Perhaps the principal moral of *this* cautionary tale is simply that in the field of cardinal choice prophecy is precarious and moral certainty hard to justify.

Yet the views that I am about to sketch were held with great conviction not only as to their truth but also frequently as to their being the only moral views possible. I have mentioned that the Lindemann versus Tizard-Blackett controversy illustrates the passionate way in which men of science when they enter practical affairs may be divided about inherently uncertain matters. The opposing views of American scientists since the War have exhibited such tenuously founded feelings of certainty even more intensely than the emotions stirred up by the bombing controversy in England in 1942. American scientists altered their strategic views drastically and suddenly, turning 180 degrees, but the opposing factions remained in opposition, almost exactly changing place. Even if the cast of characters were new in each of the three periods I shall describe, these 180-degree turns in the dominant beliefs would be striking. But in fact some of the principal characters remain the same, that is, the individuals reversed field from Period I to Period II, or from Period II to Period III, or throughout, making the changes still more startling.

I will limit my illustration mostly, though not exclusively, to the changing and opposing views on the subject of defense in a broad meaning which includes not only (1) active defense by manned and unmanned interceptors, but also (2) civil defense by dispersal, evacuation, or shelter, (3) the bombing of the enemy offense force as a device to limit damage to oneself, and (4) the use of self-restraint in applying offensive force as an inducement to restraint on the other side.

The role of efforts to limit damage to oneself by these four methods is a complex issue which is not well understood today. I choose it partly because it offers some perspective for evaluating the passionate views that are currently being expressed on the subject. One such view enjoying a great vogue among natural scientists and engineers today is the notion that any preparations to limit damage to ourselves in the event of war, by active defense or otherwise, will make it more likely that the war will come. A paradoxical consequence of this view has it that it is wholly immoral to prepare to bomb military targets (like opposing offensive military forces) and that the only moral behavior is to prepare to concentrate exclusively on the bombing of cities (and incidentally, therefore, on the killing of noncombatant civilians).

At first blush this seems very strange indeed. On second thought, it may be made to seem less so. If we can talk about "third thought" or "third blush," however, I believe such careful further thought confirms the original impression. Analysis of the substantive questions raised by these and other paradoxical views on air defense is not possible in this paper. But a brief outline of the history of the views of natural scientists on this subject may implant a few doubts. In any case it will illustrate the fact that moral certainty and feelings of prescience have been a pretty uncertain guide to the future—even to the immediately next future beliefs of the prophet.

An outline history.[77] Just after World War II there was very widespread agreement among articulate scientists associated with wartime technical achievements. They held that (1) the spread of nu-

---

[77] Anything like a fully documented history takes many pages. In fact, in successive drafts of this essay the space devoted to the history doubled, then doubled again, and then again, until it was well beyond the bounds of an essay. The history now forms a substantial part of the book, *Scientists, Seers and Strategy,* to be published in the spring of 1964. The book elaborates this sketch and presents detailed evidence.

clear weapons to many other countries was imminent, (2) war if it came would be nuclear, and (3) in this war there was no hope of adequate defense. On defense specifically, (a) techniques for intercepting the bomb carriers were unlikely to increase significantly the cost to the aggressor of destroying his victim's cities, (b) shelter was of doubtful value, and (c) dispersal of cities and war industry were the best of the bad lot of defense measures, first because cities were the only targets for A-bombs and second because stockpiles of A-bombs would be relatively small. (This last assumption was connected with the common belief that the economics of uranium ore would make it scarce.) While dispersal was supposedly far better than active defense or shelter, even its utility was transient.

(4) Preparing for defense in fact was futile. Or worse, it would ruin the structure of our society by (a) the enormous military budgets it would impose, (b) the indirect effects of militarization, bringing about a garrison society, and (c) by the effects of large-scale dispersal itself which would lower industrial efficiency and standards of living and sacrifice free institutions. In this Period I, which passed its peak at the end of 1946, the only solution was international control of atomic energy. There was no defense. It was one world or none.

Near the end of 1946 and for the rest of the decade, this quite uniform view received a sequence of political shocks. The Russians rejected the Baruch Plan, entrenched themselves in Eastern Europe, threatened Berlin, exploded their first nuclear weapon in 1949, and supported the aggression in South Korea in 1950. By 1950, Period II was well under way. There had been drastic changes in view in most of the scientific community and a sharp and widening split.

The largest section of the articulate scientists now held that defense was not only feasible, but that an adequate continental defense should be built. This would include (1) a very "high attrition" active defense, that is, highly effective techniques of interception, with (2) civil defense as a necessary supplement. (a) Dispersal was regarded not merely as a transient measure of civil defense, but of long-term importance. Its side effects on society moreover were now benign, talked of in terms of green grass and sunlight replacing crowded urban streets. (b) Near the start of the 1950s these scientists emphasized evacuation of cities on the basis of hours of radar warning, a shift from the earlier Federal Civil Defense Administration assumption that there would be only 15-minute warning and shelter therefore necessary. (c) By the end of Period II, formally marked by Sputnik and the Gaither Committee in late 1957, the scientists had shifted their emphasis in civil defense to shelter.

(3) Limiting damage to the United States involved, as an essential part, the long-range bombing of enemy bombers, the destruction on base as well as in the air of the vehicles capable of destroying the United States. Views varied here, but many of the scientists regarded such targets as morally right, in contrast to city targets. Almost everyone now understood that A-bombs could be potent weapons against military targets—and stockpiles could be large. However, much as in Period I they thought the A-bomb adaptable only to urban targets, now in Period II they interpreted the H-bomb to be usable solely against cities, and at that only a few of the largest ones. (4) And one final method of limiting damage to the United States was frequently linked to self-imposed restrictions or selectivity in long-range targeting, that is, self-restraint calculated to induce restraint on enemy action.

Such limitations in long-range bombing paralleled ideas for restraints on the battlefield. Large stocks of A-bombs made possible the use of small nuclear weapons in ground warfare, and these scientists advocated such use and called for a development of the stockpile not only for this purpose, but also for air defense and antisubmarine warfare. In this Republican era of budget emphasis, a bigger-bang-for-a-buck, and attempts at economy in defense, they pressed for larger budgets as necessary to the security of the United States, and specifically for defense. The goals of an adequate defense were defined in extremely ambitious terms—preserving the continuity of war production in a long thermonuclear war. Finally the defense of the United States was regarded as (a) a necessary help in deterring attack on the United States, also (b) in deterring attack on our allies, and (c) as an aid in obtaining arms control.

The scientific community was of course divided on these matters. A numerically smaller faction bitterly opposed these views. As in the Lindemann-Tizard controversy, moreover, neither of the opposing factions was a reliable witness to the views of the other side. Once again the differences were not all or none, but questions of emphasis and allocation. The acrimony nonetheless reflected strong differences. The smaller faction emphasized the big bomb, and strategic bombing in the traditional sense of destruction of war-making capacity. They fought with passion what they regarded as an extreme (some thought total) diversion of resources from the Strategic Air Command to air defense and theater war.

Since 1957 there has been a remarkable shift. The opposing factions have almost exactly changed place. The minority now emphasizes the importance of battlefield nuclear weapons and, in the long-range war, would limit bombing to military targets exclusively. They also stress nuclear weapons for active air defense and back large-scale civil defense programs. They take defense to be deterrent, not provocative. The principal articulate faction of scientists meanwhile have returned to something like their views in Period I. They regard an effective civil defense and active defense against the ICBM as infeasible. Moreover, they presume that the fact of this infeasibility is good. For they take both active and civil defense (and also the bombing of military targets) to be provocative, not deterrent. They believe them to be destabilizing in the sense that they (a) foster an arms race, (b) make war more likely, and (c) are inimical to arms control. Many of these scientists deride self-restraint, a controlled nuclear response, as theorizing about chess games. They place their immediate hopes on a small deterrent force armed with H-bombs and aimed solely at cities and on small budgets and stockpiles, and they urge early international control.

Perspective. What is the significance of these sudden and repeated dramatic reversals in strategic doctrine by the natural scientists and engineers? People do after all change their beliefs, even on rather fundamental matters and it is a good thing they do. Is it rather small-minded perhaps to center much attention on the fact of change? Memories for the most part have been blissfully short on these matters, and to cover some of the memorably odd shifts by figures like Bertrand Russell (who moved from advocating preventive nuclear war in 1948 to the Campaign for Nuclear Disarmament in the 1960s), a standard and rather brusque answer has been developed:

the world changes; beliefs must change to adjust to the changing world.

Such an explanation has a good deal of appeal. In fact there were many internal inconsistencies in the position of individuals at any given time, and they are not without interest. My interest here, however, is not in such inconsistencies but rather in the question of the foresight of the scientists both in anticipating innovations in technology and in deciphering the strategic implications of recent existing hardware. This outline history is directly relevant for that. The standard explanation, the world changes, while appealing, has almost too wide an application. It is too easy. Between the utterance or writing down of any two statements a finite period of time elapses and, in between, the world has always changed. There are several questions underneath this blanket explanation that need looking at. Even if we were to assume that the views in fact had changed to meet the changing world, that is of some considerable significance for our purpose in this essay; it is evidence that being a seer in this line of work is hard. Such changes illustrate the difficulties of prophecy, of anticipating events, rather than adjusting to them after the fact. Secondly, such an experience by rights should have tempered the harshness of the strategic disagreements among the scientists. Antagonists, one would think, might be made a little tolerant of an opposing view that they have so recently abandoned. Having only just surrendered the belief, it should seem less than totally foolish—or totally malign. Heresy normally presupposes a rather stable set of orthodox doctrines. Simply to have lagged a little in changing in a dynamic world seems a pardonable sin.

But in the third place the mere fact of change is no blanket excuse for all changes in doctrine. The world changed and so did the scientists' beliefs. But in many cases, some of which I will pinpoint, the world and the scientists moved in opposite directions. Moreover, the changes were based not so much on evidence and reasoning as fervent desire. In fact what is constant amid all these changes is a kind of impatience, a desire for a final solution, free of uncertainty.

Fourthly, weighing the evidence relevant for these beliefs would have meant going far beyond physical science and engineering. The feasibility and costs of dispersing urban populations, the economics of uranium ore supply, the appropriate targets for fission and fusion weapons, the feasibility of continuing war manufacturing under atomic bombing, the interacting operations of bombardment vehicles and interceptors under alternative modes of attack and defense, the deterrent or provocative effects of various forms and amounts of active defense, and the utility of continental defense in deterring attack on our allies—are any of these simply questions of physics or electrical engineering or the like? Clearly not. Yet these are the matters dealt with by both principal factions of the scientists.

The opposing views surveyed were violent and angry. Emotions have run high; suspicions and accusations of disloyalty on the one hand and of insanity on the other have disfigured the debate. Hopefully this review should make us less dogmatic and a little more thoughtful and tentative about these awesomely complex, cardinal choices.

It was not my purpose in this essay to make a point by point evaluation of the positions taken by each of the factions in each of the periods. At this date the mere outline given of the changing opposing views makes it plain that time and again these highly competent, professional physical scientists and engineers were far from clairvoyant on the feasibility or timing of impending changes in technology or in prophesying the strategic implications of already existing but recent technology. In spite of the folklore, our history suggests that almost none has been regularly successful at foreseeing future technologies. Even the acquisition by foreign countries of a nuclear technology already possessed by the United States has not really developed as expected. Then there have been surprises in the developments of fusion technology, rockets, and many others. Surprise should be regarded as normal in research: "You pay your two bits . . . you go in and you don't know what you're going to see." Predicting these innovations would have involved more than physical research. Finally, in this area so close to the cardinal issues of human conflict our views on the feasibility of an innovation are likely to get mixed with our emotions. I said earlier that it is hard not to guess that something is feasible if you would like it to happen. It is also true, and of course closely related, that it is hard not to prophesy a catastrophe if its imminence would make urgent an action you are recommending. A good many of the prophecies of the scientists, both those that turned out to be right and those that are wrong, fall in this last category. This was true for both the right and wrong prophecies of nuclear diffusion.

In particular the scientists have not been outstanding as seers on the strategic implications of the weapons they have made. Brilliant inventors of hardware are not automatically first-rate inventors of strategies for its use or restraint. They frequently exclude by definition uses they fail to see. So in Period I the A-bomb was supposed to be useful only against cities. And in Period II when it was evident that the A-bomb was a potent weapon against military forces, an analogous misconception of the H-bomb was current—which was cleared up by Period III. Programs for population shelters, not to say urban dispersal, have long lead times. Yet plans for civil defense shifted from an assumption of 15-minute warning to depend on many hours of warning, and they did this just about the time the United States vastly accelerated its own program to build ICBMs whose total time of travel is measured in minutes. The notion of the relative efficiency of city dispersal as compared to other defenses had a curiously long and bipartisan life. The history of the dispersal concept illustrates that the changes were not always made simply to accord with changes in reality. Even if this were so, the suddenness of the transformation makes the prevalence of the gift of foresight on strategic choices hard to believe. *However, as has already been said, a good many of the changes went in the wrong direction, moved further from reality.* So the transient utility of dispersal lengthened to permanence, while the realities of the bomb stockpile moved the other way. There was no defense against the A-bomb yet. Though no breakthrough of genuinely comparable importance had occurred in defense, a quite adequate defense was claimed against the H-bomb.

Or take the one major contemporary instance, the notion in vogue that defense is, without qualification, destabilizing. This can be shown to be more farfetched in Period III than in Period II, when its present proponents believed that defense was, without qualification, stabilizing. In Period III almost nobody claims to be able to assure very low levels of damage, even in the unlikely event that we should strike first. But in Period II the claim was very widespread that the defense recommended was adequate to achieve a quite remarkable protection against a massive surprise attack aimed mainly at our cities—that a mixture of active and passive defense of our cities could assure even the continuing manufacture of war goods during a long nuclear war. Thus on the destabilization theory we should have behaved much more aggressively and provoked legitimate fears of preventive war on our part, and made attack by the Russians more probable. The destabilization theory, of course, needs a much more extended analysis. These remarks are intended to suggest that it is especially implausible in a period when an increment in defense, even if it significantly limited damage, would admittedly leave us open to an enormous catastrophe.

However, these substantive issues are too difficult and uncertain to permit handling in brief. The most important lesson to be learned from this survey is precisely that these issues *are* extremely complex. They are not really the sorts of questions on which one can expect a revelation. On these complex cardinal choices foresight of the answer is not given. It is won—precariously and intermittently, in the course of hard empirical study of the major factors affecting choice. Intuition and intelligence help, but do not make superfluous the study not only of the vital technologies, but also of the behavior of men and nations using and affected by the use of such technologies. No one has the gift of reliable foresight on these cardinal choices. The primary thing then is *not* to be positive. The basic failures of the physical scientists and engineers in this turbulent history is not their lack of prescience but their acting frequently as if they had it. This means a failure to deal with contingencies other than those foreseen, and it is likely to mean a passionate intolerance of the views of those on the other side of the fence.

TIME FOR THE METHOD OF SCIENCE?

The sense of mission and urgency. There are more extreme views of the character of those on the other side of the fence: they are not simply *wrong.* Bertrand Russell wrote recently: "Indignant atomic scientists, after Hiroshima, inaugurated a monthly review, *The Bulle-*

tin of the Atomic Scientists, which has continued ever since to present the sane view on atomic weapons and atomic warfare." [78] Russell, of all people, knows the meaning of the three-letter word "the" in the phrase "the sane view." Once upon a time he wrote two whole chapters of a book to explain it, and his Theory of Descriptions attempted its first rigorous formulation. Its usage here implies that aside from the view of the "indignant atomic scientists" there are no other views except insane ones. And in fact Russell's writings have become increasingly salted with statements about the insanity of the politicians and generals and of the scientists with whom he disagrees. His February, 1962, speech to a mass meeting in London accusing Messrs. Macmillan, Kennedy, and Khrushchev of plotting the butchery of millions was not untypical.[79] He also has written:

If the negotiators on either side were sane men or less immersed than they are in detail, they would realize that a nuclear war, entailing these awful consequences, is far the greatest risk that is being incurred, and that a reasonable give and take leading to agreement is the only policy compatible with sanity or humane feeling or with reluctance to condemn ourselves, our children, our friends, and our nation to a totally futile death. Meanwhile, pride, love of power, and belief in the possibilities of unending bluff, blind the statesmen of East and West to their obvious duty to humanity and allow them to pursue their murderous game unchecked.[80]

And "If the world could live for a few generations without war, war would come to seem as absurd as dueling has come to seem to us. No doubt there would still be some homicidal maniacs, but they would no longer be heads of governments." [81] And "Eatherly [who gave the signal for the dropping of the bomb at Hiroshima] was repentant and certified; Truman was unrepentant and uncertified." [82]

Such extremity unfortunately is not confined to Lord Russell. All of the organizations, many of them thickly populated with scientists, with titles like "SANE" suggest by this self-designation that their views are the only ones that could be held by people who are not lunatics. And books like *Common Sense in Nuclear War* or *Common*

---

[78] Russell, *Has Man a Future?,* p. 19.
[79] As reported in the New York *Times,* February 26, 1962.
[80] Russell, *Has Man a Future?,* p. 103.   [81] *Ibid.,* p. 46.
[82] *Ibid.,* p. 41.

Sense in Defense have titles based on the assumption that the issues are clear-cut, and obvious to common sense. Any difference, if not crazy, is at least cantankerous or insincere, or otherwise unworthy of sober intellectual examination. And such assumptions have been spelled out by a sizeable number of psychoanalysts who have been diagnosing the specific sort of insanity of those who disagree.

Russell's stress on the question of sincerity is characteristic: "In negotiations there is no genuine wish on either side to reach agreement, but only to avoid any semblance of a diplomatic victory by the other side." [83] In fact sincerity is what distinguishes the scientist from the politician in Russell's mind and in the mind of many other Western scientists. A good many of them have a rather naïve skepticism about politicians and "power politics." Snow's own view of politics, as essentially a struggle for personal power, has as a consequence that politics is the same in a Cambridge College as on the world scene— world politics is seen on the model of petty campus feuds.[84] Szilard's suggestion in *The Voice of the Dolphins* that his Dolphin Institute need only buy off troublesome senators at the rate of $200,000 a year is related to the pastoral view of the scientist as a simple but pure soul. He is the country boy outwitting the city slicker. In fact Snow has a moderate form of this self-exaltation: "The scientists I have known (and because of my official life I have known as many as anyone in the world) have been in certain respects just perceptibly more morally admirable than most other groups of intelligent men." [85]

It is the scientists' sincerity and their related lack of political experience which recommend them for the job of converting the Russians. In his House of Lords speech in 1945, Lord Russell suggested:

I think one could make some use of the scientists in this matter. They themselves are extremely uneasy, with a very bad conscience about what they have done. They know they had to do it but they do not like it. They would be very thankful if some task could be assigned to them which would somewhat mitigate the disaster that threatens mankind. I think

---

[83] *Ibid.*, p. 44.
[84] See, for example, Snow, *Science and Government*, p. 59.
[85] Snow, "The Moral Un-Neutrality of Science," p. 256.

they might be perhaps better able to persuade the Russians than those of us who are more in the game; they could, at any rate, confer with Russian scientists and perhaps get an entry that way toward genuine cooperation.[86]

I cannot help thinking that if that were put in a perfectly frank and unpolitical manner to the Russians they would be as capable of seeing it as we are—at least I hope so.[87]

The declarations of the various Pugwash Conferences stress similarly the belief that scientists would serve both as a model and as an agent for international understanding. It is ironic that a group so riven by feuds should think of themselves so much as a model of cooperation and harmony.

Conferences between Eastern and Western scientists as well as diplomats can be useful, but there is no evidence whatsoever that progress along these lines will satisfy the enormous sense of urgency felt by the scientists in the West. On this very matter of sincerity our scientists have been poor prophets in judging the Russians. Hans Bethe, for example, had great hopes for an agreement with the Russians on international control in 1946. But these were dashed when Dr. Oppenheimer told him in January, 1947, of the total Russian intransigence.[88] Again, on March 29, 1960, in a letter to the New York *Times,* he expressed the belief on the basis of his many conferences with Russian scientists that: "The Russians have shown that they are just as anxious as we are to reach a workable agreement, satisfactory to both sides. And even in the unlikely case that they should violate the moratorium. . . ." In mid-air Dr. Bethe's hopes were once again in the process of deflation, and by this very "unlikely" case. In January, 1962, he had to say:

[T]he Russian procedure showed bad faith. Their test series was so elaborate that it must have been prepared for many months, perhaps longer. It is likely that they had started preparations by March when the test ban conference reconvened in Geneva; thus they negotiated for six months in bad faith. They did so at the time when we were showing most

---

[86] Russell, *Has Man a Future?*, p. 23.   [87] *Ibid.*
[88] Bethe's testimony in the Atomic Energy Commission, Personal Security Board, *In the Matter of J. Robert Oppenheimer* (Washington, D.C., USGPO, 1954).

clearly by our attitude and proposals at Geneva that we were sincerely interested in the test ban. . . .[89]

Judging the political intent of a Soviet physicist is not a problem in physics.

The sense of mission of these scientists is charged with urgency. A great many have written ominously about the accumulating probability of war. Russell believes that world annihilation in a rather near future is more probable than not.[90] Snow tells us that nuclear war is a "statistical certainty" before the decade is out. The belief that the choice is immediate between world annihilation and "a world of glory and joy" [91] has led to some of the most paradoxical aspects in the behavior of scientists. They sometimes bear a strange and uncomfortable resemblance, as I suggested earlier, to the militantly pacific Anabaptists in medieval and Reformation Europe. These Anabaptists also saw the issues as clear and simple, were armed with the gift of prophecy, and were charged with a unique and stupendous mission,[92] the establishment on earth of a Kingdom of Peace. When they took up the sword against their opponents, they were destroying only the enemies of peace, the unrighteous. Like them, some scientists have at one time or another contemplated ushering in a totally peaceful world by the threat or practice of war. Russell's advocacy of preventive war against the Russians in 1948 betrayed the same moral certainty and the same impatience:

Atomic bombs, if used, will at first have to be dropped on West Europe, since Russia will be out of reach. The Russians, even without atomic bombs, will be able to destroy all big towns in England, as the Germans would have done if the war had lasted a few months longer. I have no doubt that America would win in the end, but unless West Europe can be preserved from invasion, it will be lost to civilization for centuries.

Even at such a price I think war would be worthwhile. Communism must be wiped out, and world government must be established.[93]

---

[89] "Nuclear Testing," Cornell University Lecture, January 5, 1962.

[90] See, for example, Russell, *Has Man a Future?*, p. 36.

[91] Lord Russell's phrase. See *ibid.*

[92] For this see Norman Cohn's fascinating and scholarly *The Pursuit of the Millennium* (New York, Harper and Bros., 1961).

[93] Russell, letters to the editor of the *Saturday Review of Literature*, XXXVII (October 16, 1954), 25. See also the New York *Times*, November 21, 1948, reporting a speech at the New Commonwealth School in London; also Russell's

In 1954, however, he said that the situation had changed. The Russians now had the bomb. "[W]e cannot defeat Russia except by defeating ourselves." [94]

Russell's views at each of these times, despite his moral assurance today, had a curiously expedient and contingent character. In fact in 1948 he postponed his urgent appeal to threaten war on Russia on the advice of some professional strategists who told him that in a few years Russia would still not have the bomb, and the West would be in a still better strategic position.[95] His strategist friends had not "the gift of foresight," however, and the Russians, contrary to expectations, tested nuclear weapons in 1949 and plunged into an intensive and successful program of fission and fusion weapons production. Russell's early position then amounted to saying that he was in favor of coercing the Russians with nuclear weapons to eliminate communism, since the West could get away with it. He was against it only when he believed the West could not. Yet here again Russell's over-simple picture of relations of nuclear power played an unconscious role. He has held and to some extent still holds the view that the mere possession of nuclear weapons assures retaliation against attack. In fact it need not unless a great deal of care has been taken to prepare a second-strike capability. In the early 1950s, the Russians had taken no such care. If Russell had known that, unlike many better informed men who were against preventive war then and now, he would have continued to advocate preventive war. There is then a sense in which Russell has not changed. His views continue to be based on a very tenuous factual understanding of the capabilities of the two sides, and the measures useful in increasing stability, and an exceedingly pressing desire to assure a total peace once and for all, even though attaining this assurance might entail desperate nuclear risks.

In less extreme but more widespread and nonetheless emotionally violent form, such impatience and moral certainty about the one path to peace and the end of international conflict has been directed against the internal "enemies of peace." For example, it has been

---

lecture "Values in the Atomic Age," in *Sir Halley Stewart Lectures, 1948* (London, Allen and Unwin, 1949).
   [94] *Ibid.*   [95] *Ibid.*

directed against those men who currently advocate measures of civil defense: "Civil defense preparations . . . are diabolical inventions calculated to tell lies and to deceive." [96] Passionate exorcism of such discordant devils is not inconsistent with the hostility to the fact of hostility which I discussed earlier—it illustrates it. The enormous sense of urgency of many scientists fosters a kind of anti-intellectual violence, and, at the very least, by spreading the belief that there is no time, discourages our taking the time for careful exploration of the complicated problems that beset us.

Durability of the problems. The problems for cardinal choices are persistent as well as complex. Perhaps a patient inquiry into them is discouraged not merely by the millennial sense of urgency of so many scientists, but also by the heritage of the way scientists worked during World War II. In a war emergency crash studies were the natural mode of operation. Some of the same atmosphere pervades much of the participation of scientists today on committees.

During a wartime emergency the very shortness of time helps determine the way decision-makers use their experts. This is in fact how Churchill explains his relation to Lindemann:

There are only twenty-four hours in the day, of which at least seven must be spent in sleep and three in eating and relaxation. Anyone in my position would have been ruined if he had attempted to dive into depths which not even a lifetime of study could plumb. What I had to grasp were the practical results; and just as Lindemann gave me his view for all it was worth in this field, so I made sure by turning on my power-relay that some at least of these terrible and incomprehensible truths emerged in executive decisions.[97]

But have *we* no time? Dr. Bethe himself wrote some five years ago, in pleased astonishment: "It is true, no definite steps have been taken to make [an all-out nuclear] war impossible but at least we have survived thirteen years without one, more than many of us expected." [98] One of the things the scientists did not prophesy and

[96] Bertrand Russell, interview in *Playboy*, February, 1963, p. 46.
[97] Churchill, *Their Finest Hour*, pp. 382–3.
[98] "Review of *Brighter Than a Thousand Suns*," *Bulletin of the Atomic Scientists*, XIV, No. 10 (December, 1958), 427.

something they found it hard even to conceive of was the continued existence for eighteen years and more of a divided world with conflicts unresolved. Their imagination vaulted but fell far short of envisaging the present state of affairs and its possible persistence.

It is high time that we recognized the extreme implausibility of the notion that war may become "impossible" in the next short space of time. On the other hand, neither is nuclear war "inevitable" in the next ten years—or many more. Since reducing the likelihood of war will preoccupy us for many years to come, it is appropriate to think of the probable consequences of this persisting preoccupation, some of which are already visible.

Decision-makers are likely to acquire a deep familiarity with these problems in the course of time, and to grow in professional competence in the continuing work on their solution. This is happening today for example, in the Department of Defense. In 1962 the New York *Times* published a statement of the Secretary on the issues in the choice of strategic bombardment vehicles for the late 1960s and after.[99] Whether or not we agree with the specific choice it explains, the document is impressive. In its thoughtful treatment of the uncertainties and the essential technological as well as operational and economic problems, it compares very favorably in sophistication with the analyses done by scientists to aid decision during World War II. Moreover, anyone who follows the congressional hearings will be quite convinced that such statements are comprehensively understood by a good many current decision-makers. These cardinal strategic decisions in general *are* made by them.

There is a good deal of hocus-pocus in Snow's pronouncement that the decision-makers "cannot have a first-hand knowledge of what these choices depend upon." [100] There is, of course, a sense in which nobody can have first-hand knowledge of all the things such decisions depend upon. They depend upon a great many things besides technology, in many fields. However, the choices that Snow dwells on, for example, in his cautionary tales are not all that obscure, and a

---

[99] The New York *Times,* March 16, 1962.
[100] Snow, *Science and Government,* p. 1.

first-rate Cabinet officer or military man can master the essentials of much more complicated matters, especially if they keep coming up—and they do.

It is one of the many oddities of this history that recently systematic and analytic consideration of the factors in cardinal choice has come under identical fire from the radical right and left. Snow and Blackett [101] are joined by Barry Goldwater [102] in attacking civilian "calculations" and in appealing to the "conventional military wisdom." [103] However, the deliverances of the conventional wisdom of both military and civilian decision-makers diverge. This imposes the need for choice, and, hopefully, for careful thought. Even so fortified, the judgments of decision-makers will be far from infallible; but given the novelty, depth, and persistence of our problems systematic thought is called for and all the current invective about "computers" and "cold strategic thought" is not likely to discourage an increasing professional competence in defense decision-makers.

The other side of this picture is that the natural and behavioral scientists, who offer advice or do analyses to assist decision, may experience a growth of professional competence too. Offhand judgments of individuals and crash studies by committees will always be with us—and should. But expertise and committee activities have limitations. An expert on the whole range of problems involved in even one of these complicated choices is hard to find, and, if one is discovered, the way in which he reaches his conclusion may be difficult to reproduce and verify. This in turn affects whether his judgment will be subject to criticism by more than a "handful of men." Inexplicitness is likely to be even worse with committees, since they proceed frequently by bargaining rather than reason. But explicit statement of the way conclusions are reached and of the evidence is part of the normal method of science, and what I mean by "conflict-systems studies" is simply the application of the method of science to the analysis of political-military strategic alternatives.

---

[101] Lecture by Blackett with commentary by Snow, *Journal of the Royal United Service Institute*, 1961.

[102] *Los Angeles Times*, March 24, 1963.

[103] Blackett's phrase; see *ibid.*, and "Critique of Some Contemporary Defence Thinking."

This suggests a little of the answer to at least one of the large questions with which we began: both the physical and the behavioral sciences have a role to play in component research on cardinal choices. And in the course of studying strategic alternatives the methods of science can be used to reach conclusions going beyond the skills of any of the individuals involved.[104]

---

[104] I am indebted for information or comment to Michael Arnsten, Janina Bonczek, James F. Digby, Noble Frankland, Emma Gee, S. M. Genensky, F. S. Hoffman, R. V. Jones, Nathan Leites, Joseph Loftus, Albert Madansky, A. W. Marshall, Robert Merton, Edward Purcell, E. S. Quade, Harvey Waterman, Charles Wolf, and in particular Daniel Ellsberg. Some of these suggestions could be accommodated only in the longer work from which this essay is extracted, *Scientists, Seers and Strategy,* to appear as a book in the spring or fall of 1964.

The Scientific Strategists

BERNARD BRODIE

Senior Staff Member of the RAND Corporation,
Santa Monica, California

One of the most remarkable changes in the intellectual landscape over the last dozen years, especially in the area of public affairs, is the entry of civilian scientists into the field of military strategy. Some of these persons, because of their publications, are very much before the public eye; others, often of no less talent and accomplishment, are less known among the general public but known and much respected among the specialists themselves.

The people we are describing, though civilians, are fully professional in their approach to military strategy—which is to say that they are highly trained in relevant disciplines and that their full-time labors over a period of years have been devoted to that field, to which they seem to have committed themselves wholeheartedly and permanently. Their special abilities have been recognized and utilized, often with enthusiasm, by the military services, and the relations between these scientific strategists and members of the military profession are on the whole quite close. Although their numbers are still small compared to the numbers in the ranks of other scientific disciplines, collectively they have been of very considerable public influence. Most of the distinctively modern concepts of military strategy that have been embraced by the military services themselves have been evolved by them. Although their special research efforts are generally in the field of systems analysis, and hence confined to very special problems in the fields of tactics and strategy, a few of them have also striven to develop comprehensive concepts.

CONTRAST WITH THE PAST

Despite the relatively small numbers of these specialists, there is a spectacular contrast between the situation today and that existing before 1950, or at least before World War II. Before World War II theoretical strategy, like ancient Gaul, was divided into three parts. In the field of naval strategy the figure of Alfred T. Mahan was still supreme. Mahan, though a naval officer, was primarily an historian, and his strategic concepts represented mostly rediscoveries of principles that had held sway in days of sail. Another distinguished though less-known figure was his civilian British contemporary, Sir Julian Corbett, also a naval historian. In the new field of air strategy there was only one noteworthy publicist, the Italian General Giulio Douhet, whose fund of experience was confined to World War I. In land strategy the situation was more chaotic. There had been no really outstanding publicist since the great Karl von Clausewitz, who died in 1831, and the very influential though lesser figure of Antoine Henri Jomini, both career officers of the Napoleonic period. More recent work had been devoted largely to restating, and often to vulgarizing, the ideas of these two early-nineteenth-century giants.

We should notice also that none of these figures, including the most recent, had been much interested in applying quantitative measures to their data. Douhet's neglect to apply even elementary arithmetical calculations to his concepts resulted in exaggerations which oblige us to account him a failure in his efforts to predict the character of World War II, or even to predict the influence of strategic bombing in that conflict. Besides, even if we were to add the names of all the lesser figures whose writings on strategy are worth mentioning at all, the total number of names in the hundred years preceding 1950 would still be remarkably small. The field of military strategy, at least on the level of theory, was one of the most sparsely populated of intellectual pursuits, despite the periodic recurrence of important wars.

During those same hundred years the important strategic decisions and the thinking that went into them were the work of men who though professional soldiers were rarely specialists in strategic analysis. The generals or admirals who carried responsibility for the major decisions were in the main older men who had spent most of their lives in pursuits that though military were primarily concerned with tactics and especially with administration. A talent for leadership rather than strategic insight was, and largely remains, the main qualification for advancement to high rank, and one cannot quarrel with the justification for this requirement. Thus, strategic decisions were usually made on a basis of personal experience, of intuition, and also of dedication to axioms and other encapsulated concentrates of strategic insight known as "principles." In each of the major military services of the world there were also important national traditions that helped guide the decisions. Naturally, not all services were alike; the German Imperial Army, especially under the elder von Moltke and later von Schlieffen, placed an important emphasis on precise mobilization planning. That in itself was almost enough to account for the great German victory in the Franco-Prussian War of 1870–71. But in a calling where aristocratic connections were so important, the number of serious, dedicated persons ruminating on strategic problems could never be considerable. At any rate, careful military analysis after 1871 remained tied to "war plans" that were essentially plans for mobilization and for initial deployment or attack. What to do if enemy actions spoiled one's plan was hardly ever considered.

Insofar as the system worked prior to World War II it did so because (1) it was fairly universal, so that each side tended to work under the same disadvantages of inefficiency, and (2) changes in military technology, though they might indeed be very rapid, were confined to instruments having only tactical significance. For example, although the naval gun underwent drastic development following 1850, it remained from any strategic point of view essentially the same instrument.

However, by any pragmatic standard we have to concede that the system worked very badly. The tactical and strategic lessons presented by the experience of successive wars had to be learned over and over again, always at great cost in lives and resources and often at the cost of defeat. Cavalry charges against intact lines of infantry proved useless at Waterloo, and in the American Civil War it was repeatedly demonstrated that the proper way to use cavalry was to exploit the horse for mobility while doing the major fighting dismounted; but this experience had no effect on the tactics of the French in the Franco-Prussian War. They resorted to cavalry charges against strong infantry in practically every battle. Almost always the only result was heavy losses. Further examples could be repeated without end. The most horrendous failures were those of World War I, where the simple lesson provided in the American Civil War and reconfirmed in the Franco-Prussian and Russo-Japanese Wars—that direct frontal attacks on entrenched infantry armed with modern hand rifles were bound to be extremely costly and usually fruitless—was not taken seriously even against strong forces armed with machine guns.

CHANGES WROUGHT BY WORLD WAR II

World War II produced two critical factors of change. The first was the introduction of the atomic bomb at the very end of the conflict, which not only presented a basic strategic change of the greatest dimensions and importance but also signaled the beginning of an era of extremely rapid, and incidentally also extremely costly, technological development. The second was the wartime role of scientists in assisting top military commanders and even heads of government to reach critical tactical and strategic decisions. The use of such people was particularly prominent in the new field of strategic bombing, where experience was so completely lacking and where a flow of new inventions was drastically affecting the capabilities of the bombing forces. The outstanding application of analytical skills was in the field of strategic target selection, where economists proved especially invaluable; but even in such technical and tactical matters as whether or not bombing forces should use "chaff" or "window" to confuse enemy radar, the matter was, at least among the British, largely debated by the scientists and decided by the Prime Minister.

The atomic bomb differed from all previous military inventions in that its effects could not clearly be confined to the tactical. The airplane had already taken war beyond the battlefield by means of strategic bombing, but nuclear weapons guaranteed that strategic bombing would be all-important. And since so little was known about the conditions of nuclear war, the value of combat experience seemed drastically depreciated. Furthermore, the destructiveness of nuclear weapons meant that general wars, that is, the nonlimited variety, would be fought with forces existing at the outset—a change that effectively pushed the major strategic decisions, involving choice of weapons systems, deployments, and targets, into the pre-war period. In addition, the rapidity of change resulting from the development of nuclear weapons both in numbers and in range of sizes, combined with the development of fantastic new vehicles for carrying them, produced a requirement for something besides military experience and intuition as a means of selecting weapons systems, particularly in view of the tremendous sums of money involved in the choices. There was obviously much work for people with analytical skills, which is to say for scientists, whose prestige had been enormously enhanced by the very achievement of producing the nuclear bomb.

THE FOUNDING OF THE RESEARCH
INSTITUTIONS ON MILITARY AFFAIRS

In the United States a revolutionary occurrence resulted from this new military prestige of scientists and from certain sobering experiences in World War II. This was the founding of a number of institutions, associated with but outside the military services, in which people with various kinds of scientific training and with full access to classified information could devote themselves on a full-time basis to the consideration of tactical and strategic problems. The prototype and, with respect to our subject, the most conspicuous of these organizations has been The RAND Corporation, working primarily for the U.S. Air Force. RAND and other comparable institutions have played a role very much like certain great universities and research centers in the past, where some dedicated scholars and their students have opened up whole new fields of knowledge.[1] It

---

[1] Prominent among those other autonomous institutions where strategic analysis is carried on today are the Research Analysis Corporation, the Operations

should also be stressed that thus far this has been almost entirely an American movement. There are essentially no comparable institutions abroad. The Institute for Strategic Studies, with an international membership and headquarters in London, provides a valuable forum for public discussions of strategic questions and has sponsored certain very useful publications, but it is in no way a research institution patterned after RAND.

The use of scientists for assistance in making tactical decisions goes back at least to World War I, when such distinguished British scientists as Ernest Rutherford were employed to think up new ways of dealing with the German U-boats. At that time the British mathematician F. W. Lanchester laid the groundwork for what later became known as operations analysis. His book, entitled *Aircraft in Warfare* and published in 1916, is a landmark in the field.

Such employment of scientists was carried a long step forward in World War II, where several experiences of the air war probably helped convince General H. H. Arnold, then Chief of Staff of the U.S. Army Air Forces, that scientists had to be retained on a continuing basis in peacetime to assist the Air Force with its many tactical and strategic problems. For one thing, the U.S. Strategic Bombing Survey, carried out on the heels of the advancing or occupying armies first in Germany and then in Japan, had disclosed that the bombing attacks might have been much more effective if certain modest and easily achieved improvements had been made in weapons and techniques. Even more disturbing than the findings of the Survey was the fact that the Allied air forces had clearly lost several important technological races. The Germans had developed the missiles; first the HS-293 glide bomb used in the Mediterranean, then the V-1, and finally the V-2. They had also developed the ME

Evaluation Group, the Institute of Defense Analyses, affiliated with the Army, Navy, and Joint Chiefs of Staff, respectively, and the Stanford Research Institute, which does not have a specific affiliation. Within the Defense Department and attached directly to the Director of Defense Research and Engineering and the Joint Chiefs of Staff is the Weapons System Evaluation Group. In the university world the few relevant centers tend to be very small but contain some distinguished names; one must mention especially the Harvard University Center for International Affairs, the Columbia University Institute of War and Peace Studies, and the centers for international studies at Princeton and at the Massachusetts Institute of Technology.

262, a jet bomber of remarkable performance, and the rocket-powered fighter ME 163. The German wind tunnels were experimenting with swept-winged aircraft models that anticipated our F-86's and the Soviet MIGs. Their jet engines alone, if they had been applied to fighters rather than to bombers, as Hitler had insisted, might have been enough to stop the U.S. air offensive entirely (the ME 163's had too brief a cruising endurance to do the job, even if they had existed in somewhat larger numbers).

The initial interest of the Air Force in the RAND Corporation was no doubt primarily for the sake of technological advice, and thus the physics division and the several kinds of engineering divisions were basic. But those who organized RAND included in it at the outset a division of mathematics and within two years divisions also of economics and social science. As we shall see, the inclusion of an economics division turned out to be of critical importance.

The vital influence of the institutional framework in guiding and developing the interests as well as the skills of the participants is demonstrated by the fact that most past and present members of RAND who are now publicly distinguished in the field had done no work in military problems at the time they joined RAND. Others had shown some interest and accomplishment in the field before but received a strong and apparently permanent impetus toward full-time absorption with strategic problems as a result of their association with RAND. One must mention also the "consultantships" by which various ex-members of RAND, as well as others who have never been associated on a full-time basis, maintain a mutually stimulating and fruitful contact with the organization. Naturally, close contact is also kept up with members of similar research institutes as well as with those few individuals who have contributed significantly to the field while remaining in the university world.

At RAND an institutional learning process characterized the first few years of endeavor. Early work depended heavily on "inputs" provided by the Air Force, that is, upon assumptions or hypotheses about weapons performance and about other factors, including strategic needs. It was inevitable, however, that with time these assumptions and hypotheses would be increasingly challenged. One could have expected that putting together talented and highly trained persons to work full-time on military problems would certainly result in some of them becoming interested in reexamining the basic assumptions of the field, which is to say interested in the comprehensive problems of strategy rather than in limited tactical or technological problems.

CONCEPTUAL PARALLELS BETWEEN
STRATEGY AND ECONOMICS

In an article published in 1949 [2] this writer called attention to the remarkable similarities in both method and objectives between the science of economics and what could become a science of strategy. Both fields are essentially concerned with optimum utilization of scarce resources for the efficient achievement of certain objectives of society. It was argued that most of the concepts basic to economics could be transposed to the field of strategy with considerable resulting clarification—for example, the concepts of marginal utility and of opportunity cost. Events have confirmed this article to a totally unexpected degree. Most of those who have made their mark today as theorists in strategy have been trained as economists, or at least have more than a bowing acquaintance with the concepts and principles in that field. The modern training of economists, with its heavy emphasis on tools of quantitative analysis, tends to fit one peculiarly well for grappling with some characteristic problems of strategic analysis, and especially for making choices between weapons systems.

On the other hand, appropriately trained political scientists have a distinctive contribution to offer. It would be hard to overestimate the importance of being sensitive to the political issues that are omnipresent in strategic questions and of exercising good judgment where these political issues and their resulting research problems are concerned. It is an element often lacking in the equipment of talented men in other fields. Much is gained from putting the representatives of the several relevant disciplines together and

[2] Bernard Brodie, "Strategy as a Science," *World Politics*, I, No. 4 (July, 1949), 467–88.

getting them to work jointly on the same problems, along with physicists, engineers, and other technologists; but the interdisciplinary transference of insights is not always easy.

A major contribution to modern strategic thinking that emanated from the economists was the idea of using the dollar as a common measure of value in comparing the relative performance of competing weapons systems. The only known way to compare objectively the claims advanced in favor of each of two or more competing weapons systems is to examine how much it costs in each case to achieve a common objective, such as the destruction of a given number of targets in a given enemy area. The cost is measured not simply by the purchase price of the various weapons and vehicles involved, but by the whole material and manpower structure that goes into the system, extended over a suitably prolonged period of time to include the factors of amortization and of peacetime maintenance.

This kind of "cost-effectiveness" analysis has been greatly refined over the years, so that many factors which at first glance might not seem to be amenable to dollar-value comparison turn out to be so on closer examination. A simple example is the costing of reliability in a system, where the designer usually has some degree of choice between spending more money on each instrument to increase its reliability or increasing the total number of instruments so that the failure of one will be offset by the success of another.

All this is not to deny that good judgment, that is, intuition based on experience and other forms of educated insight, remains enormously important in the decision-making process. Some of the important factors relevant to determining the performance of a system are not finally reducible to dollar value. Besides, there is always the larger context—often with its special political and psychological overtones—into which the weapons systems must be fitted. Nevertheless, it is one thing to recognize the limits of cost-effectiveness analysis, and quite another to deny or depreciate the necessity of this and comparable techniques within the limits of their utility.

The overriding fact is that we are living in a world in which the whole agglomerate of strategic questions is essentially baffling, and in which choices, besides involving tremendous sums of money, commit us to future strategic positions that may determine the safety of the nation or even of civilization. Because of the large "leadtime" required between testing the feasibility of a new technological conception and actually being able to put the resulting hardware into production, the research and development decisions made at any one time usually have to derive from conceptions of what the strategic universe will be like some eight or ten years hence.

In view of the ongoing rate of technological change, such prediction can be a fearsome responsibility. The sums involved in developing a major weapons system are likely to be enormous and very difficult to predict accurately. Because of new technological discoveries, systems under development often turn out to be obsolete before they are completed, and therefore have to be abandoned and their heavy costs written off. Thus, at every stage, decisions are made which are difficult at best, and which are impossible to make wisely without utilizing all the tools that modern concepts of economic and strategic analysis have made available to us. This is a new condition which is now permanent; a state of the world undreamed of in 1939.

THE COMPLEXITIES OF STRATEGIC ANALYSIS

As we move to a larger context we see that we have hardly begun to measure the complexity of the major issues of strategic analysis. A nation makes its strategic dispositions not against a more or less predictable state of nature but against an opponent or group of opponents who are endowed with cunning as well as resources and whose intentions and capabilities have to be analyzed for the present and predicted for the future. The problems of decision in such a context are thus in part "gaming" problems—though the term is no doubt an unfortunate one in this context. It is obvious, for example, that to make optimum use of a given fund of resources for, say, antimissile defense, it is necessary to consider and make allowance for the kinds and numbers of offensive weapons that the opponent is likely to have at the time when one's defensive system will be ready for operation. Moreover, one has to adjust to a range of possible situations—the single most likely situation does not necessarily have a high degree of likelihood. And, obviously, one's defensive preparations will affect the offensive designs of the opponent, as well as vice versa.

This example tends to fall in the category of what is called a "zero-sum game," that is, a game in which one side's gain is the other side's loss. But not all strategic problems, and perhaps not even most of them, fall into this category. The opponent's interests are not always in direct and reciprocal conflict with one's own. Both sides obviously have a common interest in avoiding wars which are utterly ruinous, and this interest is distinctive from, though obviously similar to, that of avoiding wars altogether. The former interest is one that has already had a profound effect on strategy.

For example, we have already referred to the difficulties resulting from the fantastic speed with which military technology is developing. The layman may feel that after a nuclear weapon has reached a certain level of power further increases in its power are likely to be of little importance. In particular categories of weapons there may indeed be some justification for that view, but if we are seeking to use a weapon as the warhead on a missile, we are bound to be critically concerned with its over-all weight as compared to yield. As the opponent installs and augments passive protection around his missiles, we not only have to make ours more accurate but we may also have to fit more and more powerful warheads on them in order to restore some part of our capability to destroy his offensive power. Or we may have to devote some payload weight to decoys. In addition, we may desire to make our warheads "clean" rather than "dirty," or we may decide for comparable reasons that we have to use air-bursts rather than ground-bursts. All these changes directly and significantly affect our requirements in weapons development.

To consider only one category of weapons or instruments, however, inevitably oversimplifies the problem. It is a broad spectrum of weapons in which change is occurring at so alarming a rate—alarming because of all the elements of uncertainty, with resulting fallibility, that are bound to be introduced. In the seventeen years since the initial introduction of nuclear weapons, developments in the character, variety, and abundance of these weapons, as well as of the vehicles designed to carry them, have effected not one but several distinct revolutions in military technology; and these are not the only instruments of military technology with which we have to be concerned.

In our past studies we have often found ourselves struggling to "locate the exact peak of a rather flat curve" when the problem was really to get on to some entirely different curve. In other words, one has often seen "studies which try to determine the exact best way to perform an operation which shouldn't be performed at all." [3] This is one reason why analytically trained people of mature strategic insight may not be willing to accept as given those postulates traditional to a military service which is often ruled by the conviction that one particular kind of function is essential to its being.

This point also suggests another insight that happens to be one of the recent breakthroughs in the science of strategic analysis. Where the tendency used to be to try to find the optimum method of dealing with the single most expected contingency, the realization that the enemy might not want to play the game that way—the realization, in other words, that the enemy is both cunning and intent on injuring us—has prompted us to seek instead that complex of solutions which does rather well over a complex of contingencies. For example, it does no good to perfect a defense against high-altitude bombers that leaves us entirely open against low-altitude bombers. Within a given budget and depending on the actual figures involved, a solution is likely to be preferable which also has some capability against those entering at low-altitudes even if it does less well against the high-altitude craft. What we need are systems that will work well under widely divergent contingencies, and perhaps even give some sort of reasonably satisfactory performance under major catastrophe. In analysis aimed at policy-making, the relevance of the many factors and contingencies which affect our problem is more important than the mathematical or economic sophistication of the analytic techniques applied. This is where we must rely on good judgment, which must include a disposition to see beyond the limits of the assignment in hand.

[3] See Albert Wohlstetter, "Defense Decisions: Design vs. Analysis, abstract of paper presented to Second International Conference on Operational Research, Aix-en-Provence, France, September, 1960.

THE USES AND LIMITATIONS OF GAMING

It is appropriate at this point to say a few more words about the use of gaming techniques in strategic analysis, because in the minds of laymen the importance of this aspect of strategic analysis has been exaggerated to a considerable degree. The refinements of game theory as developed for the most part by the late mathematician John von Neumann are generally of little importance to the strategic analyst. Actually, many analysts do exceedingly good work without having much familiarity with game theory, though they will unquestionably utilize some of its concepts. What matters is the spirit of game theory, the constant awareness that we will be dealing with an opponent who will counteract our moves and to whom we must in turn react. It is amazing how little this simple conception of reciprocal response has characterized war plans in the past. Perhaps the greatest merit of the war-gaming technique is that it stimulates this kind of awareness. It does not matter how simple or complex the particular game, as long as the enemy is represented by a player who will see to it that the initiative and capabilities accorded him by the terms of the game will mean something in practice, and who will make the most of the tokens he is given to play with. It is really remarkable what immunities the usual war-plans designer has taken for granted as belonging by right to his own forces, and how quickly his roseate fantasies have collapsed the moment he has played on paper (or otherwise) a simple war game in which the enemy is allowed something like comparable power and perhaps the initiative to boot. Another benefit of war games is that they force the players to consider the problem beyond the opening moves, which it is otherwise very difficult for a war planner to force himself to do. There are other advantages in war games, but there are also some disadvantages. Chief among the latter is the tendency, especially in the more complicated games, for the play to induce in the player the illusion that he has really tested his hypotheses or presumptions in a conclusive manner. Another is the tendency to design an opponent who will be aggressive and imaginative enough to make the game interesting, rather than one who is as close as possible to the real life opponent.

THE IMPERFECTIONS OF SCIENTIFIC STRATEGY

We come now to the inevitable limitations and imperfections of scientific method in strategic analyses and decision-making, and especially to the imperfections and limitations in the practitioners, whose greatest limitation is that they sometimes fail to observe true scientific discipline. Such lapses illustrate one respect in which the practitioners are human, and thus disposed to sharing the infirmities of humanity. There are also others.

For one thing the most basic issues in strategy often do not lend themselves to scientific analysis. This is usually because they are laden with value judgments. They therefore tend to escape any kind of disciplined or searching thought. These are the issues on which official judgments simply reflect the traditional thinking of military or civilian bureaucracies, heavily overlaid with service or departmental prejudice. Such prejudice is not confined to stupid or unsophisticated men. It also limits the thinking of the most gifted and the most highly trained.

As this writer has said on another occasion:

Those of us who do this work are beset by all kinds of limitations, including limitations in talent and in available knowledge. Where the object is to predict the future, for the sake of appropriate action, we simply cannot wait until all the relevant facts are in. Besides, we can make progress only as we cut off and treat in isolation a small portion of the total universe of data and of problems that confront us, and every research project is to that extent "out of context." In addition, we are dealing always with large admixtures of pure chance. These are sometimes difficult to take into full account without seeming to stultify our results, and that human beings are naturally loath to do. The same is true of the large range of variables which deal with enemy intentions and capabilities. Finally, we are immersed in bias, our own and that of our clients or readers. With our audience, in spite of our strong efforts to be objective, we cannot avoid being influenced by what we know it likes to hear. Feelings of loyalty and friendship are involved, as well as a normal liking for applause.[4]

Even in the areas in which strictly scientific analysis is appropriate, the temptation always exists to short-cut some of the analytical

[4] Bernard Brodie, *Strategy in the Missile Age* (Princeton, N.J., Princeton University Press, 1959), p. 407.

difficulties and to pretend to analytic objectivity where it has ceased to operate. This is due to the complexity of the field, the impossibility of conclusively testing one's planning factors or deductions, and the fact that one is constantly running up against the region of value judgment or simply the region where the mysteries of the future remain impenetrable. Scientific method is not what we always accomplish but what we always have to try to adhere to, and the great merit of the scientifically trained analyst is that he tries more persistently than do persons without this training, and he can be more easily made aware of his lapses when they occur. When we do succeed in using scientific method for the systematic exploration and comparison of alternative courses of action, we are simply doing the best we can to bring some order into the vast, chaotic mass of technological, economic, and political facts and predictions which form the universe of data in which reasonable military decisions have to be made.

RELATIONS BETWEEN THE ANALYSTS AND THEIR MILITARY CLIENTS

Finally, a word on the relations between the civilian scientific strategists and their military clients. On the whole these relations have been thoroughly good and mutually profitable. Where it has not been so, it is usually because we are dealing with character weaknesses on one or both sides. Most military officers know their own worth, and their indispensable qualifications for service, and are content to recognize the limits of their training and experience. Some are not. The same holds true for the analysts. Also, it has always been true that creative abilities are not necessarily combined in the same person with such character endowments as tact and modesty. Besides, special new conditions having to do with the appearance of new personalities in high civilian and military office may set up extra frictions; these stand a good chance of being at least partially smoothed out with time, which includes the certainty of further changes.

For example, the coming to office of Mr. Robert S. McNamara as Secretary of Defense has introduced, among other things, a much tighter and more thorough degree of civilian supervision of military decisions than has ever prevailed before. In such a circumstance it is inevitable that the civilian analyst may find himself in a condition of special strain with his military clients, who find themselves harried from above and perhaps no longer enjoying exclusive jurisdiction over the analyst's output. Questions of service interest are involved, and the close confidence essential to mutually profitable collaboration may be tested.

Yet a dominant consideration that must affect one's evaluation of the change is its impermanence. Certainly a number of important trends existing before the present administration, and brought to fuller fruition under Secretary NcNamara, represent long-term and largely irreversible changes. One, for example, is the new method of budgeting according to strategic functions rather than to services, and another is the tendency for decision-making on major weapons systems to be brought into the direct purview of the Office of the Secretary of Defense. Yet, there seems to be little chance for institutionalizing the pervasive and searching kind of civilian control of the whole gamut of important military decisions that a very special kind of secretary with a most unusual array of assistants has undertaken. Most future secretaries will very likely not want to shoulder that kind of responsibility.

One must therefore conclude that the military chieftains are likely to continue to have primary responsibility for major military decisions and for making recommendations to their political superiors regarding national security for a long time in the future. The civilian strategic analysts will in the main continue to understand and appreciate the distinctive role of the military in the guidance of national security affairs, and the military will undoubtedly continue to appreciate their need for objective analysis of a kind which they have neither the freedom nor the appropriate training to undertake themselves. This collaboration can be expected to continue and to prosper for the common good.

It is doubtless also true that the conditions of the relationship are in a state of flux, and that the pattern of the future will probably not permit as much accent on exclusiveness in the appropriate connections as was true in the past. The new sophistication in military affairs represented in a small but growing section of the intellectual public is bound to have a large and enduring effect on national security policy. Can anyone regret such a development in today's world? The fantastic new gadgetry of attack and defense, with its awful potential of destructiveness, creates a need for all the brain power that can be brought to bear on issues of national and indeed international security which so deeply concern every citizen.

Scientists and the Establishment
of Science Affairs

CHRISTOPHER WRIGHT

*Executive Director of the Council for Atomic Age Studies
and Lecturer in the Department of Public Law
and Government of Columbia University*

Science has untold ramifications for the rest of society, both as a human enterprise conducted by scientists and as a systematic body of knowledge and methods. These ramifications, together with the reciprocal effects of society on science, constitute the substance of science affairs or the external relations of science.

The major feature of science affairs in the period beginning with World War II has been the continuous effort to build better bridges between the science community and the government. They have been built in an effort to promote cooperation, yet little attention is paid to the meaning of "cooperation" in this context, to understanding the nature, volume, and direction of traffic over the many bridges, to assessing the impact of this traffic in the adjacent areas, or to regulating it by means other than the brute-force technique of building up or breaking down the structures themselves. Without expert understanding and practice of science affairs, coupled with statesmanship of the highest kind, national policies involving science will at best remain precarious and at worst contradictory, for both scientists and nonscientists are actually laymen when it comes to understanding their mutual interests and complementary capabilities. The style and conduct of science affairs as they affect national policy-making has nevertheless been influenced more by the state of science and the professional characteristics of some scientists than by formal organizational arrangements or policies about how to make policy. This essay identifies and assesses characteristic features of this influence in terms of four primary functions of science affairs: mobilizing scientific and technical resources, developing the interests and institutions of science or of government, analysis and review, and creating goals and guiding change.

With the benefit of hindsight we now know that we have been living in a new age of science for over twenty years without understanding many implications of this fact. A substantial percentage of America's best physical scientists left the Manhattan Project and the M.I.T. Radiation Laboratories at the end of World War II expecting to return to their universities to engage in the pure basic research and the routine training of graduate students that had been interrupted by the War.[1] But the nation's expenditures on research and development since the War have accelerated the growth and drastically altered the character of scientific research and education and the careers of scientists and engineers. Science and its practitioners have moved from the eddies to the mainstream of our nation's activities. Now many social decisions involving industrial production, resource allocation, organizations, manpower, foreign relations, and military security are dependent on specific scientific facts and analyses and on the activities, ideas, and opinions of natural scientists.

The growing volume and social importance of science and of technologies directly based on science has produced new intellectual and practical problems for many working scientists, such as the rapid obsolescence of their most specialized talents. It is having a still more profound effect upon a small number of scientists and others who actively, and often on a full-time basis, help mediate between science and government in ways that go far beyond engineering and science administration as traditionally practiced. These activities involve the giving of advice, the analysis of major policies and programs, the imaginative development and screening of ideas about how science might affect national policies and how it will be affected by them, and other activities appropriate to the custodians of scientific discoveries whether these custodians be research scientists or not.

While the quality of truth itself may be inviolate, the quality of the quest for truth is not. The direction and design of experiments,

<hr />

[1] Dr. Seaborg has referred to this as "the great hegira to fundamental research" in an address before the annual meeting of the American Association for the Advancement of Science, December 27, 1961.

interpretation of data, theoretical speculations, dissemination of results, and relations of scientists to students, to each other, and to outside authorities have all undergone qualitative changes attributable in part to the changing character of science affairs and to the related intellectual and social development of science and scientists.

Some of the most fundamental features of contemporary science affairs affecting the formulation of national policies were identified by President Eisenhower in his Farewell Address to the Nation in 1961 in which he suggested that research was the key to our technological revolution; that we were in danger of distorting and perhaps drying up the source of free intellectual ideas and scientific discovery in favor of military research and development; and "that public policy could itself become the captive of a scientific-technological elite." [2] This third observation was subsequently clarified by George B. Kistiakowsky, who at the time of the address was President Eisenhower's Special Assistant for Science and Technology. He stated that the danger referred to was meant to be associated with a specific scientific-technological elite within what could become a highly undesirable combination of special interests in industry, the press, and perhaps institutions of higher learning as a result of the nation's emphasis on military research and development. In contrast, the true nature of basic research was held to be "a cultural endeavor and a source of advancing welfare to the people." [3]

Both the content and context of these observations about the nature of contemporary science affairs should alert us to the need for detailed understanding of the scientific-technological elites and the various possible relations between scientific research, military security, human welfare, social values, and the policy-making and policy advice of scientists. In the absence of Kistiakowsky's gloss, it would have been possible to interpret President Eisenhower's remarks as meaning that whatever the particular character, balance, or thrust of scientific research and discovery, the indiscriminate exploitation of the results by scientists and technologists could have the effect of making public policy the captive of these persons and their organi-

[2] *Department of State Bulletin*, XLIV, No. 1128 (February 6, 1961), 181.
[3] "Footnote to History," *Science*, CXXXIII, No. 3450 (February 10, 1961), 355. (An Editorial embodying a statement made by George B. Kistiakowsky.)

zations. Indeed, President Eisenhower's concluding assertion in his train of thought was that it is "the task of statesmanship to mold, to balance, and to integrate these and other forces, new and old, with the principles of our democratic system—ever aiming towards the supreme goals of our free society." [4]

Governmental and other national policy-making activities of natural scientists at the present time have been useful and even essential contributions to the fulfillment of new functions which may, however, be performed by others in the future. Since the beginning of World War II new roles have been forced on scientists in greatly increased volume and variety. Perhaps these roles are necessary and suitable extensions of science and the work of scientists. Perhaps they are merely transient experiments in response to the obvious national need to perform certain complicated, difficult, and frequently new governmental functions, for there are clear indications that these functions are being weaned away from the community of scientists as such. The community of persons involved in science affairs is becoming increasingly differentiated from the community of scientists as a whole. Although the members of this new community are still mostly scientists or ex-scientists, only a very small proportion of all scientists are members. The many functions of this new community are giving rise to a complex structure of institutions which is evolving according to a discernible pattern that is itself influenced to a considerable extent by the methods of science and the natural scientists. A special new kind of Establishment may be in the making.

In the early 1940s the newest features of science affairs of special interest to government and to the making of major national policies were the concern of a few prophetic scientists, science statesmen, and established men of public affairs for whom attention to the uses and problems of science was often only one of many responsibilities. Awareness of the critical importance and scarcity of specific scientific knowledge led to the growth of a science affairs community composed primarily of persons who were also outstanding experts in a few critical fields of science. Now, the membership of the science

---

[4] "President Eisenhower's Farewell to the Nation," *Department of State Bulletin*, XLIV, No. 1128 (February 6, 1961), 181.

affairs community is beginning to include specialists and generalists adept at performing many governmental and policy-making functions presently performed by research scientists at the expense of their concentration on the pursuit of science.

The need for a very special kind of statesmanship to cope with contemporary science affairs is becoming evident. Science and technology inherently tend to upset the established order. Our government is geared to respond to traditional kinds of disruptive forces such as war, crime, natural disaster, or economic upsets for which patterns of response can draw on precedent or be tested by experience. New mechanisms must be devised and new talents perfected to fill the interstices created when, as a result of an endless succession of new challenges related to science, the pinnacle of responsible authority and leadership lacks supporting institutions and expertise based on conditioned responses.

Experience can be of some help. Thus far America has, in fact, responded constructively and deliberately to the challenges presented by scientific advances, although the incidence of upsetting surprises is increasing. Efforts have been made to fill the gaps created in the governmental structure with persons and mechanisms that will bring new ideas, opportunities, and lines of inquiry to the attention of individuals and groups which can supply the most relevant information, analyses, and support. Enough experience has been acquired concerning these mechanisms so that it is now possible to identify characteristics of their new functions, the means used to perform them, and the sorts of persons involved in this effort over the past twenty years.

THE MAKE-UP OF THE SCIENCE AFFAIRS COMMUNITY

The science affairs community is comprised of individuals who directly and significantly influence national science policy or the role of science in the development of other national policies. It includes some articulate persons who have original scientific minds or can at least understand and interpret established scientific theories and techniques. It also includes those who are in positions to command large research teams or their supporting facilities, to control the dissemination of scientific information, or to speak for significant numbers of scientists on any one of a number of matters. Some members belong because of their willingness to serve or because of their status among scientists; others, because of the power over science activities vested in them by outside authorities or supporters. These persons tend to communicate with each other on matters directly involving the interactions of science and society. They share a special and sometimes extremely detailed interest in the subject. In this sense they form a primitive community.

This community has some evidence of stability and structure including hierarchies, patterns of mobility, and avenues of entry which tend to make membership only partly determined by the functions which the community itself performs or by its internal needs. In this sense the science affairs community is established, although it possesses but a few of the exclusive, autocratic tendencies one might associate with an Establishment. It is, in fact, expanding, and both its responsibilities and composition are changing in rough accord with each other.

For the most part, active involvement in science affairs is by participation in small-group activities or by writing for popular or semipopular publications. It is possible to list virtually all the groups and their leading members at any given time, even though it is impossible to ascertain the exact importance or interrelations of these groups for national policy-making. The lists overlap considerably and are short enough to remind us of the influence of individual personalities but long enough to remind us that members of the President's Science Advisory Committee (PSAC) and his Special Assistant for Science and Technology are not the only members of the science affairs community.

Individual and group positions directly involved in the conduct of science affairs can now be found on many policy levels of government, among government contractors for research and policy studies, within private and quasi-governmental organizations concerned with science and engineering, in the administration of facilities for large-scale research and development, and to a lesser extent within private nonscience organizations. It is sufficient to point to the existence of these groups and individual positions, to use them as a basis for identifying participants in the science affairs community and to note the main trends affecting the role or composition of these groups without attempting to assess their relative importance or adequacy. Such an assessment is complex and beyond the scope of this paper, for the importance and value of the various groups and offices appears to depend in large measure on the intelligence and energy of the particular participants rather than on formal authority.

Three significant formal features of these groups, offices, and other positions are, however, (1) their novelty, (2) the increasing expectation that the persons involved will be fully attentive to specific aspects of science affairs without dividing their time or their loyalties, and (3) the general movement of these groups upward in the organization charts of government and private institutions. Mechanisms for giving attention and weight to science and technology and to the contributions of scientists are thus being built into the general fabric of major national policy-making. Very few of the positions listed below existed before 1945 and most of them acquired their present structure and status only after the launching of Sputnik I in 1957. Whether the particular position is nominally old or new, many of the functions to be performed are quite new or at least have taken on new dimensions of importance and interdependence in response to the times. They reflect our tradition of interdependence between public and private initiative and policy-making, but they also involve new solutions to new problems which it would be misleading to describe as either a gathering-in or an alienation of prior governmental responsibilities.

Government organization for science affairs. Although some states, for example, New York with its Office of Atomic Development, have offices concerned with aspects of scientific and technical research and development, virtually all specific governmental attention to science affairs is associated with the federal government. With some notable exceptions in Congress, the greater part of this attention is now found within the Executive. On rare occasions, and then on an *ad hoc* basis, the Judiciary has gone beyond the adversary style of judicial decision-making and consulted scientific experts and utilized the results of scientific research.

In addition to the Joint Committee on Atomic Energy (JCAE) of Congress there are individual committees and subcommittees with jurisdictions over one or another of the many federal offices, departments, and agencies having some responsibility for scientific research and development. Still other committees and subcommittees act on related appropriations. The House of Representatives Committee on Science and Astronautics is the only committee, however, with a mandate to consider science research as a whole and prepare for the consequences of new scientific discoveries and applications that do not fall under the present jurisdiction of any other committee.

Typically the congressional committees with the greatest influence in science affairs have been powerful for other reasons and are not especially concerned with this area of activity. In recent years committees having scientific or technological agencies as their primary concern have, however, developed increased influence, and that of the JCAE has even spread from Congress to the Executive to an extent that has alarmed some participants and been a source of satisfaction to others.[5] In any event, the mechanism of the Joint Committee was not followed in the creation of congressional machinery for overseeing programs having to do with outer space.

Some congressional committees are acquiring professional staff members with expert knowledge of science or of science affairs. Other committees make use of scientists as consultants and hold hearings at which scientists and others testify about matters that often have more to do with science affairs than with science itself. The Committee on Science and Astronautics even has a permanent panel of scientists to provide guidance and counsel concerning science and engineering. Individual Senators and Congressmen with interests in science and technology that go beyond their ordinary

---

[5] Harold P. Green and Alan Rosenthal, *The Joint Committee on Atomic Energy, A Study in Fusion of Government Power* (Washington, D.C., The National Law Center of George Washington University, 1961) and H. L. Nieburg, "The Eisenhower AEC and Congress: A Study in Executive-Legislative Relations," *Midwest Journal of Political Science*, V, No. 6 (May, 1962), 222–29.

committee responsibilities are tending to acquire their own science advisers or are participating in other private efforts to inform themselves about science and science affairs.

In the formulation of national policies involving science, the Executive makes extensive use of scientists and others who are not necessarily full-time federal employees. These individuals generally serve on science boards, councils, committees, and advisory panels, or as individual consultants. Such positions are now a fixture, if not a fashion, in many federal agencies and may range in their demands from intense but intermittent intellectual involvement to perfunctory assemblies three or four times a year. Sometimes, as with the Advisory Committee on Weather Control (1953–57), an independent body is set up by act of Congress. In this case the Committee included some Cabinet officers and some private members. Other outsiders serve on a full-time basis for periods of a year or more as science adviser, assistant secretary, director for research and development, chief scientist, science attaché, or a similar position subordinate to Cabinet officers, heads of agencies, chiefs-of-staff, or ambassadors.

The separate agencies and offices most exclusively concerned with aspects of science and technology, include the Atomic Energy Commission (AEC), the National Science Foundation (NSF), the National Aeronautics and Space Administration (NASA), the Office of the Director of Defense Research and Engineering, the National Institutes of Health, and most recently the Office of Science and Technology (OST) in the Executive Office of the President. They are headed by officials who are not only among the prime movers in science affairs but also tend to have a background in science or some other close identification with the science community. The trend is clear. Future scientific and technical breakthroughs of major proportions are likely to force the creation of further agencies or other centers of administrative power. In the meantime, and perhaps in an effort to forestall this possibility, an increasing number of established departments and agencies are creating science advisory committees. This step tends to be followed by the establishment of a full-time science adviser or even an officer of high administrative rank whose task is not only to mobilize the resources of science for the benefit of the agency, drawing upon his science background for this purpose, but also to integrate these resources with others that come under his administrative command.

Professional staffs closely associated with many of these advisory and policy-making positions often do not have advanced science training and research experience. If any trend is discernible it is toward a relaxation of the requirements for scientific originality in favor of executive and political ability mixed with some acquaintance with science and an ability to communicate with scientists about matters pertaining to science affairs.

A number of interagency policy-making and coordinating groups at different levels within the Executive, and composed exclusively of full-time officials, are devoted to specific aspects of science affairs. The permanent ones include the National Aeronautics and Space Council, the Federal Radiation Council, the Federal Council for Science and Technology (FCST) and its subsidiaries, and the AEC-DOD Military Liaison Committee. Although the National Security Council (NSC) has a wider mandate, its deliberations involving matters of science affairs must be of crucial importance to it and to the future course of the relations between science and government.[6] As with many other positions referred to here, these groups have had a varied history in terms of their activity and their inclusion or exclusion of "private" members. The chief participants in most such councils are political officials whose primary loyalty must be to the President or the government as a whole, and yet even here it is possible to note a decided trend toward the inclusion of officials otherwise identified with science affairs by virtue of their executive responsibilities, their professional loyalties, or their status as representatives of scientists as constituents, or of the interests of science as an enterprise.

A review of the policy-making activities associated with the groups mentioned above would indicate that a useful but by no means sharp line can be drawn between science affairs and science. The govern-

---

[6] The fact, although not the substance, of NSC reviews of technological capabilities is occasionally brought to public attention. One such review is discussed in Morton H. Halperin, "The Gaither Committee and the Policy Process," *World Politics*, XIII, No. 3 (April, 1961), 360–84.

ment does, of course, enlist the services of a great many outside scientists and engineers for advice on matters within their areas of special technical competence that do not bear directly on science affairs. These matters may involve advising on selections for research grants or fellowship awards, the setting of scientific standards, or the design of a special experiment or weapon. Thus, members of the NSF Advisory Panels, for example, are not ordinarily concerned with science affairs, whereas the National Science Board, the various Directors, and the Divisional Advisory Committees may contribute directly to the formulation of national science policy. The same distinction exists between the committees and the councils associated with each of the National Institutes of Health. Similarly, while the AEC General Advisory Committee is *ordinarily* involved in science affairs the other advisory committees of the AEC are not. In other instances, as with the Department of Defense, a committee's work may be purely technical while the direction of its efforts is a sufficiently delicate policy matter so that the chairman performs a function in science affairs while the other members do not.

It is characteristic and noteworthy that initial involvement of individuals and groups in science affairs is often associated with the fact some phenomenon about which they are technically expert has become an object of high policy concern. In connection with national security particularly, matters of technical or tactical interest have a way of suddenly taking on major strategic importance and catapulting technical experts or administrators to high policy-making or advisory councils where they sometimes remain.

Nevertheless, it is not too difficult to find the dividing line at a given time between those individuals and groups which are expected to advise or pass judgment on significant issues of science affairs and those that are not. It is in the nature of science and working scientists to obscure this line, and yet the close identity of science affairs with science and scientists also facilitates this division because the natural scientists, and more particularly the physical scientists, have a well-developed system of classifying and honoring fellow scientists according to ability. They also have a tradition whereby each scientist tends to represent himself alone. Thus, although in science affairs the matter of ability and the issue of representation are necessarily more complicated than in science, the recognized caliber of the physical scientists known to be drawn into the government's organization of these activities and their reluctance to accept direction from others makes it unlikely that there are many other scientists playing equally authoritative but unrecognized roles at policy-making levels. The same may not be said for contributors of advice on issues of science affairs that do not seem to require or stem from special scientific competence.

On the basis of this distinction between science affairs and science, there are now approximately fifty full-time positions and five to ten major interagency committees in the Executive directly concerned with science affairs and probably several times these numbers of supporting professional staff positions. There are also about fifty established public advisory or policy-making groups most directly concerned with science affairs. Each of these groups has an average of ten to twenty members and is public in the sense that it includes members who are not full-time government employees. At any one time there are as well many *ad hoc* public committees or special study groups.

Few of these positions existed prior to World War II. For the most part they have been created in response to the urgencies of national security and the government's commitment to the support of scientific research and training on a large scale. If any other trend is detectable it is an increasing number of full-time positions in government carrying the same kinds of advisory and review responsibilities earlier vested in a part-time committee. As the public groups are relieved of these specialized functions they dissolve or else assume broader and often more honorific responsibilities concerning science affairs. They also appear to integrate, or at least represent, a greater variety of expertise by acquiring a more heterogeneous membership.

Government contractors for research and policy studies. Closely related to the government's organization for science affairs is the attention paid to them in nonprofit corporations that contract to do management, research, or policy studies for the government in national defense and other areas. The RAND Corporation and the Institute for Defense Analyses (IDA), for instance, have full-time personnel concerned with aspects of science affairs and make use of advisory groups and part-time consultants in ways comparable to those employed by the government. The Jason Division of IDA, for example, is composed of some leading young physical scientists who, on a part-time basis, help it produce analyses intended to assist high policy-making. In this process Jason attempts, apparently, to live up to the reputation of its namesake.[7]

One of the prime functions of such organizations is, in fact, to engage in the kind of synoptic forward planning that depends, among other things, on understanding science affairs. This function has often been performed on an *ad hoc* project basis by specially assembled study groups. The tendency to organize and formalize the arrangements is almost always present and as a result there has been a proliferation of "RAND-type" organizations.

Science organizations. The National Academy of Sciences-National Research Council (NAS-NRC), the American Association for the Advancement of Science (AAAS), and to a lesser extent the many specific professional associations of scientists and engineers play significant roles in science affairs. The NAS now has a self-perpetuating membership of about 0.6 percent of the high-status scientists in the nation. Its charter specifies that it shall advise the government when asked to do so. The associated Research Council was established primarily to be of research assistance to the government. Either *ex officio* or as a matter of practical convenience the President of the Academy also occupies many governmental positions dealing with science affairs. He now receives a full-time salary as President, although until recently this office only involved partial compensation and fifteen years ago it provided none at all. Under his direction the Governing Board of the NAS-NRC and the committees which it establishes have a long record of participation in science affairs by determining when and how to encourage the development or application of particular fields of science. In the 1950s the Academy

---

[7] "Jason, rightful heir to the throne, came anonymously down to Iolcos to claim his kingdom. He taunted Peleas with a recital of Minyan misfortunes and accused him of cowardice for failing even to attempt to recover the Fleece from its sanctuary at the far end of the Black Sea. The upshot was that Peleas appointed him leader of a recovery expedition and agreed to relinquish the throne on successful completion of the mission." *IDA Annual Report III* (Washington, D.C., Institute for Defense Analyses, 1958), p. 1.

went beyond its traditional advisory functions to assume general administrative responsibility for the American contribution to the International Geophysical Year (IGY) in order that the IGY might not only be a scientific success but also a valuable contribution to international cooperation. In 1962 the Academy created the Committee on Government Relations, subsequently renamed the Committee on Science and Public Policy, to consider and help solve some major problems of contemporary science affairs. Because of tradition the National Academy has endeavored to avoid permanent responsibility for operating programs. Hence the Academy's increased responsibilities with respect to science affairs are by no means rising in proportion to the nation's total involvement in science and hence in science affairs. Formidable new demands are nevertheless being placed on the Academy and are reflected in the increases in the professional staff and in the activities of such Academy officials as the President, the Foreign Secretary, and other members, and in their increased reliance for expert judgments and policy advice on scientists and men of experience in science affairs who are not members of the Academy. It would even appear that membership in the Academy is occasionally conferred on creditable scientists whose distinctive excellence is, or is expected to be, more in the area of science affairs than of science.

Unlike the NAS-NRC, the AAAS is open to anyone interested in science. It has an elected Board of Directors and appointed committees concerned with such issues in science affairs as science and the promotion of human welfare and the social aspects of science. On occasion these committees conduct organized discussions or issue reports. In 1958 the AAAS itself convened the Parliament of Science, which consisted of several hundred persons invited with a view to securing a good balance with respect to fields of science, types of background and employment, and geographical representation. The Parliament issued a statement about the organization of science with special reference to proposals for creating a Department of Science in the federal government.

Some professional societies, such as the National Society of Professional Engineers, have executive or other committees which consider aspects of science affairs and, through congressional testimony or otherwise, take positions on controversial issues related to them. In this Society, for instance, the Committee on Federal Engineering and Scientific Activities prepared a report on the organization of engineering and scientific activities in the federal government which recommended legislation to establish a high-level coordinating body in the Office of the President that would include representatives of the engineering and scientific community.

Some members of the science community have, on occasion, engaged in science affairs through special organizations of scientists rather than through their professional organizations. Most notable among these are positions of leadership in the Federation of American Scientists, the *Bulletin of the Atomic Scientists* (which describes itself as the only journal devoted to issues of science and public policy), the American Academy of Arts and Sciences, the American Continuing Committee for the Conferences on Science and World Affairs (formerly known as the Pugwash Conferences), and less well-known groups such as the Society for the Social Responsibility of Science and the American Association of Scientific Workers. Members of the science community have also engaged in less formally sponsored activities of a collective nature, including special studies and the preparation and marshaling of public support for policy recommendations on matters such as radioactive fallout, nuclear bomb testing, and shelter programs. Again, the trend is for increased activity bearing on science affairs. In these situations it is founded on the common bonds of scientists rather than of science. The notion of who is a scientist becomes more obscured and participation is governed more by a common political purpose than by any common background of professional methods or training.

Administration of large-scale research facilities. The complexity of science affairs as an area of policy planning and programmed activity necessitates several levels of policy-making and more or less abstract planning between the working levels and the pinnacle of political leadership. The intellectual exercises involved in these processes must not, however, neglect the fact that ultimately the opportunities and difficulties arising from the interactions of science and society depend on the substance of specific scientific research and related technological developments, and on the interests of those who make these possible. For the most part, these activities require organized support now frequently centered in large research facilities supported by the government directly or through universities, special nonprofit or limited profit corporations, or industrial concerns. The scale and changing character of many of these facilities requires that their directors and intellectual leaders be concerned with matters of science policy and national policy and not merely with laboratory administration.[8] In rare but notable cases the intellectual power of one man's mind may not only be focused on matters fraught with national policy implications but may be equal to or a superior substitute for the work of a large research facility. An individual may for this reason occupy a significant position in science affairs.[9] But the specific research activities of most scientists are not in themselves a basis for participation in science affairs, even though the scientists may be extremely competent and their work extremely important, albeit of less crucial relevance to the making of national policies.

Nonscience organizations and publications. To an increasing extent scientists are included in the activities or direction of organizations, publications, and other mechanisms for developing thought on a great variety of subjects not directly associated with science and technology. The scientists or their surrogates who, for example, participate in committees of the National Planning Association, write for leading journals of public affairs, or serve on boards of trustees of universities and philanthropic foundations may thereby play signif-

---

[8] An exaggerated but no less revealing indication of the policy interests and implications of directing large teams of scientists and advanced technologists is found in the fact that of the approximately 130 young men and women from the "take over" generation that were singled out in all fields of endeavor from the arts and sciences to business, government, and theology for mention by the editors of *Life* (September 14, 1962), no less than twenty are participants in science affairs because of their responsibilities for research programs while at least another five to ten fall into other categories of participants.

[9] Scientists sometimes appear to be driven by their awareness of the fact that one individual's intellectual insights may have profound effects on science affairs and on the work of many scientists and technologists. Enrico Fermi and John von Neumann are notable examples of persons who participated in science affairs on this basis irrespective of their many other contributions and who are universally revered by fellow scientists for this reason.

icant parts in the conduct of science affairs. In much the same category are the increasing numbers of professional science writers who do not limit themselves to explaining the content of science to the layman but articulate the ways in which science depends on society or will, together with technology, affect areas of social affairs such as defense, education, health, international relations, and resource development.[10]

The size of the science affairs community. A list of individuals occupying the positions described in the above paragraphs probably would not total more than about 800 to 1,000 names at any one time, although, because of multiple participation by some individuals, the number of positions may be larger. As additional types of positions are included, the list expands very rapidly and the special characteristics of the science affairs community are lost among those of the larger communities of persons involved in science or in public affairs generally.[11] If, on the other hand, the positions of obviously less crucial importance in science affairs are discounted, the number of those most intimately and deliberately involved is reduced to 200 or fewer. At present there appears to be no reliable *a priori* basis for further eliminations from this nucleus.

The size of this community probably does not vary much from that of other communities actively and influentially involved in complex matters of national concern because its size is influenced by

---

[10] Notable examples of this kind of reporting are to be found in the section "News and Comment" of *Science,* and in the coverage of the IGY and other activities of scientists provided by the New York *Times.* A striking example of this aspect of science affairs is found in the reactions Rachel Carson's book on biocides, *The Silent Spring,* has produced in the public, in industry, and in a panel of the PSAC. See, for example, "Experts Studying Pesticide Dangers to Man, Wildlife," *Washington Post,* September 1, 1962, p. A4.

[11] Estimates vary, but there seems to be rough agreement on the size and character of the following categories within the community of scientists and technologists:

"High status" scientists	100,000
"Acceptable" scientists	200,000
Engineers	650,000
Physicians	250,000

Adapted from Walter A. Rosenblith, "On Some Social Consequences of Scientific and Technological Change," *Daedalus,* XC, No. 3 (Summer, 1961), 510.

the simple fact that the more important and socially complex the problems and their solutions, the fewer will be the number of individuals equipped to discuss them meaningfully and responsibly.

STRUCTURAL CHARACTERISTICS
OF THE SCIENCE AFFAIRS COMMUNITY

Because the immediate interrelations of science and government are at the core of science affairs, whatever structure exists in the science affairs community as a whole tends to be displayed most clearly in the executive branch of the government. In this context one cannot help but be impressed by the implications of the proposition suggested by some scientist participants to the effect that "the government needs us more than we need it." The characteristic authority structure and standards of participation and promotion are, in fact, closely related to the methods of recruitment and types of factional differences familiar to participants, and the modes of participation most congenial to them as individuals.

Recruitment. The existing bridges between science and government convey many more scientists than nonscientists. The historical development of science affairs from the special professional concerns of scientists and the difficulty of achieving respectable competence in science subjects make it understandable that members of this community should have been scientists or have had science training. It is nonetheless remarkable that nonscientists and representatives of nonscience organizations have participated in science affairs only incidentally or by enlisting the aid of scientists as mediators. In general they have been intimidated by the assumption, not always warranted, that the technical features of an issue are more difficult to comprehend than the nontechnical ones. It may also be that the sciences have attracted a disproportionate number of persons with the highest inherent intellectual abilities, and that this asset is more important in the conduct of science affairs than any particular formal training, special conditioning, willingness to act as a representative, or possession of a special sense of responsibility. Recruitment from the science community for this reason nevertheless tends to transfer some of the special characteristics of that community to the science affairs community.

The science background of members inclines them to represent only themselves and the best knowledge and methods that science has to offer, rather than any particular discipline, laboratory, professional association, or political party. The characteristic patterns of entry into this community do not, however, make the intellectual elite among scientists the automatic and sole participants in science affairs. Nevertheless, the prestige of this elite inside and outside the science communities, through such recognition as membership in the NAS or the winning of a Nobel Prize, permits its members to be especially influential if they so choose and if the functions of science affairs do not clearly require some other kind of competence.

For most scientists entrance depends on a special area of knowledge or kind of scientific or administrative ability being in short supply and being urgently needed in connection with national policy determinations. The waves of interest in military and peaceful uses of atomic energy, electronic defenses, bomb-delivery systems, oceanography, seismology, outer space, meteorology, and technical assistance overseas, for example, have each brought to the forefront of science affairs persons who may then remain there for reasons unrelated to their specialty.[12] Through purely technical work of a classified nature a scientist may per force be in a specially advantageous position to recognize and deliberately influence higher level strategic and policy implications of the work with which he has become familiar. The possession of a security clearance for purely technical reasons undoubtedly facilitates recruitment into the government's organization for science affairs, although it need not, of course, and often does not result in active participation in science affairs unless the individual so chooses. Much of the government's urgent need for technical expertise in connection with national policy re-

---

[12] The apparent persistence of influence in science affairs of persons who on the basis of wartime experience would qualify for membership in a "Los Alamos Alumni Association" leaves unanswered the question of whether this is due to the bonds produced by this experience or to the prescience inherent in the process of recruiting only the most able physical scientists for Los Alamos.

view and reformulations has been associated with the physical sciences and engineering rather than with the life sciences, thus leaving less personal choice for the life scientists. In the future this emphasis may be altered as problems in epidemiology, drugs, biocides, ecology, and population control become of more immediate national policy concern.

Characteristically the individual scientist's opportunities to cultivate his interest and develop his understanding of science affairs have also depended on his being in a very special kind of environment which has developed at only a few locations since World War II. Not even a minimal awareness and knowledge of science affairs is now developed or taught in any formal way. It must be absorbed within an environment the most significant features of which seem to be (1) a large pool of research scientists who have some individual control over their time and the opinions they may express, (2) a university atmosphere including some opportunities for intellectual exchange between natural and social scientists and humanists, and (3) opportunities, preferably provided by the scientists' teachers or senior colleagues, for contact with and a chance to solve crucial real problems of science affairs. In practice these conditions may limit participation in many categories of science affairs to individuals situated where there are large-scale scientific activities in reasonable proximity to established centers of higher learning.[13] The fact that such activities often attract our ablest scientists for reasons having to do with science itself makes it still more likely that these persons will at least be able to participate in science affairs.

Factions? In general the intrusion of science into public affairs has had the effect of blurring traditional distinctions between the conservative and the radical, between government bureaucracy and independent initiative, between responsible officials and advisers, between policy-makers and planners, between interested parties and disinterested parties, between pure research and applied re-

---

[13] Of the 70,000 scientists and engineers engaged in research and development at colleges and universities in 1958, 65 percent were at the 36 institutions absorbing 77 percent of the total amount expended on research and development at 377 colleges and universities. Each of the 36 institutions had staffs of over 500 persons engaged in research and development. *Review of Data on Research and Development* (Washington, D.C., NSF, 1961), No. 27.

search, between the brilliant innovator and the technician, and even between the scientist and the nonscientist. This state of flux leaves no room for basic splits within the science affairs community, although temporary fractures have on occasion developed.

For apolitical persons such as the scientists participating in science affairs it would still seem inappropriate to attach much significance to traditional political party labels, although this may not be the case in the future.[14] If the traditional radical image of scientists, as opposed to engineers, was ever significant, it must have been greatly dissipated by the augmented prestige, position, and legitimacy which science received during the Eisenhower Administration. The increased legitimacy of scientists as active participants in science affairs does not necessarily ensure a lack of political friction, but as yet there are no obvious basic ideological splits within or between categories of participation. There may be differences in general outlook which vary according to discipline affiliation but with the possible exception of differences between physical and life scientists, these are probably less significant than those resulting from individual temperament or allegiance to pet scientific or technological programs.[15]

Nor are there now clear organizational or functional separations. Individuals often serve in various capacities simultaneously. Even within the Executive it is not uncommon for one individual to occupy two or more advisory positions that do not obviously require this overlap. Indeed, this conscious lack of institutional loyalties and disparagement of the more crass forms of competition may well hamper the effective contributions to the making of national policies that

[14] In connection with the presidential campaign of 1960 both the Democratic and the Republican Parties prepared statements concerning science and technology. The Democrats appointed a group of scientists to prepare and endorse these statements and both presidential candidates had science advisers for the campaign. This was the first campaign with such extensive use of science and scientists, although they were both drawn in on specific issues during the campaign four years before. It is hard to imagine how science can be kept out of campaign politics and hence out of administration politics.

[15] Where special interests may generate factional differences, individuals with quite different outlooks have been brought together, as for instance in PSAC panels related to arms control matters in order to discover, starting with purely technical questions, the extent of possible agreement on issues involving homogenized technical and political questions.

must ultimately be decided, in a democratic society, by an adversary procedure. Nevertheless, in their avoidance of petty loyalties scientists of all sorts, whether drawn into science affairs or not, tend to emphasize their loyalty to truth alone.

Interlocking memberships thus become a virtue in the eyes of a participant because they increase the range of information accessible to him and, assuming he not only observes but also actively contributes, makes most efficient use of what is presumed to be a rare talent. However, even now, a detailed reading of events in science affairs would suggest the presence of more adversary procedures in the making of national policy than the introduction of "scientific" objectivity might require. The PSAC, for instance, is only advisory but it was not only created to provide the President with scientific advice when needed. In the national security field, if not in the field of planning for science, it has also served to counterbalance advice already being given. In helping to assess and interpret technical presentations advanced by one interested party with access to skilled technical personnel, the PSAC is not always in the position of judge but may be in the position of a technically proficient devil's advocate, leaving the ultimate decision to the President. In helping identify and support policy issues concerning scientific research and manpower requirements, the PSAC is pleading a special, albeit important, interest which must ultimately be reconciled with other claims on the nation's attention and resources.

Modes of participation. The most significant differences in outlook among members of this community are based on individual estimates of how science and scientists can suitably or legitimately contribute to the government of society. And this, in turn, depends in part on different views about government, society, and human relations and not just on the participant's area of technical competence or his organizational affiliations.

Some participants focus on science or technology, others on scientists, and a few on both. In the first category there has in the past been little overlap between involvement in matters having to do with defense or weapons systems, with promoting pure basic scientific research, and with using science programs such as the IGY and international exchanges to promote aspects of world peace or general welfare in addition to science. Such splits tend to reflect individual priorities and a convenient division of labor, rather than firm convictions. And in recent years even these fairly discernible and somewhat separately organized activities have overlapped.

Participants who concentrate on the assets of scientists and on what they conceive to be vital public policy issues, including the matter of saving the world and the consciences of scientists, rather than on science and technology have tended to extend to the political sphere the scientist's characteristic style of analysis of problems and his ability to communicate unambiguously, at least on matters of science.[16] Those that approach science affairs in this light sometimes have a persistent influence despite changes in subject, climate, or experience. Even their rationale for expecting such influence changes, with the result that the participants do not. Participation often appears to be defended progressively on the basis of: (1) the virtues of innocence and the introduction of a fresh approach, (2) the capacity to inject specific crucial facts, (3) the ability to use scientific methods regardless of the subject or the specialty of the user, (4) the advantage of already being privy to the problems and issues that one might be called to advise upon, (5) the utility of already knowing your way around government bureaucracies, and (6) the necessity of being able to talk to key government officials, a small but increasing number of whom speak the language of science.

Other participants who focus on the role of scientists have tended to promote or speak for the scientists, or some segment of them, as a professional group. In a simpler day these spokesmen for scientists were among the chief participants in science affairs and the latter were primarily concerned with promoting science as a cultural exercise for a few gifted persons. For reasons which have to do with the inherent qualities of science, with the scientist's traditional individualism, and with his antipathy to the public and publicity

[16] This style and ability has, for example, provided the impetus for the Pugwash Conferences and for the proposals of some scientists for systematically influencing legislators. It has also provided the basis for vigorous differences in analyses of military strategies and related weapons systems. For an illuminating account of the effect of different political outlooks on scientists concerned with weapons policies see Robert Gilpin, *American Scientists and Nuclear Weapons Policy* (Princeton, N.J., Princeton University Press, 1962).

features of a system of representation, this kind of participation in science affairs is at present much less pronounced than one might expect.

Participants may not only be divided in terms of the direction of their special efforts, but also in terms of the methods used for effective participation. Indeed, this formed the basis for our description of the make-up of the community. The major operational divisions here are between the roles of adviser, of administrator or planner, and the role of the publicist articulating issues, facts, and opinions. Sometimes circumstances force an individual to combine these roles to the obvious detriment of each and sometimes they force separations that may be ineffective. Except possibly for some publicists, these categories, like those discussed above, would seem to be conditional and for the most part reflect practical considerations and interests of the moment. On occasion some of the government's most respected advisers have played the role of publicist while prolific publicists have assumed major advisory and administrative or policy-making roles in close association with the executive branch of the federal government.

Standards of participation and promotion. Underlying these patterns of participation in science affairs is the participating scientist's haunting awareness that as a scientist this activity is not quite legitimate. The values of science do not recognize merit in human affairs as such and hence they cannot provide standards for judging the quality of involvement in science affairs. Participation is often "bootlegged" away from research, teaching, or local administrative responsibilities. Even membership in the PSAC or an official position in the NAS, the AAAS, or another professional society is likely to be felt by the participants to require special justification. The paramount concern of participants to remain in good standing with the science community is partly responsible for the design of governmental part-time advisory systems, special summer study projects, policy-making positions, and other organizational features of science affairs.

The emphasis on advising makes it intrinsically difficult and often inappropriate to test abilities by examining specific results. For this reason and because of the feasibility of combining advice-giving with other activities, the extensive use of advisory systems in science affairs may be an accommodation to scientists. Now, circumstances and the quest for improved policy-making are forcing more full-time attention to science affairs outside government as well as inside, and as a consequence new standards of legitimacy may evolve.

In any case, the structural elements in the science affairs community are not now indigenous to the subject but are rather reflections of science and the science community. They incorporate standards familiar in the physical sciences, if not in all the natural sciences, which reject formalism and place a premium on flexibility, on close contact with real problems, on hard data, on a reputation in one's science specialty, and on the ability to use quantitative methods and styles.

The antiformalism of the science community favors the dissolution of specific science affairs activities unless they gain legitimacy by demonstrably performing nonformal functions. It also encourages participation and collaboration of individuals, regardless of their formal affiliations, so long as the basic operating standards and objectives borrowed from the research community are preserved. The organizing principles based on these standards are probably most clearly seen in the large segment of science affairs devoted to the exploitation of science in the formulation of effective national policies, and especially defense policies. They emphasize logic and the use of intellect more than the accumulation of evidence and experience. Ideally, they appear to call for:

Positions of authority granted or assumed according to merit with a premium on the virtuoso manipulation of facts and arguments;
Debate of issues with appeal to specific facts and rational argument and without regard to personal feelings;
Decisions by unanimous, but tacit, agreement after intellectual debate.

In practice these ideals have been actualized by invoking the standards recognized by the science community for singling out the best minds, the best manner of inquiry, and the best kinds of problems to focus on. In the extreme each of these three standards runs counter to the basic requirements of all our social affairs, including science affairs, that our policy-making institutions should avoid excessive reliance on genius and on secrecy, and that they should exercise moderation.

Yet persons possessing the best minds for science are more readily identified than their counterparts in many other areas of activity. They are often revered as a natural elite. Some of them are recognized by election to the National Academy, which is commonly regarded by scientists as a necessary, but not sufficient, condition for policy participation in policy-making affecting the more crucial aspects of science affairs.[17] The fact of our nation's reliance on these few persons is dramatized by their constant emphasis on the excessive demands placed upon them in the course of science affairs. This is coupled with an absence of efforts to distribute the burden more widely on the grounds that other persons may not have all the requisite qualifications or that the tasks require the integration of interests and attention provided by one man serving in many roles and performing several functions in each.

The best manner of inquiry as practiced in the science community is for discussion and publication of evidence and analysis as well as conclusions under conditions which are familiar within this community but may be unintelligible or inaccessible to the layman. Although scientists as such may regard all their deliberations as public, the public is the science community as a whole or more likely some single science discipline. The distinction between private and public deliberations nevertheless inheres in the science community whose members are typically much more anxious to prove their point with their colleagues than with a larger public. Within the science affairs community, and especially in relation to government policies, the distinction necessarily becomes more important because of the privacy with which policy advice must be given and the delicacy with which policies must be formulated and expressed. The "open world"

---

[17] Membership in the Academy opens doors and permits participation in a kind of consensus-building in the science community that is not otherwise possible. The fact that neither of the two Directors of the NSF since its founding in 1950 has been a member of the Academy, whereas many scientists serving on the National Science Board have been, is subject to various interpretations. Yet this circumstance may well inhibit the Foundation's potential for leadership in important areas of science affairs,

of the scientist participant in an advisory role may be restricted to the committee or panel of which he is a member, and as a result the self-correcting aspects of debate in a larger community may not operate. There is instead a tendency to argue in public that the quality of deliberations carried on in private must be accepted on faith and that more restraint and judiciousness prevails there than is possible in public forums where political pressures often force the overstatement of diverging positions.[18] This rationale is understandable, given the professional scientific background of many participants in science affairs, but it should not obscure the contrary view that in social affairs public debate might better strive for more accuracy than private debate so that the public can readily and responsibly form the judgments it must make while private councils continue without inhibitions to explore and debate viewpoints that are still more expressions of opinion than well-founded positions.

The best kinds of problems to tackle, from the scientists' point of view, are those that lend themselves to decisive solutions either by theoretical analysis or by crucial experiment and that will yield results which will advance knowledge significantly. When extended to science affairs this approach not only presumes the existence of neat solutions to problems of science affairs but also places a premium on first identifying crucial tests and analyses that can be done and then insisting on doing them. The ultimate dilemma inherent in the extension of the principle that what can be done should be done was already well recognized at Los Alamos and elsewhere at the end of World War II. In one example it was stated in the form of the question: "Might a super thermonuclear bomb actually ignite the oceans?" To which the usual only half-jesting reply was: "We think not but the only way to be sure is to test and if our calculations are in error no one will be alive to prove us wrong anyway."

Scientist members of the science affairs community have usually been advisers rather than operating agents. The practical consequences of the tendencies described above have been more limited and colored more by predispositions than by experience. The Office

---

[18] Lee A. DuBridge, "Policy and the Scientists," *Foreign Affairs*, XLI, No. 3 (April, 1963), 588.

of Scientific Research and Development, the M.I.T. Radiation Laboratory, the Manhattan Project in World War II, and some postwar projects have, however, provided significant demonstrations of the ability of some members of this community to assume and carry out operational tasks and to alter their standards of judgment as a result. The various space programs and other science projects of equal magnitude will again put this ability to the test and thereby affect advancement within the community. Nevertheless, the current ideals of science as expressed in the emphasis on flexibility, on quick accomplishment, and on theoretical analysis with minimal but crucial experimentation are more compatible with the roles of informed critic and influential adviser than with that of responsible administrator or policy-maker. This compatibility depends, however, on acceptable standards of excellence borrowed from the science community and perpetuated without invoking performance tests in the science affairs community itself.

As the science affairs community matures it rediscovers the tradition of respect for seniority and acquires its senior science statesmen,[19] but it also acquires its own standards of performance for promotion within its ranks even though the nature and importance of an individual's participation is still very much determined by informal circumstances. The PSAC takes advantage of its advisory panel system to identify individuals who have the interest, ability, and devotion that might make them especially useful on the Committee itself as well as on other panels, or in full-time policy-making positions. Large science-oriented agencies such as the AEC, the NSF, and NASA also make some promotions from within their ranks or from a reservoir of prospects who have had earlier experience with

---

[19] The Scientific Advisory Panel to the Army has grown in ten years from an original ten to over fifty. Excluding those who are deceased, it has a total of only eighty-five past and present members. As of September, 1962, the Scientific Advisory Board to the Chief of Staff of the U.S. Air Force actually had a category of membership entitled "Senior Statesmen." In 1961 the President created the category of Consultants-at-Large to his Science Advisory Committee. These consultants are selected from among the members of the PSAC who would normally be rotated off the Committee. Routine rotation of membership in any particular group may well be impeded by the remarkable practice of placing key scientists in science affairs in a number of official positions simultaneously.

the agency. Scientist-commissioners of the AEC and sometimes the other commissioners as well have had close previous associations with atomic energy matters.

The mechanisms now employed in the science affairs community to recruit, integrate, and utilize persons, and evaluate their contributions, are themselves clearly influenced by the specific topics of concern and also by the backgrounds of participants both as scientists and as earlier participants in science affairs. The adequacy of these organizing mechanisms and the best direction for their further refinement or for their general reorganization have yet to be judged carefully. When this is done it is likely to be in terms of the basic functions which science affairs as a whole should perform in the development of wise national policy-making.

FOUR FUNCTIONS OF SCIENCE AFFAIRS

Science affairs probably constitute our society's most ambitious effort at rapid integration of practice and theory. This process involves at least four distinct mediating functions between science and government, two of which are most closely associated with immediate practical considerations while the other two involve theory, foresight, goals, and values. In this order the first function is to mobilize advanced technologies and the government of science in order to accomplish specific practical objectives. The second is to protect and develop the institutions of science and government by articulating and justifying their distinctive features and promoting the interests of each by means of the other. The third is to use apt scientific knowledge and techniques of the very highest quality in the analysis and review of complex projects and programs often required for meaningful national policies. The fourth is to exercise foresight and generate creative and constructive ideas, institutions, styles, and social objectives that will be responsive to the full potentiality of the permanent interactions of science and government and the resulting condition of perpetual physical and intellectual change.

These four functions place distinctly different demands on the skills and knowledge of participants in science affairs, even though the performance of each is strongly influenced by a mixture of the same policy perspectives graphically described by Warner Schilling, in his essay in this volume, with reference to the characteristic predispositions of physical scientists which affect their views on national security policy issues. The first requires that much of science be grafted to the upper reaches of engineering. In practice this has often meant that scientists and their facilities forego exploration of new frontiers in order to conduct or oversee advanced engineering work with which they are intellectually familiar but which is beyond the reach of conventional engineering establishments. The second requires that the sciences and scientists prepare to justify their priorities within science as well as between science and the rest of society and that they see the justice and relevance of the claims of others (politicians, for example) on them and their work. The third requires the maximum use of special expertise at selected new frontiers in order to evaluate proposed programs and policies against the unknown or unfamiliar features of nature and society. The fourth requires the expert generalist who is not just able to understand the constraints of nature but has a taste for the challenge of deliberately fashioning attitudes toward change and the direction of changes in our civilization in order to maximize their accord with our society's most basic and unambiguous goals and principles.

Without being fully aware of the differences between these functions, the science affairs community as now constituted and organized has made serious efforts to contribute to each of them. But the success of these efforts can easily be frustrated if we do not learn from a critical review of the past and come to recognize that the different functions often require different kinds of abilities, interests, loyalties, and organizational machineries if they are to complement and restrain each other. With such recognition it should be easier to localize and resolve debates about whether or not scientists are to be on top or on tap, are specially gifted in foresight, are the best available talent, and are wise or merely well-intentioned.

Advanced engineering and the government of science. The bulk of science affairs activities today are concerned with estimating, overseeing, and developing or mobilizing the capacity of the science community to respond to the advanced engineering needs of the nation or with the complementary function of furthering science and improving the conditions for scientific work. The formal predecessor to the PSAC was, in fact, established in 1951 to maintain awareness of developments and to be ready to advise the President on how the scientific talent of the country should be mobilized in case of an emergency.[20]

If this function is to be performed adequately it is necessary to acquire and make full use of information about the specific technical needs of the nation and the capacity of our scientific and engineering facilities to satisfy them. It is remarkable how much reliance is now placed on technical expectations and necessarily partial information about advanced technologies. This has long been true in the area of national security. More recently there have been congressional debates and legislation concerning, for instance, the organization of satellite communication services, even before the techniques involved had been clearly demonstrated.

Under present circumstances the problems of disseminating scientific and technical information and ideas to the right individuals at the right time appear to raise sensitive issues in science affairs which neither scientists nor others are now able to solve with complete satisfaction.[21] Both the bulk and the secretive nature of information concerning possible projects of national importance require systems of selective dissemination. It is not hard to imagine that a great many of the public scientific advisory groups in the government could be justified solely as devices for exchanging information and ideas, whether or not any other functions are also performed. But if this is their purpose it serves no useful end to expect more from them.

Still more serious problems exist with respect to information about the condition of our research facilities and manpower, their adaptability, and the circumstances under which they can or cannot operate

[20] DuBridge, "Policy and the Scientists," p. 578.

[21] The NSF has an Office of Scientific Information and many information services have developed. But no one would pretend that these are sufficiently selective as to the materials covered and the audience addressed. A further step in this direction is being attempted by NASA which has established an office to facilitate the application of developments made for NASA to independent civilian uses. A panel of the PSAC has issued a report, "Science, Government and Information" (1963), which reviews the entire problem of the responsibilities of the technical community and the government in the transfer of information and suggests further improvements.

most efficiently. Knowledge about these matters is not adequate for forming sound judgments and is unlikely to be so until science administration itself becomes more systematic than it is now.[22]

For instance, the PSAC report "Meeting Manpower Needs in Science and Technology" (1962) identifies eleven major national challenges which it asserts will depend on scientific and technical manpower. Accordingly it proposes that we train a great many more engineers, mathematicians, and physical scientists than we do now, and it finds that this is a feasible undertaking. What the report fails to consider, however, is the central question of whether existing manpower resources in these areas are capable of fashioning a suitable response to the challenges and whether a simple quantitative increase is necessary, sufficient, or the most effective way to a more adequate response. There is an obvious shortage of skills required to analyze requirements and plan responses. The use of scientists as engineers has, to be sure, proved feasible and has a record of major successes as well as some notable failures, even though one must expect difficult problems in the effective use of science and scientists in the upper reaches of engineering projects because of the inherent duality involved in being temperamentally attuned both to the search for original discoveries and to application of the best that science now has to offer in practical situations.[23] Yet, the scientist's characteristic interest in acquiring the whole picture of the problem he is tackling and his tendency to restrict himself to problems permitting specific accomplishment are in harmony with the engineering tradition. Perhaps the additional special qualifications needed by leading scientists attempting to perform this func-

---

[22] For an account and assessment of manpower studies see Thomas J. Mills, "Three Years After the Hauser Committee Report on Scientific and Technical Personnel Data," in *Scientific Manpower* (Washington, D.C., USGPO, 1961), NSF 62-22.

[23] Atomic energy and radar development owe a very great deal to scientists, although there are also instances where the design requirements set by scientists have proved unfeasible given available materials and necessarily average manpower skills for routine production and operation. Oppenheimer has observed that "the great lesson of the last decades has been that men of science who have spent their whole lives in the quest for new knowledge may be among the most gifted practitioners of technology." *Symposium on Basic Research* (Washington, D.C., AAAS, 1959), Publ. No. 56, p. 10.

tion are an interest in human beings and an ability to arouse the necessary enthusiasm in order to accomplish difficult tasks in advanced engineering.[24]

Science affairs is thus comparatively well organized to perform this general management and design function. The individuals presently most knowledgeable about practical aspects of science affairs, including the three men who have been Special Assistants to the President for Science and Technology, have had intimate personal experience with some of these problems and the responsibility for solving them. Particularly challenging problems of this nature, both with respect to the military, and even with respect to some civilian concerns, have received considerable, although obviously not enough, attention. Knowledge and opinion about advanced engineering and the administration of science is still exploited through the mechanisms of advisory committees and occasional consultants, yet there are noticeable increases in the numbers of positions for policy-makers and planners which will allow them to accumulate and use specially relevant experience and competence. Following the establishment of the NSF there were created such offices as that of the Director of Defense Research and Engineering, the Assistant Secretary of Commerce for Science and Technology, and most recently the Office of Science and Technology in the Executive Office of the President.

It remains to be seen, however, whether these offices can reconcile their performance of this function with the other functions for which they are responsible. The direction of large programs in applied research and development is often thought to provide precarious pro-

---

[24] In discussing the qualifications for someone directing research facilities, John von Neumann suggested that "he has to have a good understanding and has to know the subject very well. It is not decisive that he should have made original contributions. It is more important that he should be able to understand human relations very well." U.S. Congress, H.R. Subcommittee of the Committee on Government Operations, *Hearings, Organization and Administration of the Military Research and Development Programs*, 83rd Congress, 2d Session (Washington, D.C., USGPO, 1954), p. 378.

It will be recalled that one of the accusations which the AEC Personnel Security Board deemed important in the Oppenheimer case was Oppenheimer's known lack of enthusiasm for the H-bomb program and the effect this had on the morale of a major research laboratory.

tection and support for pure basic research or for speculation on the broader implications of the program. Even basic studies in science administration and related manpower problems may very well be disparaged if they appear to contradict established national policies or existing mechanisms for the training and research of scientists and the utilization of engineers.

The interests and institutions of science and government. It is obvious enough that advances in science are very much dependent on continuing material support and that many elements in society ranging from local political constituencies and industry to the mass media and the federal government are increasingly aware of what science enterprises may offer them. The problem of appropriate representation of these diverse interests and the means for reconciling them are not well recognized, although they are obviously more political than technical in nature. Many of the individuals and activities associated with science affairs are devoted to impressing the public and its leaders with both the cultural and the ultimate practical benefits to be derived from science. As yet, they show few overt signs of authority or inclination to negotiate a position for science in the total social picture that might place any responsibilities or other requirements on the science enterprise in return for support. Of necessity such a place is being established, albeit without benefit of full analysis within the science affairs community.

At the same time that a holding action is thought to be necessary in order to maintain the tradition of pure basic research, efforts are being made to expand the scale and scope of this activity and give it institutional permanence. The NSF and the National Laboratories of the AEC have helped establish science on a new scale which universities alone could not have accomplished, although at one time some of our largest philanthropic foundations made major contributions along the same lines.

The persistent problems of providing for pure basic research appear to have occupied the sympathies, if not the undivided attention, of science policy-making and advisory groups in the government.[25] Yet the skills required for protecting the essence of science by de-

---

[25] See the essay by Kreidler in this volume.

veloping new social institutions are not necessarily those possessed by scientists. Some knowledge of science and scientists is obviously required, but, as with the use of science for advanced engineering, many other skills are also required. It may even be that the best scientists are temperamentally unwilling to plead the cause of science or accept compromises in the manner which our political system requires of all interest groups that are to be heard.[26] As suggested by Robert C. Wood, scientists may possibly achieve certain political purposes because of the apolitical image of themselves which they and others hold.[27] Thus, for instance, politicians, government agencies, and other groups sometimes wish to be publicly identified with outstanding scientists or have the advice of scientists in order to enhance their prestige and the authority with which they speak.[28] To this extent scientists may be able to specify conditions of service which will also protect and maybe enhance the essence of science and not result in the misinterpretation, slighting, or other abuses of scientific opinion. Often these doubts seem to be overcome by giving support to basic research, creating vast science enterprises and laboratories, and honoring the accomplishments, talents, and integrity of scientists.

In this manner new apportionments of resources and influences are developed between representatives or spokesmen for science and politicians, whether they be civilian administrators, military officers, Congressmen, or Senators. But it is likely that this function of science affairs will in the future require increasing expert attention to the long-range plans and internal constitution of science and of other social institutions that might be directly affected by these plans. It is not obvious that scientists who are personally dedicated to one particular line of inquiry will have the inclination to perform this second function.

Difficult problems, such as the matter of priorities in science, which have been neglected while there has been steadily increasing

---

[26] See the essay by Sayre in this volume.

[27] See the essay by Wood in this volume.

[28] This political contribution of scientists is recognized by Harvey Brooks, himself a scientist engaged in PSAC activities. See the essay by Brooks in this volume.

over-all support for science, will have to be solved. A cursory glance at the material and manpower demands of possible lines of scientific inquiry suggest the eventual need to supplement the case for science with assessments of priorities within science.[29] This task is not now performed within the organization of science affairs except perhaps for the specific recognition that research and education must proceed hand-in-hand. The PSAC and the OST appear to argue that their responsibilities are to the President and not to science as such and that the over-all assessment of priorities within science is a responsibility of the science community itself. Yet traditional science institutions, including the universities and the NAS, and the NSF, which is their specific source of government support, tend to be committed to established categories of science and are extremely reluctant to engage in comparisons or to augment the list. At the same time, the public interest as expressed by Congress, for instance, tends to assign priorities within science on the basis of specific practical uses of anticipated discoveries rather than on the likelihood of making the most significant discoveries.

The issue of priorities and other similar issues can, of course, be settled by competitive bargaining, and often are. But the special function of the science affairs community in this regard would seem to be to use systematic knowledge and reason to help find and establish priorities that will satisfy as many interests as possible both within and beyond the boundaries of science. These two different approaches to the resolution of issues are reflected on both sides of the debate over the establishment of a Department of Science which occurred in the years following the launching of Sputnik I.[30] Some

[29] A number of projects that involve "big science" but are nevertheless basic, are now underway or being seriously considered. These involve major new investments in facilities and programs for such areas of interest as high-energy physics, IGY-type activities, oceanography, mathematical computation and data processing, meteorology, and space sciences. The problem of justifying special consideration for a particular research program is humorously and poignantly stated by Warren Weaver in "Report of the Special Committee," *Science*, 131 (November 20, 1959), 1390.

[30] Sputnik I was launched in October, 1957. This debate has been carried on since then at congressional hearings, the AAAS Parliament of Science (1958), and in a number of magazine articles.

of those in favor emphasized the need to prepare a united front for science, and some of those in opposition emphasized the opportunities to maintain and develop independently specific harmonies of interest between various sciences and various other social enterprises. This is only the beginning of a debate which undoubtedly will continue to preoccupy segments of the science affairs community and will draw into this community more surrogates for the sciences and defenders of other interests who can communicate with and influence the community of science.

Analysis and review. In many ways this third function of the science affairs community is the most exciting and challenging for its participants drawn from the physical sciences, and has done much to establish the present make-up and character of the community. The government is now enlisting at its highest levels the knowledge and sophisticated methods possessed by some of our best scientists in order to review proposed policies and the extravagant claims sometimes made by proponents of particular weapons systems or other complex and costly technical systems. Undoubtedly, policies and strategies affecting such matters as defense systems, space programs, deterrence, arms control, and the "nth" country problem, have been subject to this kind of review as have specific projects involving the ICBM, the anti-ICBM, the RS-70, a nuclear-powered aircraft, nuclear testing, the manned lunar landing program, and various detection and communications systems.

To perform these reviews, some scientists have been assembled into committees, *ad hoc* panels, or study groups, assigned to be mentors of ongoing programs, or appointed to full-time high-ranking positions. Often the scientists involved are accustomed to the lack of hierarchal authority in universities and to a self-confident, free-wheeling, and frank collective approach to their subject. This approach appears to be essential to the performance of this function both in the analytical phase and in the process of injecting the outcome into that place in the government where it can be most useful. At least in an ideal sense, this function exploits the skill (often highly developed by scientists) of starting with some proposition or proposal that lends itself to quantification, then mixing knowledge, ideas, and analytical skills until the group has worked its way to a unanimous judgment on the merits or demerits of a particular proposal.

Because physicists are the generalists among physical scientists (if not among all scientists), some physicists seem particularly well equipped for this work. If the participants are to detect obscured difficulties and make judgments on proposals they must not only be adept, if not experienced, in the domains of those who draft the proposals but must also be able to put the proposals in a somewhat wider context. This analytical task would thus seem to be particularly congenial to the scientist because of its limited character and the high probability of successful accomplishment. For instance, the apparently successful use of panels of physicists for analysis of proposed weapons systems suggests that superior mathematical and other methodological skills of the physicists have been found to be more important for such a task than specific military experience.

Since World War II, if not before, a number of the very best physical scientists in the United States have performed this function in a unique and invaluable way.[31] There was then no other source of persons with equally important skills. But a favorable judgment of this contribution must not lead us to the conclusion that better skills cannot now be developed. In examining the past in order to learn for the future it appears that persons who are not necessarily renowned as physical scientists or even trained as such can develop and use more appropriate techniques of analysis and review than have been developed thus far. This has to do with the breadth of the context in which one must study national problems, as distinct from problems studied under laboratory controls. The effort to solve prob-

---

[31] "The question is not whether all recommendations were 'right' or were free from criticism or controversy, but whether they were based upon the best scientific thinking of the time, whether they were made by earnest, able individuals, and whether in the long run such advice and recommendations have been in the best interests of the country." DuBridge, "Policy and the Scientists," p. 587.

This defense of scientists in the making of past policies does not dispose of the need to assess their participation as a first step in the development of new skills. This, I take it, is a primary purpose of Albert Wohlstetter's essay in this volume and his article based upon it, "Scientists, Seers, and Strategy," *Foreign Affairs*, XLI, No. 3 (April, 1963), 466–78.

lems of national security, for instance, by rigorous scientific analysis may spread the illusion that a problem is technical when in fact it may be a human problem.

Obviously this function of science affairs requires that analyses be made as inclusive as possible without impairing their quality. Breadth and quality tend to be in practical opposition, since a team of analysts must consist of persons equipped with similar methodological tools and information even though such a group might arrive at a consensus about questions that exceed their comprehension. Yet any attempt to broaden the range of competence might transform the group from a technical arbitration tribunal to a forum for negotiation and compromise among panelists. As the quality of proposed programs and policies improves there is less likelihood of discovering purely technical fallacies. The general function will therefore have to be broadened if it is to continue to be of assistance at high policy levels. Opportunities for broadening are already evident in the emerging role of the scientific strategists who draw more heavily on the techniques of the economists than on those of the physicist for the common language that is needed to perform this analytic function.[32] The need for the broadest possible scope of analysis increases very rapidly as the uses of analytic techniques are extended from military policies, where the objectives are so crucial that social costs usually seem insignificant, to major policies and programs related to resource development and the earth sciences, technical assistance programs, information handling, to other ventures which draw on science and technology, and even to the policies bearing on the detailed interdependence of these areas of major policy concern.[33]

Whatever the feasible breadth of analysis at any one time, one major contribution of these analytical exercises is that they offer a means for sharpening policy issues by identifying and clarifying

---

[32] See the essay by Brodie in this volume.

[33] Problems concerning the breadth of analysis are illustrated by the proposal for a very large linear accelerator at Stanford University and the sequence of reviews which it received by a joint panel of the PSAC and the AEC-GAC, and the JCAE. The first review emphasized the requirements of high-energy physics. In the course of successive reexamination, consideration was later given to the long-range implications for the field of physics generally, for the pool of trained scientists, and for the whole of science.

some of their technical ingredients. This role is a negative one, however, in that it is more likely to expose fallacious reasoning and factual errors, or to introduce alternate viewpoints of seemingly equal validity, than it is to generate and demonstrate the viability of programs or policies involving qualitatively different alternatives. It is adept at applying the laws of science but not necessarily at identifying where scientific knowledge is weak and possibly incorrect. It can spot unconvincing proposals but it cannot spot those that may turn out to be sound but are advanced by right intuition supported by wrong reasons.

The problems and pitfalls peculiar to this function deal with the style of science itself and the difficulty of understanding the meaning and basis of major national policies and programs. It is not easy to identify the crucial components in a program that lend themselves to technical analysis without being drawn toward those components which may also be susceptible to analysis but are relatively minor. The real meaning and bases of major policy proposals are not always clearly articulated, and if no one fully understands them members of the science affairs community cannot be expected to do so either. Yet, like the linguistic analysts among contemporary philosophers, scientists find strength in insisting on clearly stated definitions and purposes and discounting that which is not clear or is beyond the boundaries of precise observation and control even though the essence of a political problem may be in the imponderables.

Technical and policy analysis cannot be kept apart. They must be integrated with increasing care and thoroughness, despite the difficulty of linking precise knowledge and the real policy considerations within an analytic framework. This difficulty, which is no new occurrence, has been described vividly with regard to the drafting of NSC-68 for the National Security Council in 1950.

What troubled Kennan about the study project was the very idea that the vast and complex problems of American foreign policy could be set down on a few sheets of paper without transforming them into crude and clumsy oversimplifications . . . he saw this new appraisal of American policy developing characteristics which he had already learned to distrust: the systematization of policy-making by which a simplified, co-ordinated, and programmed general solution was adopted, but which submerged the real issues and eliminated flexibility in policy-making and diplomacy.[34]

Similar dilemmas have undoubtedly recurred many times since 1950 and as scientists have been drawn into national policy-making they have tended to aggravate the inherent tension. In discussing the role of the scientist in the processes of judgment and action affecting public policy in 1962, the Secretary to the NSC emphasized the need for these scientists to contribute their special awareness of the possible and the impossible and to participate in all phases of policy-making with an understanding of the rules and procedures of government.

It may be important over the next ten or fifteen years that there should be more scientists who are ex-scientists. . . . For the interpenetrations of science and government, science and public policy, science and politics, are bound to increase and the processes of communication from man to man thick as they are and thickening steadily, are not yet as deep, as thick, as varied—are not above all as much taken for granted—as they need to be.[35]

The difficulties of interpenetration are no more solved by ex-scientists who abandon their special knowledge and methods than by scientists who insist on reducing all public policy issues to the kinds of terms they customarily manipulate. While the emerging skills of scientific strategists may sometimes replace those of the physical scientist in the performance of part of this third function, they are more likely to supplement them. Nor is it likely that these new skills will go very far toward expanding the boundaries of this function or solving the dilemma associated with these limitations. Technical, strategic, or other systems analysis may undermine a policy or program that is actually valid but difficult to articulate or defend with logical rigor, and yet the neglect of this kind of synoptic analysis is likely to prove increasingly risky. The very potency of this third function thus suggests the need to assist it by deliberately

[34] Paul Y. Hammond, "NSC-68: Prologue to Rearmament," in Warner R. Schilling, Paul Y. Hammond, and Glenn H. Snyder, *Strategy, Politics, and Defense Budgets* (New York, Columbia University Press, 1962), pp. 315–16.
[35] Remarks by McGeorge Bundy at the annual meeting of the AAAS, December 27, 1962.

generating and clearly articulating major new ideas, institutions, and objectives which will be feasible, acceptable, and appropriate in this age of science and will also serve as guidelines for the independent function of analysis and review. This must be the job of the fourth function of science affairs.

Creativity and change. It must be a function of the science affairs community to probe the nature of the changes which science and technology may effect and the relevance of these changes to the goals of the nation and the well-being of mankind. Concern about the relation of facts and values is not new although the importance and malleability of their relation in the present context is unique. In practice, performance of this function is incidental to any one individual's other concerns. It obviously cannot be performed in total isolation from other inquiries into the relations of means to goals or from the other functions of this community. Nevertheless, the trend toward increased division of responsibility and improved performance of the functions already discussed applies here with equal necessity, albeit with less significant evidence of development thus far.

It would be unrealistic to expect rapid progress in the conscious and wise conduct of science affairs so as to achieve existing goals and to create only those new goals and values which will contribute to the total well-being of our society. It is first necessary to distinguish this function from the three already discussed and to recognize the possible need to develop new skills for its performance and to avoid burdening an individual with multiple functions when the performance of one might impair performance of the others.

We have suggested that the third or analytic function of science affairs draws on the best traditions of scientific objectivity by validating the means to an end, but it loses its special value and falls into disrepute if, as often happens, it is confused with the function of imagining suitable objectives and canvassing all means for achieving them. The second function is concerned with building the institutions and otherwise furthering the interests of science and of government. Hence it would be naïve to claim without evidence that the general promotion of science is a panacea to the problems already resulting from science or politics. Finally, because this fourth function involves scrutinizing our social objectives, it cannot be combined with the first function of efficiently mobilizing science and our technical resources to achieve specific programs.

This fourth function would demand of a person a sense for what is scientifically possible and for what among our figments is not known to be impossible. Such a person would also have to have a profound understanding of a nation's goals and of man's dreams, as well as insight into how these may be reconciled—a task which cannot be carried out merely as a cooperative effort among scientists, philosophers, and politicians, unless there is an appreciable synthesis in the minds of single individuals.

Features of the scientific community which are a characteristic source of strength in science may impede the successful scientist's contribution to this highest function. It is hardly appropriate, for instance, for participants to employ the philosophy of "back to the drawingboard" and "this proves you cannot predict the future," no matter how appropriate this philosophy may prove in the scientific laboratory or in the performance of the other three functions.

The traditional emphasis among scientists on clearly demonstrable achievement is an asset in scientific work which may be particularly distracting to this fourth function. In graduate school the student of science is impressed with the idea that he must limit his attention to problems which are clearly statable and for which he can reasonably expect to find solutions, given the state of the art, the time, and the resources at his command. Overoptimism may be taken as proof of inadequacy. This piecemeal approach has contributed significantly to the release of physics from metaphysics and the resultant remarkable advance of science. But while the avoidance of difficult problems in the natural sciences until they are ripe for solution may actually contribute to their more rapid solution, social goals and values and the quest for them can be effectively destroyed if these objectives and the problems associated with them are neglected.

The characteristic emphasis on clear definitive achievements is not, of course, equally pronounced in all scientific disciplines. The physical scientist tends to be concerned with scale and the magnitude of quantities that can be mathematically modeled. His world can involve both extremely small and extremely large phenomena and extremely short and extremely long periods of time. In contrast, the life scientist is necessarily bound to the scale of living organisms and the social environment. He is constantly reminded of the problems of balance and adjustment and of environment, ecology, and the concept of the organic whole. The extension of one or the other of these contrasting modes of thought to the realm of science affairs helps determine the problems which are identified or overlooked and proposes solutions to them. One outlook encourages attention to a single objective and neglect of side effects because they are deemed relatively unimportant or impossible to calculate. The other outlook is more sensitive to the possibility that apparent side effects may turn out to be crucial to the main mission.

The requirements for the performance of this fourth function are sensitive to differences in outlooks among scientists and between scientists and nonscientists. Of the four mediating functions between science and government, this one may be the least likely to require the assistance of any particular recognized scientific competence. No training beyond a general education in science and its institutions would be needed were it not that a specific scientific fact may sometimes have tremendous importance. Thus, for example, atomic bombs were made possible by the fact that the average number of fast neutrons emitted on fission just happens to be above the value needed for self-sustaining chain reactions. The need for scientific alertness and imagination is thus as important to this function as it is to the third, yet, the scientific knowledge and ideas that scientists may provide are only a stimulus to action and do not complete the mediating function between science and the development of social objectives. When this function is lacking, scientific and technical innovations tend to be exploited for the most firmly established social goals regardless of the possibility that the acceptance of the innovations may not be entirely appropriate and may even be self-defeating. Thus, to take but one example, atomic energy has been more firmly linked to the objectives of national security and international power than to other national goals even though its utility for defense may become more limited than we realize and its utility for social goals requiring large independent sources of energy is obviously undeveloped.

TOWARD THE PROFESSIONALIZATION
OF SCIENCE AFFAIRS

This summary view of the make-up, structure, and functions of science affairs has focused on the dominant influence of science and of some natural scientists. Scientists have had the most to offer and, in personal and institutional terms, they have had the most immediate stakes in the conduct of science affairs. Now the specific interests of the rest of society are more evident. The various functions of science affairs can and should be separated and mechanisms devised to make it clear when one function rather than another is being performed. Even though the actions of few major participants in science affairs bear on one function only, examination of these four separate functions, and there may be others, as ideal types having practical import is a first step to better recognition of the present immaturity of science affairs. There is need for increased self-consciousness about what needs to be done if science is to maintain its dynamism yet is to achieve a stable position in the social fabric through the mature operation of science affairs. Toward this goal one must expect and welcome intensive competence and devotion to improvement of these operations rather than an unending proliferation of participation by existing experts as one after another is seen to possess information or techniques that must be taken into account in national policy-making.

There is a place for both scientists and nonscientists in the performance of each function. Because scientists had to assume major responsibility for the deliberate performance of these functions in the early postwar period, the most noticeable development since has been the recruitment of persons with nonscience skills to help in their performance. The science administrator often needs to be more of a skilled administrator than a scientist. The protector and promoter of science is sometimes more effective if he is a surrogate who is a skilled negotiator and architect of new institutions rather than a research scientist. The analyst of technical programs and strategies may be more useful if he is skilled in economics and political science rather than in physics. Finally, it is evident that the creative function requires the vision, statesmanship, and wisdom that come from profound understanding of human values and goals, broad social experience, a sense of history, and a vivid imagination that will help us realize that more is to be learned from the discontinuities of the past than from the continuities if society is to establish values and goals on a basis commensurate with this new age of science.

It remains questionable whether enough practicing natural scientists can or should undergo the strenuous training and experience necessary to acquire the further skills, or will commit themselves to the sustained social or political action, now required by science affairs. In any case, clear delimitation of these four functional specializations permits the nonscientist, as well as the scientist, to concentrate on acquaintance with new subjects in accordance with his primary function in the science affairs community.

It is not necessary for the social scientist, politician, or philosopher to become a research scientist in the natural sciences, or vice versa. But it is clear that some persons starting from one or another of these disciplines will have to become professionally competent in science affairs if national policy-making is to gain the full assistance of relevant and integrated knowledge and is not based just on the opinions of diverse laymen and specialists.

Index